CONTENTS

HBJ material copyrighted under notice appearing earlier in this work.

i

HBJ material copyrighted under notice appearing earlier in this work.

HBJ material copyrighted under notice appearing earlier in this work.

HBJ material copyrighted under notice appearing earlier in this work.

CHAPTER 1

The Parts of Speech

Although there are over 600,000 words in the English language, you need to learn only eight terms, or *parts of speech,* to classify the ways these words can function in a sentence. The eight parts of speech are *noun, pronoun, adjective, verb, adverb, preposition, conjunction,* and *interjection.*

As you study the parts of speech, try to expand your knowledge and understanding of the work they do. Mastering the terms used in language study will help you to talk intelligently about your language and to express your ideas correctly and effectively.

LESSON 1

The Noun

A <u>noun</u> is a word used to name a person, place, thing, or idea.

A <u>common</u> <u>noun</u> names any one of a group of persons, places, or things and is not capitalized.

EXAMPLES   female, lake, book, stadium, heart, fear, honesty

Nouns like *fear* and *honesty* name things that cannot be seen or touched. They name ideas. Similarly, *hope, knowledge,* and *love* are nouns; they name something we can talk about, though not see.

A <u>proper</u> <u>noun</u> names a particular person, place, or thing and always begins with a capital letter.

EXAMPLES   Barbara Jordan, Lake Michigan, *Great Expectations*

EXERCISE A. Underline each noun, including proper nouns, in this passage. If a noun appears more than once, underline it each time it appears. (Add 5 points for each correct answer.)

1   Mercury is the planet nearest to the sun. Recently, spacecraft have

2   shown astronomers that Mercury, like our moon, is covered with craters.

3   The surface of Venus also may be cratered, but thick clouds of gas hide the

4   landscape from telescopes. Craters are formed when large meteorites,

5   which are fragments of comets or asteroids, collide with a planet.

HBJ material copyrighted under notice appearing earlier in this work.

EXERCISE B. Underline each noun, including proper nouns, in this passage. If a noun appears more than once, underline it each time it appears. (Add 5 points for each correct answer.)

1   Mount St. Helens, a volcano in the state of Washington, erupted in
2   recent times. Clouds of ash and steam billowed for miles above the peak.
3   The eruption was accompanied by earthquakes, lightning, floods, and
4   fires. Fallout from the explosion drifted across the nation. Mount St.
5   Helens had been inactive for over a century.

EXERCISE C. Underline each noun, including proper nouns, in the following paragraphs. (Add 2 points for each correct answer.)

1   The formation of an island is a remarkable event. This process occurs
2   over millions of years. Erupting volcanoes build mountains on the floor of
3   the sea. Each eruption adds more lava to the pile of volcanic rock, until
4   after many years the volcanic mountain comes within reach of the waves.
5   The potential island may remain as a shoal for ages. When the island
6   finally emerges from under the waves, the cone is pushed up into the air
7   and a rampart of hardened lava is formed, protecting the new island from
8   attacking waves.
9   Plants and animals come to the island, either blown in on the wind or
10 washed in with the current. Some forms of life travel to the new island on
11 natural rafts of tree limbs and matted vegetation. Other forms are carried
12 by the birds that come to the island from other lands. In an experiment
13 Charles Darwin was able to raise eighty-two plants belonging to five
14 different species from the seeds found in a mud ball.

HBJ material copyrighted under notice appearing earlier in this work.

The Pronoun

A pronoun is a word used in place of a noun or more than one noun.

Read the two sentences below. Notice how much better the second sentence sounds than the first. The second sentence contains pronouns.

EXAMPLES   Now that Jane has finished building *Jane's* bookcase, *Jane* is ready to stain the *bookcase* dark brown.
Now that Jane has finished building her bookcase, she is ready to stain it dark brown.

By itself a pronoun conveys no clear meaning. Its meaning becomes clear and specific only when you know what noun it stands for. The noun on which the pronoun depends for its meaning is called the *antecedent*. In the second sentence of the example above, "Jane" is the antecedent that makes the meaning of *her* and *she* clear.

The following words are pronouns:

I	me	myself	my, mine	who	someone
you	him	yourself	your, yours	whom	anyone
he	her	himself	his	whose	everyone
she	us	herself	her, hers	whoever	none
it	them	itself	its	whomever	somebody
we		ourselves	our, ours		anybody
they		yourselves	their, theirs		everybody
		themselves			nobody

EXERCISE A. Fill the blanks in the following sentences with pronouns which may be used in place of the italicized nouns. (Add 10 points for each correct answer.)

1   *Edith Cavell* was a British nurse .... served in Belgium

2   during World War I. In 1907 *Dr. Antoine Depage* had asked Miss Cavell

3   to come to Brussels. .... wanted .... *hospital*

4   modernized according to the principles of Florence Nightingale. With the

5   outbreak of the war in 1914, ... became a Red Cross hospital.

6   The Germans marched into *Belgium* although .... was a

7   neutral country. The hospital was filled with many casualties of the war.

8   Edith Cavell joined an underground *group*. .... gave aid to

9   Belgians of military age and to escaped Allied prisoners. The *Germans*

10   discovered the group and in 1915 .... arrested Edith Cavell

11   and thirty-four other members. *Edith Cavell,* because of ....

HBJ material copyrighted under notice appearing earlier in this work.

3

12 religious convictions, refused to lie, even in order to protect

13 .... was sentenced to death and executed by a

14 firing squad on October 12, 1915.

The following words may be used as pronouns. They may take the place of nouns. (Like some of the pronouns in the first list, these pronouns may also be used as adjectives, as you will see later.)

which	these	neither	few	most	other
what	those	all	many	several	another
this	each	any	much	some	
that	either	both	more	one	

EXAMPLES   The journalism students work together beautifully. **Many** report the news. **Several** do the typing. A **few** edit the copy and send it to the printer. (The pronouns *many, several,* and *few* take the place of the noun *students.*)

Mark showed me a white sweater and a green sweater. "**Which** do you think is appropriate?" he asked. "**Either** is," I replied. (*Which* and *either* are pronouns used in place of the noun *sweater.*)

EXERCISE B. List in order in the spaces below the ten pronouns in the following story; after each pronoun write the word or words it stands for. (Add 5 points for each correct answer.)

Taking part in the teachers' convention as student volunteers, we worked hard all Saturday. A few of us stood at the main door to distribute programs. Some wrote out name tags. Several served as ushers.

Beverly and Randall listened in during a discussion period. They were surprised by the comments of two teachers. One argued for tougher grading standards. Another protested that grades do not represent the true ability of the student. Neither seemed to win the argument. Each, however, took a firm stand.

1. ....   6. ....

2. ....   7. ....

3. ....   8. ....

4. ....   9. ....

5. ....   10. ....

HBJ material copyrighted under notice appearing earlier in this work.

The Adjective

An <u>adjective</u> is a word used to modify a noun or a pronoun.

To modify means *to limit*. An adjective limits the number of things or ideas to which a word can refer, making the meaning more definite. Notice how the adjectives below limit the words they modify, so that each word has a more definite meaning. Notice, too, that some of the words listed as pronouns in Lesson 2 are adjectives when they modify a noun or pronoun.

a big joke, a good joke, a new joke   all cars, both cars, one car
a tall tree, a scrubby tree, an oak tree   each one, another one

An adjective may answer one of three questions about the word it modifies. It may tell *which one, what kind,* or *how many.*

WHICH ONE?   this puppy, that room, the short one
WHAT KIND?   black ink, a rough street, delicious pudding
HOW MANY?   fifty cents, several signs, a few pages, one hit

An adjective does not always stand next to the noun or pronoun it modifies. Sometimes other words separate an adjective from the noun or pronoun modified.

My uncle is tall.

We might have been tardy.

Everyone on the rink looked cold.

The most common adjectives are *a, an,* and *the.* They are sometimes called *articles.* Unless otherwise advised, ignore the articles when adjectives are required for exercises.

EXERCISE A. Circle each adjective in the following paragraph and draw an arrow from the adjective to the word it modifies. (Add 5 points for each adjective and 5 points for each modified word.)

1   In Japan, people grow dwarf trees that have had a famous history and an

2   important place in horticultural art. Through pruning and fertilization, the

3   trees are trained to keep the shape and proportion of larger trees. The trees

4   have an old and windswept appearance, as though they had grown in the

5   out-of-doors. Gardeners can create realistic landscapes in pots and carry

6   scenes of mountain crags or vast plains into their homes.

HBJ material copyrighted under notice appearing earlier in this work.

EXERCISE B. Draw a circle around each of the twenty-five adjectives in the following story. Treat hyphenated compound words like *spine-tingling* as one word. Remember that an adjective modifies a noun or a pronoun. (Add 4 points for each correct answer.)

BEWARE OF THE BEAR!

1   On hot summer nights, Julio and the other boys sleep out in the yard.

2   They put up a tent in a dark corner, where the trees and bushes are thick.

3   That way the boys can easily imagine they are in wild, uninhabited

4   country.

5   One evening Mike suggested that they tell ghost stories or tales of bear

6   hunts. After a particularly spine-tingling story, Mike couldn't sleep; he

7   was too nervous.

8   About midnight he saw something move in the shadows. "Yeow!" he

9   cried out. "There is a black bear! It is really big!"

10   In the sudden confusion, the tent collapsed on top of the boys; each one

11   seemed eager to go in a different direction. Anxious parents ran down

12   from the house. They found a coal-black dog. Like a bear, this animal was

13   very curious. It was sniffing at the writhing, yelling tangle of arms, legs,

14   and bodies under the tent.

HBJ material copyrighted under notice appearing earlier in this work.

Review of Nouns, Pronouns, and Adjectives

EXERCISE A. Each of the following sentences contains two pronouns. In the first column at the right, write the first pronoun in the sentence and the noun it stands for. In the second column, write the second pronoun and the noun it stands for. Words like *my, our, his, her, its, their* should be considered possessive pronouns, not adjectives. (Add 5 points for each correct answer.)

1. Laura passed the ball to Ann, who caught it easily.   ....

2. Otis called his sister, but she didn't answer.   ....

3. When asked about the game, Mike said, "I didn't see it."   ....

4. Since Gabriella found the money, it belongs to her unless claimed.   ....

5. The children like the new bus driver who takes them to school.   ....

6. Although Elliot studied French in school, he didn't feel comfortable speaking it.   ....

7. Denise brought sandwiches with her on the hike and carried them in a knapsack.   ....

8. "You," Jerry said to Lee, "surprised me."   ....

9. Because Sheila enjoyed musical comedies, she tried to see them as often as possible.   ....

10. Paula enjoyed volleyball so much that she played it every day after school.   ....

HBJ material copyrighted under notice appearing earlier in this work.

EXERCISE B. Write in order in the spaces at the right the part of speech of the italicized words in each line. Use these abbreviations: *n.* (noun), *pron.* (pronoun), *adj.* (adjective). (Add 5 points for each correct answer.)

1   *Ernest, who* is invited nearly everywhere by   . . . .

2   friends, has his *favorite definition* of "life of the   . . . .

3   party." *He* believes that a *person* can be in the   . . . .

4   *limelight* merely by being a *good* listener.   . . . .

5   *"People* at a *party,"* he says, "welcome a   . . . .

6   *chance* to make a *big* impression. If you are   . . . .

7   *quiet,* listening attentively, *you* give them an   . . . .

8   opportunity to make a *grand display* of their   . . . .

9   *talents.* If you let *other* people impress you, ...

10   *they* will be impressed by your *graciousness."*   . . . .

EXERCISE C. Underline every adjective in the following passage and draw an arrow from it to the word it modifies. Ignore *a, an,* and *the*. Then draw a circle around every pronoun, including possessive pronouns. (Add 10 points for each correctly marked sentence.)

EX.   Magic tricks have great fascination for me

1. Many tricks are simple.

2. This stunt, however, is different.

3. Four people, who use only their forefingers, can lift a heavy boy.

4. He doesn't jump up; they actually lift him.

5. Two people stand on each side of the boy, who is seated in a chair.

6. First, they slap their hands on his head, with one hand on top of the other, taking turns.

7. Then, both people quickly place their forefingers under his knees and armpits and easily lift him.

8. Everyone has a particular version of the explanation.

9. Some say the body becomes stiff; many claim breath control is the key.

10. Apparently, though, nobody knows the true solution to the mystery.

HBJ material copyrighted under notice appearing earlier in this work.

The Verb

A <u>verb</u> is a word that expresses action or helps to make a statement.

Action verbs express either physical action or mental action. The verb *think,* which expresses mental action, is just as much an action verb as the verb *kick,* which expresses physical action.

EXAMPLES   Carl <u>trains</u> animals for television shows.
Alicia <u>ran</u> in the Boston Marathon.
She always <u>remembers</u> my birthday.

EXERCISE A. Underline each verb in the following paragraph. There are twenty-five of them, and all are action verbs. There may be several verbs in a sentence. (Add 4 points for each correct answer.)

1   Mark, Louisa, and Lynn formed an art group. Since they needed a
2   clubhouse, they planned the construction of a small geodesic dome. The
3   group financed the structure through the sale of some of its work. Louisa
4   sold a portrait and an abstract painting. Mark constructed a Tiffany lamp,
5   and the Posnicks quickly bought it for the room they redecorated in their
6   brownstone apartment across the street. Lynn sketched several local
7   scenes, fashioned the sketches into linoleum blocks, made greeting cards
8   with the blocks, and sold the cards through a local novelty store. The
9   group carefully studied *The Whole Earth Catalog* for instructions.
10   Louisa, Mark, and Lynn decided on a 10½ × 8-foot building. Louisa, the
11   math whiz, performed the necessary mathematical calculations. Mark, an
12   expert bargain finder, shopped for the materials. With the group's
13   earnings, he purchased wood struts, spoke hubs, and plastic covering.
14   The group asked Mark's parents for the use of part of their backyard.
15   They started the construction work on Monday. Louisa cut the wood to
16   the necessary dimensions. Mark formed the cut wood into triangles, and
17   Lynn fastened the triangles together in the shape of a dome. They finished
18   the skeletal structure on Friday. On Saturday they attached the plastic
19   covering. That evening the group celebrated its success in the new
20   clubhouse.

HBJ material copyrighted under notice appearing earlier in this work.

9

A few verbs *link* a noun with a noun or a noun with an adjective. These verbs are called *linking verbs*. To be a linking verb, the verb must be followed by a word that names or describes the subject.

LINKING VERBS   am, is, are, was, were, (will) be, (has) been, become, get (when it means *become*), seem, appear, look, feel, smell, taste, remain, sound

EXAMPLES   Mother **is** a good cyclist.   (mother = cyclist)
This room **has been** empty all day.   (empty room)
George **will be** our leader.   (George = leader)
The witness **remained** silent.   (silent witness)
The dog **seems** friendly.   (friendly dog)

Note: If you can put *is, are, was,* or *were* in place of a verb without greatly changing the meaning of the sentence, you may be sure the verb is a linking verb.

EXAMPLES   The bell **sounds** loud. The bell **is** loud.   (*Sounds* is a linking verb.)
The muffins **taste** good. The muffins **are** good.   (*Taste* is a linking verb).

EXERCISE B. In the left column below are nouns modified by adjectives. By supplying verbs to link the nouns and adjectives, write sentences in the space at the right. Use five different linking verbs. (Add 10 points for each correct sentence.)

EX. the stormy weather   EX. *The weather looks stormy.*

1. the dull knife   1. ....
2. the haunted house   2. ....
3. the shy child   3. ....
4. the calm lake   4. ....
5. the bitter medicine   5. ....

In the left column below are groups of two nouns, both naming the *same* person or thing. By using various linking verbs to connect the paired nouns, write sentences in the space at the right.

EX. Nero—an emperor   EX. *Nero was an emperor.*

6. Marita—treasurer   6. ....
7. Kate—an actress   7. ....
8. the lighthouse—our guide   8. ....
9. mongrels—watchdogs   9. ....
10. the movie—Western   10. ....

HBJ material copyrighted under notice appearing earlier in this work.

The Helping Verb

Very often we use verbs which consist of more than one word.

EXAMPLES   He <u>may</u> help us.

            I <u>should have</u> asked the teacher.

            The criminal <u>must have been</u> planning an escape

A verb of more than one word is called a *verb phrase*. A verb phrase is made up of a main verb preceded by one or more helping verbs. The helping verbs actually help to make the meaning of the main verb more exact.

EXAMPLES   I <u>will</u> sleep.   I <u>did</u> sleep.

            I <u>would</u> sleep.   I <u>was sleeping.</u>

            I <u>must</u> sleep.   I <u>may have been</u> sleeping.

The helping verbs may be separated from the main verb, or parts of the helping verb may be separated from each other.

EXAMPLES   **Do** you <u>believe</u> them?   **Has** one ever <u>been</u> caught?

The common helping verbs are *be (am, is, are—was, were—been); shall, will; have (has, had); do (does, did); can, could; should, would; may, might; must; ought (to).*

Note: The word *not* is not a helping verb. *Not* is an adverb.

EXERCISE A. Complete the verbs in the following sentences by writing suitable helping verbs in the spaces provided. Then underline the entire verb phrase. (Add 10 points for each correct sentence.)

1. Someone . . . . broken into the house.

2. His car . . . . going too fast for safety.

3. I . . . . waiting for Helen.

4. . . . . you met my mother?

5. It . . . . be later than you think.

6. . . . . you help me?

7. . . . . you have a good time?

8. There . . . . been serious consequences.

9. Mr. Prinz . . . . not . . . . persuaded to change.

10. If he . . . . read better, he . . . . learn more.

HBJ material copyrighted under notice appearing earlier in this work.

EXERCISE B. Each line below contains a verb phrase. First find the verb phrase and underline it. Then, in the first column to the right, copy the helping verb (or verbs). In the second column, copy the main verb. (Add 4 points for each correct line.)

		Helping verbs	Main verbs
EX.	<u>Must</u> you <u>see</u> something with	*must*	*see*
1	your eyes before you will believe it?		
2	Since the Greeks could not see the		
3	air, they did not consider it real.		
4	Anaxagoras, however, would not agree		
5	with the crowd. He had discovered		
6	that air must be something real.		
7	Anaxagoras had had a revealing		
8	experience. One day he was carrying a		
9	goatskin that had been filled with		
10	air. (This goatskin may be compared		
11	to a football.) While he was walking		
12	on the beach, he must have stumbled		
13	over a rock. He did not get hurt		
14	because the goatskin had hit the ground		
15	first and the air inside had acted as		
16	a cushion. *Something*, air, had broken		
17	what could have been a very hard fall.		
18	Like Anaxagoras, we must admit that		
19	the air does contain something real.		
20	We could not even breathe if the air		
21	did not contain oxygen. Scientists		
22	have also found nitrogen in the air.		
23	Other elements have been found.		
24	We may discover new facts about air		
25	now that we are probing outer space.		

HBJ material copyrighted under notice appearing earlier in this work.

The Adverb

An <u>adverb</u> is a word used to modify a verb, an adjective, or another adverb.

As its name suggests, an ad*verb* usually tells something about a verb. It may tell (1) *how,* (2) *when,* (3) *where,* or (4) *to what extent* (*how much* or *how often*) the action of the verb occurs.

HOW	Watch **closely**.	(*Closely* modifies *watch.*)
WHEN	We won **recently**.	(*Recently* modifies *won.*)
WHERE	Hang the picture **there**.	(*There* modifies *hang.*)
TO WHAT EXTENT	Carl **usually** walks to school.	(*Usually* modifies *walks.*)

EXERCISE A. Circle the adverb in each sentence. Draw an arrow to the verb it modifies. In the space at the right, state whether the adverb tells *how, when, where, to what extent* (*how much* or *how often*). (Add 10 points for each correctly marked sentence.)

EX. The big drawing (always) attracts a crowd at the county fair.   *to what extent*

1. For weeks merchants cheerfully give numbered tickets with purchases.   . . . .

2. My cousin Lorraine and I finally collected forty tickets.   . . . .

3. "If we're lucky," I often told Lorraine, "we will win a beautiful new car."   . . . .

4. Saturday came, and we eagerly waded through the crowd at the fair.   . . . .

5. Rules stated that the holders of winning tickets must be there.   . . . .

6. At midnight, they promptly started the drawing.   . . . .

7. "The winner of the new car is 608–1313!" shouted the announcer. "Will the holder of number 608–1313 come here?"   . . . .

8. Lorraine then surprised everybody.   . . . .

9. She walked slowly to the platform for her prize.   . . . .

10. She exclaimed, "This is the first prize I have ever won!"   . . . .

HBJ material copyrighted under notice appearing earlier in this work.

13

EXERCISE B. Fill in each blank below with an appropriate adverb modifying a verb. Choose varied, interesting adverbs. (Add 5 points for each correct answer.)

TRYOUT

1   Rena . . . . wanted to get a part in her school's production of

2   *The Diary of Anne Frank.* She was . . . . nervous about

3   auditioning, and she . . . . awaited the day for tryouts. To

4   prepare herself, she . . . . scanned the play over the weekend.

5   . . . . she went back and . . . . studied the role of

6   Anne. . . . . she began to understand how it must have felt to

7   live in hiding for so long. She wondered if she could . . . .

8   portray the girl who had . . . . written the diary.

9   Rena arrived in the auditorium . . . . she

10 looked, she saw other students . . . . thumbing through scripts.

11 She . . . . watched the first group of students read a scene

12 . . . . her turn came. She . . . . hoped

13 that her understanding of the character would come through in her

14 reading. As she began to read the part, she . . . . relaxed. She

15 . . . . enjoyed bringing the play to life.

16   After her turn, she returned to her seat. She sat . . . . waiting

17 to hear the drama teacher's decision. She smiled . . . . when she

18 heard the teacher say, "The role of Anne Frank—Rena Ross."

HBJ material copyrighted under notice appearing earlier in this work.

Adverbs Modify Adjectives and Other Adverbs

Most adverbs modify verbs, but a few are commonly used to modify an adjective.

EXAMPLE   We saw a **very** good movie.

In this sentence you can spot *good* as an adjective modifying *movie*. The adverb *very* modifies the adjective *good*, telling *how* good. Other adverbs commonly used to modify adjectives are *so, too, rather, fairly, somewhat, quite, almost, extremely,* and *unusually.*

An adverb may also modify another adverb.

EXAMPLE   They talk **too** fast.

Fast is an adverb telling how they *talk; too* is an adverb modifying *fast,* telling *how* fast.

EXERCISE A. In each of the following sentences an adverb is italicized. Draw an arrow from this adverb to the word it modifies. In the space at the right, tell whether the modified word is a verb, an adjective, or an adverb. (Add 2½ points for each correct answer.)

1. She plays tennis *well*. . . . .
2. The price seems *very* reasonable. . . . .
3. Melba *seldom* loses her head. . . . .
4. Herbert seemed *unusually* happy. . . . .
5. The *dangerously* narrow bridge scared me. . . . .
6. Bill cried out, "Don't run *so* fast!" . . . .
7. He *almost* never writes a letter. . . . .
8. A *rather* fat clown was juggling oranges. . . . .
9. "I'm *too* drowsy for words," Annette yawned. . . . .
10. Sue works *unusually* hard on Saturdays. . . . .
11. Fran answered *somewhat* sarcastically. . . . .
12. They play an *extremely* fast game. . . . .
13. Does hay *actually* cause hay fever? . . . .
14. We will play a doubleheader *tomorrow*. . . . .
15. At formal occasions, Jake speaks *properly*. . . . .

HBJ material copyrighted under notice appearing earlier in this work.

15

16. May we go to the wrestling match *now?* . . . .

17. Florence *never* eats parsley. . . . .

18. The second speech was *less* interesting. . . . .

19. He was *fully* aware of his plight. . . . .

20. Can you *really* capture chiggers alive? . . . .

EXERCISE B. Underline the adverbs in the following sentences. In the spaces at the right, tell which word or words the adverb modifies and whether it tells *how, when, where, to what extent* (*how much* or *how often*). If there are two adverbs in the sentence, list in order the words they modify and what they tell. (Add 5 points for each correctly marked line.)

EX. Shall we leave <u>now</u>? *shall leave* . . . . *when* . .

1. Come quickly. . . . .

2. I can run faster than you. . . . .

3. Sheila seems very sure of herself. . . . .

4. Later I believed him. . . . .

5. Our team was too slow. . . . .

6. Is he always tardy? . . . .

7. Your new books are here. . . . .

8. Did you work hard? . . . .

9. Marina has been there. . . . .

10. This problem is especially hard. . . . .

11. The boys work slowly. . . . .

12. What shall we do now? . . . .

13. These were expertly made. . . . .

14. She will never believe you. . . . .

15. I will be there. . . . .

16. Karen danced gracefully. . . . .

17. Joshua left yesterday for school. . . . .

18. She won easily. . . . .

19. Carla often goes to concerts. . . . .

20. The troupe rehearsed diligently. . . . .

HBJ material copyrighted under notice appearing earlier in this work.

The Preposition

A word used to show the relationship of a noun or a pronoun to another word in the sentence is called a preposition.

In the following sentences the prepositions, printed in red, tell how the underlined words are related.

EXAMPLE We store <u>wood</u> in the empty <u>barn</u>.
The school <u>is</u> around the <u>corner</u>.
Kim <u>wrote</u> to the <u>President</u>.
There was a <u>parade</u> on that <u>street</u>.

The following words may be used as prepositions. Some may also be used as adverbs or conjunctions.

about	before	by	like	to
above	behind	concerning	near	toward
across	below	down	of	under
after	beneath	during	off	underneath
against	beside	except	on	until
along	between	for	over	up
among	beyond	from	past	upon
around	but (meaning	in	since	with
at	*except*)	into	through	without

A group of words beginning with a preposition and ending with a noun or a pronoun is called a prepositional phrase.

EXAMPLES in the empty barn   after the meeting
to the President   during the day
under the oak table   below the surface

Note that the noun in the prepositional phrase may be modified.

EXERCISE A. Each of the following sentences contains two prepositional phrases. Draw a line under the phrases. (Add 5 points for each correct answer.)

EX. The books <u>of poetry</u> are <u>on the top shelf</u>.

1. Do your work in study hall or do it at home.

2. After the dance we went to Gerry's house.

3. Lorraine Hansberry's plays on Broadway were praised by critics.

4. Behind the fence I found my bicycle with a flat tire.

5. Since September she has been principal of our school.

HBJ material copyrighted under notice appearing earlier in this work.

6. As I walked from the building, I met the principal on the steps.

7. For social studies I read a book about Sacajawea.

8. Margaret lives in an apartment building on Sheridan Avenue.

9. Beyond the valley the mountains were black against the sky.

10. During vacation I kept busy working around the house.

Many words commonly used as prepositions may also be used as adverbs. If you will remember that *a preposition always begins a phrase, but an adverb does not begin a phrase,* you will be able to tell whether a word is a preposition or an adverb.

EXAMPLES I jumped **across** the deep ditch.   (*Across* is a preposition beginning the prepositional phrase *across the deep ditch.*)

I jumped **across**   (*Across* is an adverb modifying *jumped* and telling where I jumped.)

He stayed <u>under the</u> water for a long time.   (*Under* is a preposition beginning the prepositional phrase *under the water.*)

He stayed <u>under</u> for a long time.   (*Under* is an adverb modifying *stayed* and telling where he stayed.)

EXERCISE B. In the space at the right, classify the italicized word as a preposition or as an adverb. Use these abbreviations: *prep.* (preposition), *adv.* (adverb). (Add 10 points for each correct answer.)

1. Time passes *on*.   . . . .

2. I put my trophy *on* the coffee table.   . . . .

3. "Have you seen him *since?*" she asked.   . . . .

4. "I haven't seen him *since* the party," I replied.   . . . .

5. *Behind* me stood Coach Davis.   . . . .

6. He soon fell *behind* in his algebra class.   . . . .

Write short sentences using these words as directed.

7. *up* as a preposition . . . .

8. *up* as an adverb . . . .

9. *down* as a preposition . . . .

10. *down* as an adverb . . . .

HBJ material copyrighted under notice appearing earlier in this work.

The Conjunction and the Interjection

A conjunction is a word that joins words or groups of words.

Only the conjunctions *and*, *but*, and *or* will be considered in this lesson. These three conjunctions join sentence parts that are alike.

EXAMPLES   Prejudice **and** ignorance go hand in hand.   (*And* joins two nouns.)
Grandma is cranky **but** lovable.   (*But* joins adjectives.)
During spare moments the students ice-skate **or** ski.   (*Or* joins verbs.)
She speaks French clearly **and** fluently.   (*And* joins adverbs.)
Go up the hill **and** past the pond.   (*And* joins prepositional phrases.)
I told a good joke, **but** nobody laughed.   (*But* joins two statements.)

EXERCISE A. Circle the conjunction or conjunctions in each sentence and underline the words or word groups that are connected by each conjunction. (Add 10 points for each correct answer.)

EX. I recognized you (but) not your brother.

1. Every day I have to feed my dog and my cat.

2. I saw a man or a boy enter the side door.

3. Always try to do the job quietly and correctly.

4. The clown looked sad but made me laugh.

5. Would you want a blue or a red car?

6. They gave me tickets, and I plan to go.

7. I can ride my motorcycle on the road or through the woods.

8. "Slow but sure" is my motto.

9. The defendant could either pay a fine or go to jail.

10. The coach yelled at me, but I didn't mind.

An interjection is an exclamatory word that expresses emotion. It has no grammatical relation to the rest of the sentence.

EXAMPLES   Whew! I'm glad that's over.
Hey! Stop that!
Oh, never mind.

Spotting the Parts of Speech.   The work that a word does in a sentence determines what part of speech it is in that sentence. The same word may be

HBJ material copyrighted under notice appearing earlier in this work.

used as several different parts of speech. Notice how the words printed in red in the following sentences are used as different parts of speech.

EXAMPLES
We often **study** geography together.   (verb expressing action)
She has a large desk in her **study**.   (noun naming a type of room)
We finished our work in **study** hall.   (adjective modifying *hall*)

He drew a **picture** of the sea.   (noun naming a thing)
Can you **picture** me as an acrobat?   (verb expressing mental action)
Our **picture** window is cracked.   (adjective modifying *window*)

EXERCISE B. In the space at the right of each sentence, write the part of speech of the italicized word. In making your decision, ask yourself what work the word does in the sentence. (Add 5 points for each correct answer.)

1. We took an express *train*. . . . .

2. A *train* whistle sounded in the distance. . . . .

3. I will *train* your dog. . . . .

4. *Cross* the street on a green light. . . . .

5. Turn right at the next *cross* street. . . . .

6. She was wearing a gold *cross*. . . . .

7. The boss will *fire* me. . . . .

8. The *fire* department is always ready. . . . .

9. We saw a large *fire* in the distance. . . . .

10. He has a bald *head*. . . . .

11. Who is the *head* usher? . . . .

12. She will *head* the freshman class. . . . .

13. He can *field* a ball faster than any other player. . . . .

14. The new athletic *field* is ready for use. . . . .

15. A *field* mouse scampered by. . . . .

16. Everyone *left* the building in a hurry. . . . .

17. I sat on the *left* side of the room. . . . .

18. Turn *left* at the next corner. . . . .

19. Let's walk *around*. . . . .

20. They walked *around* the block. . . . .

HBJ material copyrighted under notice appearing earlier in this work.

Chapter Review

EXERCISE A. Write in the spaces at the right the part of speech described. (Add 10 points for each correct answer.)

1. modifies a noun ....
2. joins together two words or word groups ....
3. modifies an adverb ....
4. names a person, place, thing, or idea ....
5. expresses action ....
6. shows the relationship between a following noun or pronoun and some other word ....
7. takes the place of a noun ....
8. modifies a pronoun ....
9. expresses sudden emotion ....
10. modifies a verb ....

EXERCISE B. Write complete sentences using the italicized words as directed. (Add 5 points for each correct sentence.)

1. *shine* as a verb ....
2. *shine* as a noun ....
3. *shout* as a verb ....
4. *shout* as a noun ....
5. *light* as a noun ....
6. *light* as an adjective ....
7. *light* as a verb ....
8. *bus* as a noun ....
9. *bus* as an adjective ....
10. *Sunday* as a noun ....
11. *Sunday* as an adjective ....
12. *each* as a pronoun ....
13. *each* as an adjective ....
14. *pepper* as an adjective ....

HBJ material copyrighted under notice appearing earlier in this work.

15. *pepper* as a verb ....

16. *pepper* as a noun ....

17. *bicycle* as a noun ....

18. *bicycle* as an adjective ....

19. *mushroom* as a noun ....

20. *mushroom* as a verb ....

EXERCISE C. In the space to the right of each line, write the part of speech of the italicized word. Use these abbreviations: *n.* (noun), *pron.* (pronoun), *adj.* (adjective), *v.* (verb), *adv.* (adverb), *prep.* (preposition), *conj.* (conjunction). Study the way the word is used before making up your mind. (Add 5 points for each correct answer.)

1   The destructive *force* of the atom is familiar to all of   ....

2   us, but we know *considerably* less about its constructive uses.   ....

3   Materials *like* sulfur, zinc, and iodine can be made radio-   ....

4   active for *scientific* purposes. The atoms of such materials   ....

5   are said to be "tagged" with radioactivity. *Their* movements   ....

6   can be *traced* with a Geiger counter.   ....

7   By injecting the tagged elements into *live* organisms, ...

8   *American* scientists are learning much about the growth and   ....

9   *structure* of cells. Botanists using tagged atoms may at last   ....

10 discover how green leaves *manufacture* starch. Surgeons   ....

11 equipped with a *Geiger* counter can find the exact location of a   ....

12 brain tumor by tracing a dye mixed *with* radioactive material.   ....

13 Doctors have learned to treat diseases like anemia *or* cancer   ....

14 of the thyroid with radioactive *iron* or iodine.   ....

15 Industry too has found uses for tagged atoms. *They* help   ....

16 geologists to map underground oil deposits. They *can* also be   ....

17 a means of measuring the thickness of glass and *plastic,* and of   ....

18 finding flaws in metal *castings,* impurities in steel, and leaks   ....

19 in water pipes. *Undoubtedly,* the uses for tagged atoms will   ....

20 continue to grow, making possible *future* miracles of science.   ....

HBJ material copyrighted under notice appearing earlier in this work.

Usage: BRING and TAKE, GOOD and WELL

Note; In this lesson and following lessons you will encounter the terms "standard" and "nonstandard." The word *standard* suggests a model with which things can be compared. In this case, the model—standard English—is the set of widely accepted usage conventions followed in books, magazines, and most news sources. All other kinds of usage, which should be avoided in formal writing and speaking, are referred to as *nonstandard* English.

bring, take Use *bring* when the meaning is to convey something *to* the person speaking. Use *take* when the meaning is to convey something *away from* the person speaking. It's all a matter of direction. *Bring* corresponds with *come, take* with *go.*

STANDARD When you *come* to see me, **bring** your new camera.
STANDARD Please *go* to the library and **take** this book with you.
STANDARD After the dog had **brought** me the newspaper, it grabbed my socks, and **took** them into Mom and Dad's room.

good, well *Good* is always an adjective. Do not use *good* to modify a verb, that is, to describe an action. People do not perform actions good; they always do them *well.* Use the adverb *well* to modify a verb.

NONSTANDARD She spoke *good* in the debate.
STANDARD She spoke **well** in the debate. (adverb modifying the verb *spoke*)
STANDARD Her arguments were **good**. (adjective modifying the noun *arguments*)

Well, however, may be used as an adjective, too, when it has certain special meanings.

1. To appear well dressed or well groomed.

EXAMPLE She looks **well** in blue. (modifies *she*)

2. To be in good health

EXAMPLES Since his vacation, he looks **well**. (modifies *he*)
Aren't you feeling **well** today? (modifies *you*)

EXERCISE A. Select the correct one of the two words in parentheses and copy it in the space at the right. (Add 5 points for each correct answer.)

1. When I go to Estes Park, I always (bring, take) my kite along. . . . .

2. Perhaps someday I will drive a truck as (good, well) as you do. . . . .

HBJ material copyrighted under notice appearing earlier in this work.

3. Why don't you (bring, take) Rosalie when you come back? . . . .

4. Everyone agrees that she plays first base unusually (good, well). . . . .

5. "Come here this instant!" Mother called to Doug. "And (bring, take) those matches with you!" . . . .

6. If your parents give you permission, we will (bring, take) you with us on our vacation. . . . .

7. Not one of the meals at camp tasted (good, well). . . . .

8. If you will trust me with that much money, I will (bring, take) it to the bank for you. . . . .

9. Now that he is leaving, isn't he going to (bring, take) these tennis rackets with him? . . . .

10. Dennis did not trim the hedge as (good, well) as usual. . . . .

11. Come to the dance tonight, and (bring, take) your sister with you. . . . .

12. A big breakfast always looks (good, well) to Aunt Harriet. . . . .

13. When she goes for a walk, she always (brings, takes) her German shepherd with her. . . . .

14. You can (bring, take) a guest when you come to the party. . . . .

15. We did the job as (good, well) as we could. . . . .

16. When Diane went to visit her friend in the hospital, she (brought, took) six magazines, three books, and a bunch of flowers. . . . .

17. The outfield did (good, well) to make only two errors this afternoon. . . . .

18. Does that musk aftershave lotion smell (good, well), or is it too strong? . . . .

19. Did she remember to (bring, take) her sunglasses when she left for the beach? . . . .

20. We should (bring, take) our jackets when we go to the stadium tonight. . . . .

HBJ material copyrighted under notice appearing earlier in this work.

Spelling: Sounds and Spelling Patterns

The letters in our alphabet are the symbols we use to represent our speech sounds. However, we use more sounds than there are letters in the alphabet to represent them, which makes learning to spell in our language somewhat complicated. The complications may be partially overcome by learning *spelling patterns* that involve the use of combinations of letters to spell certain sounds. To show the *sounds* of a word, rather than the letters, a special phonetic alphabet has been developed.

The chart below, "Consonant Sounds and Their Common Spellings," summarizes 24 main consonant sounds of English, the symbols used to represent these sounds, and common ways of spelling them. The *symbol* for each consonant sound is written between a pair of slanted lines at the left.

Consonant Sounds and Their Common Spellings

Sound	At the Beginning	At the End
/p/	**p:** pie	**p:** rip; **pe:** ripe
/t/	**t:** ten	**t:** pet; **te:** date
/k/	**k:** kit **c:** cold;	**ck:** lick; **ke:** like
/ch/	**ch:** chin	**tch:** witch; **ch:** reach
/b/	**b:** bed	**b:** tub; **be:** tube
/d/	**d:** do	**d:** rid; **de:** ride
/g/	**g:** get	**g:** beg; **gue:** league
/j/	**j:** jet; **g:** gentle	**dge:** budge; **ge:** cage
/f/	**f:** fun; **ph:** phrase	**ff:** stuff; **fe:** life; **f:** beef; **ph:** paragraph
/v/	**v:** very	**ve:** save
/s/	**s:** see; **c:** center	**ss:** glass; **s:** bus; **se:** case; **ce:** rice
/z/	**z:** zoo	**z:** quiz; **zz:** buzz; **se:** rose; **ze:** sneeze
/sh/	**sh:** ship	**sh:** push
/zh/	**j:** Jacques	**ge:** rouge; (in the middle) **s:** treasure
/r/	**r:** run; **wr:** wrist; **rh:** rhyme	**r:** car; **re:** care
/l/	**l:** lose	**ll:** pill; **le:** smile; **l:** fail
/m/	**m:** move	**m:** Sam; **me:** same; **mb:** tomb
/n/	**n:** nose; **gn:** gnaw; **kn:** know	**n:** pin; **ne:** pine
/ng/		**ng:** strong; **n:** trunk
/th/	**th:** thick	**th:** path
/th/	**th:** then	**th:** smooth; **the:** bathe
/y/	**y:** you; **u** /yū/: use	
/w/	**w:** will; **o** /wu/: one: **qu:** /kw/; quick	
/h/	**h:** hat; **wh:** who	

HBJ material copyrighted under notice appearing earlier in this work.

The chart below, "Vowel Sounds and Their Common Spellings," shows the symbols for 14 main vowel sounds and the vowel sound called a *schwa*.

Vowel Sounds and Their Common Spellings

Fourteen Vowel Sounds

Sounds	/i/	/e/	/a/	/u/	/o/
Spellings and Examples	**i:** hit	**e:** red **ea:** dead	**a:** cat	**u:** but **o:** son	**o:** top **a:** far

Sounds	/ī/	/ē/	/ā/	/ū/	/ō/
Spellings and Examples	**igh:** high **y:** try **ie:** die	**ee:** deed **ea:** heat **e:** he **ie:** chief **ei:** deceive	**ai:** wait **ay:** pay **ei:** weigh	**oo:** root **ew:** few **ue:** Sue **o:** to	**oa:** goat **ow:** slow **oe:** hoe **o:** no

Sounds	/o͞o/	/ou/	/oi/	/au/
Spellings and Examples	**oo:** look **u:** push	**ou:** out **ow:** cow	**oi:** oil **oy:** toy	**au:** haul **aw:** flaw **a:** ball **o:** long **ough:** fought **augh:** caught

The Vowel Sound Schwa /ə/

	i	e	ea	u	o
	stir girl	were her	learn earth	burn spur	world worse

	-er	-or	-ar			
/ər/ Sound	runner father	actor navigator	liar sugar			

	-al	-le	-el	-ul	-ile	-il
/ə/ Sound	moral rural	battle circle	camel travel	beautiful useful	fertile juvenile	April council

	-en	-an	-ain	-in	
/ən/ Sound	frozen oaken	American woman	captain mountain	robin basin	

HBJ material copyrighted under notice appearing earlier in this work.

Building Vocabulary: Choosing the Right Meaning

At the end of most chapters in ENGLISH WORKSHOP, you will find a lesson called "Building Vocabulary." In some of these lessons, you will study useful methods of enlarging your vocabulary. In other lessons, you will study lists of words and meanings that you should try to add to your vocabulary. In this first vocabulary lesson, you will review some ideas about *context,* one of the basic means of building vocabulary and of using correctly the words you already know.

The context of a word is the *situation* in which it is used. The situation means both the *surrounding words* in a sentence or paragraph (the *verbal* context) and the *whole subject* of the sentence or paragraph.

The context in which a word is used shows what it means in that instance.

Many English words have several different though related meanings. In reading, we can usually tell from the context which meaning the writer intends. Often, too, we can form a good idea of the meaning of an unfamiliar word, if we know how to interpret context clues.

EXAMPLES   Mr. Seeley was a **contemporary** of my mother at college.
Our house is furnished entirely in the **contemporary** style.

Notice how much these two contexts tell you about the word *contemporary.* In the first sentence, it is used as a noun, in the second as an adjective. The first sentence means that Mother and Mr. Seeley were at college together. *Contemporary* must mean "one who lives at the same time." As an adjective, it can mean "happening at the same time," but is that the meaning in the second sentence? Here, *contemporary* means "contemporary with us —happening in the present time." Often *contemporary* is used as an adjective and means "modern."

Think of other contexts in which you might use the word *contemporary* in these two different meanings. Then, in preparation for the exercise that follows, study the meanings and examples given for the following words.

contemporary /kən tém pə rér ē/ 1. *adj.* Living or happening at the same time.—*n.* A person living at the same time as another. 2. *adj.* Like something in the present time; modern.

deliberate /di líb ər it/ *adj.* 1. Carefully thought out, done on purpose: *a deliberate lie.* 2. Slow, unhurried: *a deliberate movement.*

equilibrium /ḗ kwə líb rē eəm/ *n.* 1. The condition of an object which is acted on by opposing forces in such a way that it does not move: *The diving bell sank halfway down and stopped, in a state of equilibrium. The tightrope walker used a long pole to maintain equilibrium.* 2. A calm, well-balanced state of mind: *Herman's bad mark has upset his equilibrium.*

HBJ material copyrighted under notice appearing earlier in this work.

grapple /gráp əl/ *v.* 1. To hold tightly, as with a hook designed for the purpose: *The cruiser grappled the captured submarine to its side.* 2. To fight at close quarters: *The guard grappled with the bank robber.*

inconsistent /ín kən sís tənt/ *adj.* 1. Not in agreement or harmony with something: *a statement inconsistent with the facts.* 2. Changeable, unreliable: *inconsistent behavior.*

inertia /in úr shə/ *n.* 1. In science, the tendency of an object to keep moving or remain standing still until some force acts on it: *When the rocket engines cut out, the ship's inertia will carry it to the moon.* 2. Of persons, sluggishness, unwillingness to make an effort: *Dale failed the course through sheer inertia.*

liability /lī ə bíl ə tē/ *n.* 1. In law, the state of being responsible for a debt, penalty, or expense: *A person who causes an accident has a liability for the damage.* 2. A debt (often used in the plural); anything that lessens the worth or effectiveness of a person or thing: *Although Christopher is sometimes quite witty, his sharp tongue is more a liability than an asset.*

EXERCISE. In the blank space in each sentence, write the word from the lesson that makes the best sense in the context. Then, in the parentheses after the blank, write the number of the meaning of the word that applies in the context. In some cases, a verb may need to change form to agree with the rest of the sentence. (Add 5 points for each correct answer.)

1. Art's behavior has been rather . . . . ( ), but I think his failure to improve has been due simply to . . . . ( ).

2. The court established Mr. Chutney's . . . . ( ) for his son's debts.

3. Gertrude Stein was a(n) . . . . ( ) of Ernest Hemingway.

4. Dad likes classical music, but Mother prefers . . . . ( ) music.

5. Martha . . . . ( ) with the problem for over an hour but still could not find the answer.

6. The incoming waves and the outgoing tide held the boat in a state of . . . . ( ).

7. On the moon, an automobile would weigh about one sixth of what it weighs on earth, but its . . . . ( ) would be exactly the same.

8. Max's very . . . . ( ) way of speaking is a(n) . . . . ( ) to any group that wants to reach a quick decision.

HBJ material copyrighted under notice appearing earlier in this work.

CHAPTER 2

The Sentence Base: Verb and Subject

The eight parts of speech are of little use until they are organized into sentences to express thoughts. You can better understand what a sentence is and how its parts work together if you learn to recognize the "sentence base." This knowledge will help you to understand the grammar of your language and to write your own ideas in clear, complete sentences.

LESSON 15

Subject and Predicate

A <u>sentence</u> is a group of words expressing a complete thought. In order to express a complete thought, a sentence consists of two parts: the <u>subject</u> and the <u>predicate</u>. The <u>subject</u> of the sentence is that part about which something is being said. The <u>predicate</u> is that part which says something about the subject.

SUBJECT	PREDICATE
A heavy rain	had spoiled our plans.

PREDICATE	SUBJECT
In the distance were	low-lying black clouds.

EXERCISE A. Underline the subject once and the predicate twice. The predicate may come before the subject. (Add 10 points for each correctly marked sentence.)

EX. <u>Alice</u> <u><u>plays</u></u> the clarinet.

EX. In the doorway <u><u>stood</u></u> <u>my father</u>.

1. I frequently daydream about the future.

2. The achievements of scientists will change our lives.

3. Education will undoubtedly benefit from scientific progress.

4. Teaching machines may someday replace classroom lectures.

5. Tape recordings have already taught important facts to students.

6. Hypnotism could revolutionize teaching procedures.

7. More interesting are other speculations.

8. We may freeze a person alive one day.

HBJ material copyrighted under notice appearing earlier in this work.

9. This person might be revived after decades of the deep-freeze treatment.

10. Today's fantastic science fiction often becomes tomorrow's reality.

EXERCISE B. The groups of words below are not sentences. In some of them the subject is missing; in others the predicate is missing. Make up the missing part for each sentence and write it in the space given. Include some modifiers for each added subject or predicate. Underline the subject once, the predicate twice. (Add 10 points for each correct sentence.)

1. . . . .
decided to have an international luncheon in honor of United Nations Day.

2. . . . .
decorated their classroom with flags from other countries.

3. In the center of the room was . . . .
. . . .

4. Many friends and relatives . . . .
. . . .

5. Chile con carne from Spain . . . .
. . . .

6. . . . .
brought some fried banana chips.

7. Souvlaki and other foods from Greece . . . .
. . . .

8. . . . .
ate too much French bread.

9. Delicious mixtures of dried fruit, sunflower seeds, and almonds . . . .
. . . .

10. After two hours at the luncheon table, we . . . .
. . . .

HBJ material copyrighted under notice appearing earlier in this work.

The Verb

The <u>verb</u> is the principal word or group of words in the complete predicate.

Identifying the predicate is the first step in determining whether a group of words is a sentence. The words underlined twice in the examples below make up the *complete predicate*. The words in red are the *simple predicate,* usually referred to as the *verb*.

EXAMPLE   <u>Ralph **bought** a new typewriter.</u>

verb: *bought*

When helping verbs are used, the verb in a sentence is a group of words.

EXAMPLE   <u>Helen **has revealed** the secret.</u>

verb: *has revealed*

In a verb of more than one word (a verb phrase), the words may be separated.

EXAMPLES   <u>Ralph **will** probably **sell** his old machine.</u>
<u>**Has** Helen already **revealed** the secret?</u>

In questions, the parts of the verb are often separated. You can easily find all the words that make up the verb by changing the question into a statement. Even though the statement will not always make much sense, the parts of the verb will come together.

QUESTION   What **is** that dog **barking** at?
STATEMENT   That dog **is barking** at what.

EXERCISE A. Draw a line under the complete predicate and a circle around the verb in each of the following sentences. If the parts of a verb are separated, be sure to circle each part. In your mind, change questions into statements. (Add 10 points for each correctly marked sentence.)

EX.   The moon ⓦⓘⓛⓛ then ⓟⓐⓢⓢ between the earth and the sun.

1. That radio station reports news all day long.

2. Your help has always been valuable to me.

3. Worst of all is the multiple-choice spelling test.

4. Sea urchins have many movable spines.

5. The rusty hatchet looks dull.

6. Did the burglar have a key to the store?

7. The surgeon did not recommend an immediate operation.

HBJ material copyrighted under notice appearing earlier in this work.

8. Is the pilot light of the furnace still burning?

9. Have you ever heard of a ''devil's tattoo''?

10. A diet limited to proteins and fats will actually starve a rat to death.

EXERCISE B. Underline the verb in each sentence. Be sure to include all parts of a verb having more than one word. (Add 5 points for each correct answer.)

1. Folk tales and legends have filled the world with imaginary creatures.

2. Many of these creatures are composed of parts of various real animals.

3. The mythical manticore had the face of a man, the body of a lion, and the tail of a scorpion.

4. This powerful beast could leap across huge distances at its prey.

5. According to legend, the manticore would devour a person quickly with its three rows of teeth.

6. A glance at the Gorgon could also be a fatal occurrence.

7. The Gorgon, a creature with a woman's body and face, grew snakes from her head as hair.

8. One look into the Gorgon's eyes would turn unlucky viewers into stone.

9. The griffin was formed from the head and wings of an eagle and the body of a lion.

10. A monster with the temperament of both of these animals, the griffin was known for its predatory habits.

11. Have you read the story of the labors of Hercules?

12. The king had assigned Hercules the task of killing the Hydra.

13. Why was the task considered impossible?

14. The Hydra had the body of a dog with nine snake heads on long necks.

15. One snake head could be cut off.

16. Two more heads would immediately grow in its place.

17. Hercules seared each neck with a torch.

18. Because of this action, the heads could not grow back.

19. The Chimera is commonly pictured with the head of a lion, the body of a goat, and the tail of a serpent.

20. From the safety of winged Pegasus' back, Bellerophon slew the Chimera.

HBJ material copyrighted under notice appearing earlier in this work.

The Simple Subject

The **simple subject** is the main word or group of words in the complete subject.

The complete subject is built around the simple subject just as the complete predicate is built around the verb. In the examples below, the complete subject is underlined; the simple subject is in red.

EXAMPLES   The neighbors' children play mostly in our yard.

simple subject: *children*

Into the ring stepped the unpopular champion

simple subject: *champion*

In this book the term *subject* will be used to mean the simple subject.

To find the subject in a sentence, first find the verb. Then ask yourself *who?* or *what?* in front of the verb.

EXAMPLES   The characters in Katherine Anne Porter's novel are realistic.
1. verb: *are*
2. Who are? *characters* are
3. subject: *characters*

This new spaceship has been designed for the earth-moon run.
1. verb: *has been designed*
2. What has been designed? *spaceship* has been designed
3. subject: *spaceship*

The words *there* and *here* are not subjects although they may seem to be when they come at the beginning of a sentence. If you find the verb first and then answer the question *who?* or *what?* about the verb, you will never make the mistake of selecting *there* or *here* as subjects.

EXAMPLE   There will be a dance after the basketball game.
1. verb: *will be*
2. What will be? *dance* will be
3. subject: *dance*

Sometimes you will find the subject in a question more easily if you change the question into a statement. *Where did you find the lost wallet?* becomes the statement *You did find the lost wallet where*. Changing the question to a statement puts the subject in its more usual position before the verb.

EXAMPLE   Where did you find the lost wallet?
1. verb: *did find*
2. Who did find? *you* did find
3. subject: *you*

HBJ material copyrighted under notice appearing earlier in this work.

EXERCISE. Find the verb in each of the following sentences and write it in the verb column. Then ask *who?* or *what?* before the verb and write the subject in the subject column. Watch out for sentences beginning with *there* or *here*. (Add 5 points for each correct answer.)

	Subject	*Verb*
EX. A new bridge across the Chippewa River was built last summer.	*bridge*	*was built*
1. The town's water pipe was in the way of the new bridge.	. . . .	. . . .
2. What solution did the town adopt?	. . . .	. . . .
3. There was a good place for a new pipe along the underside of the bridge.	. . . .	. . . .
4. Last night brought the coldest weather in ten years.	. . . .	. . . .
5. At three o'clock in the morning the town was awakened by the fire siren.	. . . .	. . . .
6. In the center of town a big house was blazing.	. . . .	. . . .
7. The five hoses were useless.	. . . .	. . . .
8. The water had frozen in the exposed pipe under the bridge.	. . . .	. . . .
9. The house was owned by the construction engineer on the new bridge.	. . . .	. . . .
10. The poor man's mistake had come home to roost.	. . . .	. . . .

HBJ material copyrighted under notice appearing earlier in this work.

Finding the Subject

In command or request sentences, the subject you is understood even though the word you does not appear in the sentence.

EXAMPLES Open the window.   Leave the room!
1. verb: *open*   1. verb: *leave*
2. Who opens? (*you*) open   2. Who leaves? (*you*) leave
3. subject: *you*   3. subject: *you*

When the subject consists of two or more connected words that have the same verb, it is called a compound subject. The usual connecting words are and, or, and nor.

EXAMPLES Seniors and juniors may take this course.
1. verb: *may take*
2. Who may take? *seniors* and *juniors* may take
3. compound subject: *seniors . . . juniors*

Books, stationery, and other school supplies are sold here.
1. verb: *are sold*
2. What are sold? *books, stationery,* and *supplies* are sold
3. compound subject: *books, stationery, . . . supplies*

A compound verb consists of two or more connected verbs that have the same subject. The usual connecting words are and, but, or, and nor.

EXAMPLE I took your advice and went to the special help class.
compound verb: *took . . . went*

The subject of a sentence is never in a prepositional phrase.

EXAMPLE Two of your answers are correct.
1. Verb: *are*   2. What are? *two* are   3. subject: *two*

In this example, the subject cannot be *answers* because the sentence does not say, "Your answers are correct"; it says, "Two . . . are correct." *Answers* is part of the prepositional phrase *of your answers*. An easy way to avoid choosing the incorrect word as subject in sentences like this is to draw a line through all prepositional phrases in the sentence.

EXERCISE. Draw a line through all prepositional phrases in each of the following sentences. Select the verbs and the subjects from each sentence and write them in the spaces at the right. An understood subject should be placed in parentheses: (*you*). Be sure to include all parts of a compound subject or a compound verb. (Add 5 points for each correct sentence.)

HBJ material copyrighted under notice appearing earlier in this work.

	Subject	Verb
EX. Each of the men will help.	*Each*	*will help*
1. Do you and Maria like humorous fiction?	....	....
2. Read James Thurber's stories.	....	....
3. His funny stories are full of peculiar people and animals.	....	....
4. Can such eccentric relatives and dogs actually exist?	....	....
5. Sit down and listen to me.	....	....
6. Here are three particularly odd characters.	....	....
7. Have you ever been afraid of burglars during the night?	....	....
8. One of Thurber's aunts has such a phobia.	....	....
9. Why is she always throwing shoes?	....	....
10. The cause of this action is her fear of imaginary burglars.	....	....
11. That is the only reason!	....	....
12. A cousin in this story is also odd.	....	....
13. How does he act at night?	....	....
14. Every hour he wakes up breathless and grabs spirits of camphor.	....	....
15. One sniff from the bottle will revive the nervous cousin.	....	....
16. Otherwise there is the fear of suffocation!	....	....
17. How peculiar relatives are!	....	....
18. What are Thurber's dogs doing?	....	....
19. One of his dogs growls and bites at the air near panic-stricken guests.	....	....
20. Other dogs and relatives are even stranger!	....	....

HBJ material copyrighted under notice appearing earlier in his work.

Practice in Finding the Verb and Its Subject

EXERCISE A. Write the verb and subject in each of the following sentences; put understood subjects in parentheses. Remember to (1) cross out prepositional phrases; (2) find the verb first, then ask *who?* or *what?*; and (3) include all parts of a compound subject, a compound verb, and a verb of more than one word. (Add 10 points for each correct sentence.)

	Subject	*Verb*
1. The tilt of the earth is one reason for changes in daylight hours.	. . . .	. . . .
2. Do earthquakes cause tidal waves?	. . . .	. . . .
3. Skin the catfish.	. . . .	. . . .
4. How does a hibernating animal avoid starvation?	. . . .	. . . .
5. I have never played shadow tag.	. . . .	. . . .
6. Helena Rubinstein built a profitable cosmetics empire.	. . . .	. . . .
7. One spring there was a violent tornado in Illinois.	. . . .	. . . .
8. There are many differences between an alligator and a crocodile.	. . . .	. . . .
9. Trees and telephone wires were severely damaged by the storm.	. . . .	. . . .
10. In her purse were several dollars and some valuable papers.	. . . .	. . . .

EXERCISE B. Follow the directions for Exercise A. (Add 5 points for each correct sentence.)

	Subject	*Verb*
1. With a touch of its horn, a unicorn could purify a poisoned stream.	. . . .	. . . .
2. Do plants and animals thrive in Death Valley?	. . . .	. . . .
3. Parasol ants raise their own crop of mushrooms and eat nothing else.	. . . .	. . . .
4. What does this signal mean to an airplane pilot?	. . . .	. . . .

HBJ material copyrighted under notice appearing earlier in this work.

37

5. Hurry home and tell your parents. ....

6. Among the modern poets are Gwendolyn Brooks and Lucille Clifton. ....

7. Have the firefighters and the police been notified yet? ....

8. Did you or she write and send this note? ....

9. A flashy new sports car rounded the corner and pulled up beside us. ....

10. Open the box and look inside. ....

11. Boys and girls busily washed the dishes and cleaned the house. ....

12. Neither of my cousins has ever been here. ....

13. There are both sopranos and tenors in the choir. ....

14. Brett and Mary will probably win the election. ....

15. By how much did the committee underestimate our expenses? ....

16. At last came her long-awaited opportunity. ....

17. Watch those clever chimpanzees and enjoy their funny tricks. ....

18. Two well-known American anthropologists were Margaret Mead and Ruth Benedict. ....

19. Philip wrote the music and choreographed the dances for the show. ....

20. Costumes from many famous movies were exhibited at the Metropolitan Museum of Art. ....

HBJ material copyrighted under notice appearing earlier in this work.

A Sentence Has a Verb and a Subject

The two essential parts of a *sentence base* are the verb and its subject. If a group of words does not contain these two elements, it is not a sentence. You will need to be able to identify the verb and its subject so that you can be sure that you have written *sentences* in your own writing. A common error of some students results from their belief that a present participle (a verb form ending in *-ing,* like *going, seeing,* or *running*) can be used alone as the verb of a sentence.

Present participles are verbs only when they have a helper.

The helping verbs used with the present participle are the forms of the verb *to be: am, is, are—was, were;* and verbs of more than one word ending with *be* or *been: will be, has been, might have been,* and so on. Notice how these "nonsentences," built around the present participle, can be changed to sentences by the addition of an appropriate helping verb.

NONSENTENCES	SENTENCES
Linda *going* home	Linda was going home.
Cheryl *playing* the piccolo	Cheryl has been playing the piccolo.
Horses *drinking* from the trough	Horses were drinking from the trough.

Sentence Fragments   A group of words that does not contain both a verb and its subject cannot express a complete thought and, therefore, cannot be a sentence. It is merely a *fragment,* or piece, of a sentence.

EXAMPLES   At the end of a long dusty road
The girl in the green sweater
Running with a hose to put out the fire
Carla, my friend from Memphis
The girls in 4B
Himself winning third prize

EXERCISE. Apply the verb-and-subject test to each of the following items. If the group of words has a verb and its subject, draw two lines under the verb and one line under the subject, and write *S* for *sentence* in the space provided. (Watch for "understood" subjects.) If it does not have a verb and its subject, write *F* for *fragment* of a sentence. (Add 4 points for each correctly marked item.)

1. Acting like a mischievous chimpanzee.   . . . .

2. Acting like a mischievous chimpanzee, Joe bounced across the
   stage.   . . . .

3. His arms hanging limp, dangling almost to the floor.   . . . .

HBJ material copyrighted under notice appearing earlier in this work.

4. His arms, hanging limp, were dangling almost to the floor. . . . .

5. His arms were hanging limp, dangling almost to the floor. . . . .

6. The audience laughing at his comic appearance. . . . .

7. Mrs. Henderson, the director of this slapstick comedy. . . . .

8. Near the end of the first act. . . . .

9. Charlene was playing the part of Lady Macbeth. . . . .

10. Walking aimlessly about and rubbing her hands. . . . .

11. At the final curtain came a loud burst of applause. . . . .

12. The actors staying in character during five curtain calls. . . . .

13. The most successful performance of the season. . . . .

14. What is the director planning next? . . . .

15. In the spring she will direct the well-known musical *West Side Story*. . . . .

16. Is that story based on *Romeo and Juliet?* . . . .

17. Are you interested in musical comedy? . . . .

18. Hoping for the role of Bernardo? . . . .

19. Practice the part now and memorize the lines in time for the audition. . . . .

20. Who will play Maria? . . . .

21. A production of the play on public television. . . . .

22. The necessity of a good cast. . . . .

23. Many of the songs from *West Side Story* have become famous. . . . .

24. The performers must act, sing, and dance well. . . . .

25. A very difficult and trying task for inexperienced actors. . . . .

HBJ material copyrighted under notice appearing earlier in this work.

A Sentence Expresses a Complete Thought

To be complete, a sentence must contain a verb and its subject that together express a complete thought.

A group of words may have a verb and its subject, but it is not a sentence unless it expresses a complete thought.

EXAMPLES *When you have finished your homework* (Although it contains a verb and its subject, this is not a sentence because it is not a complete thought. It is a fragment of a sentence.)
When you have finished your homework, you may watch television. (This is a sentence because the thought is complete.)

If there is enough snow (This is not a sentence because the thought is not complete.)
If there is enough snow, we will go skiing.   (This is a sentence. The thought is complete.)

EXERCISE A. In the space at the right of each group of words, write *S* if the group is a sentence, *F* if it is a fragment of a sentence. Ask yourself whether the thought in each group is complete. If it is not, the group of words is only a fragment. Reading aloud may help you to decide. A question is a sentence if it contains a verb and its subject. A command is a sentence because the subject is understood. (Add 4 points for each correct answer.)

1. Taking a canoe trip in Canada.   . . . .

2. Sufficient food for a week's journey.   . . . .

3. Others had camped there before us.   . . . .

4. Ashes indicated the place.   . . . .

5. Where their fire had been.   . . . .

6. How clearly was the trail marked?   . . . .

7. An Ojibwa village at the end of the trail.   . . . .

8. The group spent the morning together.   . . . .

9. Talking over plans for the afternoon.   . . . .

10. As we rounded a bend in the river.   . . . .

11. Could you hear the noise of the waterfall?   . . . .

12. Before you could see it.   . . . .

13. We could not paddle against the wind unless the guide

    helped us.   . . . .

HBJ material copyrighted under notice appearing earlier in this work.

14. The wind blowing spray over us. . . . .

15. Drenched to the skin. . . . .

16. The rapids in the river were occasional hazards. . . . .

17. The excitement of shooting the rapids. . . . .

18. We steered and balanced carefully. . . . .

19. Around boulders in the stream. . . . .

20. Deciding whether to go through the rapids or portage the canoe around them. . . . .

21. On our knees in the canoe, we became painfully cramped. . . . .

22. There was no chance, however, to stretch our legs. . . . .

23. From the beginning of the rapids to the end. . . . .

24. Grazing the side of the canoe on rounded boulders. . . . .

25. After we had taken a swim in the calm water beyond the rapids. . . . .

EXERCISE B. By adding words to complete the thought, make each of the following fragments a sentence. (Add 10 points for each correct sentence.)

1. While you rest . . . .

2. . . . .
. . . . as he had often promised to do.

3. When I was a child . . . .

4. . . . . until the rain stops.

5. If you are ill . . . .

6. . . . .
. . . . since I had already heard the story twice.

7. . . . . where we camped.

8. The girls sleeping in the tent near us . . . .
. . . .

9. Holding to the stern of the boat with one hand and groping for the sinking minnow bucket with the other . . . .
. . . .

10. . . . . talking over our plans.

HBJ material copyrighted under notice appearing earlier in this work.

Chapter Review

EXERCISE. In the spaces at the right, copy the verb and its subject in each of the following sentences. Your answers will be more accurate if you draw a line through prepositional phrases, mentally change questions into statements, and select the verb first, asking *who?* or *what?* before it to identify its subject. Be sure to copy all parts of a verb of more than one word and all parts of a compound subject or verb. (Add 5 points for each correct sentence.)

	Subject	*Verb*
EX. Are all ~~of the boys~~ working?	*all*	*are working*
1. Pam and she made the popcorn.		
2. Did any of the cups break?		
3. There is a hat in the closet.		
4. Do not tell me the answer yet.		
5. Here is a copy of the play.		
6. None of the food was edible.		
7. What could he have been doing?		
8. Under the bridge was quicksand.		
9. Has either of you seen Elena?		
·10. I read Leslie Silko's story and then wrote my paper.		
11. Both of the twins are talented.		
12. You and she are the favorites.		
13. Has the bell rung?		
14. I mailed the letter on Monday and received a reply on Wednesday.		
15. When are you leaving?		
16. Beyond the lake are mountains.		
17. I washed and dried the dishes.		
18. Read three more pages.		
19. How beautiful the sunset is!		
20. How did you like the play?		

HBJ material copyrighted under notice appearing earlier in this work.

Cumulative Review

A. Above each italicized word write what part of speech it is. Use these abbreviations: *n.* for *noun,* *pron.* for *pronoun,* *adj.* for *adjective,* *v.* for *verb,* *prep.* for *preposition,* *adv.* for *adverb,* *conj.* for *conjunction,* *int.* for *interjection.* (Add 5 points for each correct answer.)

1 When *Hurricane,* my *pet* dog, does not get his way, *he* pouts. If

2 extremely *angry,* Hurricane *hides under* the sofa and sulks. Then, many

3 kind words *or* even *choice* morsels do not please him. *We* usually cope with

4 his rude *behavior* by arousing his curiosity. The curious dog *always*

5 investigates the *cause of* any excitement. We *sometimes* dash to the window

6 *and* exclaim, ''*Oh,* here comes Aunt Kate!'' Hurricane *immediately* comes

7 out of hiding, barks his way *to* the window, and *peers* out to see where

8 Aunt Kate *is.*

B. Draw a line under each adjective in the following sentences. Draw a circle around each adverb. Draw an arrow from each adjective or adverb to the word it modifies. Do not mark the articles, *a, an,* and *the.* (Add 20 points for each correctly marked sentence.)

EX. In contrast to the solid landmass of the Antarctic, the Arctic is
(completely) fluid.

1. The ice pack that covers the Arctic is not a totally solid layer of ice, as people generally imagine.

2. It consists of huge chunks and floes that vary greatly in size and thickness.

3. In fact, it contains many quite large open stretches.

4. In August 1958, the *Nautilus* became the first submarine to reach the Pole under the ice.

5. Later, another atomic ship broke through the Arctic ice to reach the Pole on the surface.

HBJ material copyrighted under notice appearing earlier in this work.

Spelling: The Unstressed Vowel Sound Called the "Schwa"

A great many of the spelling problems in English are in words that contain an indistinct vowel sound. Pronounce each of the following words. Identify the vowel sound in the *accented* syllable in each word. Can you do the same for the vowel sound in the unstressed (unaccented) syllable?

1	*2*	*3*
ác tor	tráv el	e ráse
lín en	tó tal	co coón
cél lar	cív il	a whíle

As you can hear, the vowel sounds in the unstressed syllables in these words all sound very much alike. You cannot tell whether the vowel is *a, e, i, o,* or *u.* The stressed syllables, however, have a distinct and identifiable sound. In the word *tráv el* (list 2), the vowel *a* in the stressed syllable has the sound /a/. What is the sound of the *o* in *tó tal* and of the first *i* in *cív il*? Because the vowel sounds in the stressed syllables can usually be identified, they seldom cause spelling problems.

It is the unstressed vowel sound that causes trouble. This sound, which is extremely common in our language, is called a *schwa,* and is shown by the symbol /ə/, a sort of upside-down *e.*

In the next four spelling lessons (which come near the end of each of the next four chapters), you will be given some rules and aids to help you spell words containing this difficult sound. Where no rules or aids apply, you simply have to memorize the spelling of the words.

EXERCISE A. Identify the sounds of the italicized vowels in the following words by writing *long, short,* or *schwa* in the blanks. If you wish, use the chart "Vowel Sounds and Their Common Spellings" on page 26. (Add 5 points for each correct answer.)

EXAMPLE b*a* s*i*n *long.* . . . . . *schwa* . . . .

1. l*e*s s*o*n . . . .

2. l*e*v *e*l . . . .

3. f*o* c*u*s . . . .

4. h*e*lp f*u*l . . . .

5. *a*n g*e*l . . . .

6. *e*x ter n*a*l . . . .

7. h*u* m*a*n . . . .

8. pro f*e*s s*o*r . . . .

9. pyr *a* m*i*d . . . .

10. g*o*ld *e*n . . . .

EXERCISE B. Circle any syllable in the words below that contains the vowel sound /ə/. Remember, this sound occurs in unstressed syllables, so it may be helpful to say each word softly to yourself first. (Add 10 points for each correct answer.)

HBJ material copyrighted under notice appearing earlier in this work.

1. pen cil
2. beg gar
3. fall en
4. ta ble
5. stim u lus

6. fa tal
7. cre a tor
8. stee ple
9. clar i fy
10. a way

EXERCISE C. Make a list of twenty spelling demons that are demons because they contain a schwa sound. (Use words that were not taught in this lesson.) Your teacher will write words from everyone's list on the board. (Before you suggest a word for the demon list, check in a dictionary to make sure the spelling problem in the word is caused by a schwa sound.) After all the words have been written on the board, narrow the list to the twenty most troublesome. Then copy the twenty words in a section of your notebook. When they have been copied, they should be erased from the board. Now study the twenty words, and be ready to write them from dictation in the blanks below. (Add 5 points for each correctly spelled word.)

1. ....
2. ....
3. ....
4. ....
5. ....
6. ....
7. ....
8. ....
9. ....
10. ....

11. ....
12. ....
13. ....
14. ....
15. ....
16. ....
17. ....
18. ....
19. ....
20. ....

HBJ material copyrighted under notice appearing earlier in this work.

Building Vocabulary: Words to Learn

degenerate /di jén ə rāt/ *v.* To become worse; to sink down to a lower level of conduct, physical condition, activity: *The hockey game degenerated into a free-for-all.*—**degenerate** /di jén ər it/ *n.* One who has degenerated, especially morally; a person whose inner nature is evil.

depict /di píkt/ *v.* To show in a picture; hence, to describe vividly in words: *He depicted the life of London's poor with deep sympathy.*

diminutive /di mín yə tiv/ *adj.* Very small and delicate: *The child's tools were diminutive copies of an adult's.*

ensue /en sū/ *v.* To follow something in time, often as a result: *In its last game, the football team clinched the championship, and an enthusiastic celebration ensued.*

fragile /fráj əl/ *adj.* Easily broken; hence, delicately made: *The ancient vase was so fragile that the explorers who found it were afraid to move it.*

inference /ín fər əns/ *n.* A conclusion reached by any process of reasoning from known facts or from general principles: *From the dents in Mr. Walmsby's fenders, it was a natural inference that he is not a skillful driver.*—**infer** /in fúr/ *v.*

omen /ṓ mən/ *n.* Any thing or event taken as a sign of something to come: *Breaking a mirror is often considered a bad omen.*

profound /prə foúnd/ *adj.* Deep, thorough, or intense: *A profound respect for all living things caused her to become a veterinarian.*

prudent /prū́d nt / *adj.* Careful and sensible in conduct; not rash; of actions, cautious and sensible: *A prudent executive would not have put the company's money in such a risky undertaking.*

rebate /rḗ bāt/ *n.* A deduction from or payment back of a part of an amount already charged or paid: *As a result of their heavy medical expenses last year, my parents received a rebate on their income taxes.*

EXERCISE. Fill each blank with the word from this lesson that makes the best sense in the context. In some cases, a verb may need to change form to agree with the rest of the sentence. (Add 10 points for each correct answer.)

1. The defense lawyer . . . . her client's character and home life in glowing terms.

2. Gregory had a quick, wide-ranging mind, but he was not as . . . . a thinker as his friend Mildred.

3. Mable's Department Store gives a ten percent . . . . to any customer who spends more than a certain amount per month.

4. The quality of our club meetings has . . . . considerably since the lively discussions we had at the beginning of the year.

5. That Gary Schimmel's mother is a well-educated person is a reasonable . . . . from her large vocabulary and constant reading.

6. When Geraldo found a dollar bill on the street, he took it as a good . . . . of his future financial success.

7. That ship model is very handsome, but it is much too . . . . for a small child to play with.

HBJ material copyrighted under notice appearing earlier in this work.

8. General Tom Thumb, a circus midget, was probably the most
.... person ever to achieve worldwide fame.

9. Finally, the children grew tired of playing the piano, and a delightful
period of silence ....

10. It is hardly .... to use gasoline to help start a fire.

REVIEW EXERCISE. Fill each blank with the word from the list below that
makes the best sense in the context. Some words appear twice, with different
meanings. Verbs may need to change form to agree with the rest of the sentence. (Add
10 points for each correct answer.)

contemporary	equilibrium	inconsistent	liability
deliberate	grapple	inertia	

1. Mr. Luciano did not mind Ann's arriving late, but her ....
refusal to apologize infuriated him.

2. The rocket .... itself to the space station and opened its airlock.

3. If you continue to walk at so .... a pace, we'll be late.

4. The witness' testimony was .... with the report given by the
police.

5. Any player who does not come out for practice is a .... to the
whole team.

6. For a few moments, the two men .... on the floor, and then the
detective got the upper hand.

7. The poet Anna Branch is a less well-known .... of Amy
Lowell.

8. At first, Henderson refused to pay, but the court later established his
.... under the law.

9. The pendulum gradually stopped swinging and returned to its original
state of ....

10. Next spring the company is moving from its present shabby office to a
new, ...-looking building.

HBJ material copyrighted under notice appearing earlier in this work.

CHAPTER 3

The Sentence Base: Complements

You have studied two parts of a sentence base: the verb and its subject. In this chapter you will study sentence bases that have three parts. The third part completes the meaning begun by the subject and verb. It is called a *complement*, which means "completer."

The Subject Complement

A **complement** completes the meaning begun by the subject and the verb.

As you read the following sentences, notice how the complement *completes* the meaning of the verb and its subject.

	COMPLEMENT
1. You <u>are</u>	the **winner**.
2. That <u>must have been</u>	a **surprise**.
3. He <u>is</u>	a **captain**.
4. Rosa <u>looks</u>	**pretty**.

In these sentences the complements refer to the subjects. In the first three sentences the complements are nouns that explain the subjects by naming the same persons or things as the subjects. In sentence 4, the complement *pretty* is an adjective. It describes the subject *Rosa*.

A **subject complement** is a noun, a pronoun, or an adjective that follows a linking verb. It describes or explains the simple subject. [1]

Subject complements follow linking verbs only. The most common linking verb *to be* (*am, is, are—was, were—been*) may be followed by a noun, a pronoun, or an adjective. Other common linking verbs, such as *become, seem, appear, look, feel, smell, taste, remain, sound,* are usually followed by adjectives rather than by nouns or pronouns.

A subject complement may be compound; that is, it may have two or more parts.

[1] When a noun or a pronoun is a subject complement, it is sometimes called a *predicate nominative*. When an adjective is a subject complement, it is sometimes called a *predicate adjective*. These terms are not used in this book.

HBJ material copyrighted under notice appearing earlier in this work.

EXAMPLES His favorite modern playwrights are **Lillian Hellman** and **Edward Albee**

The script was **short** but **powerful**.

To find the subject complement in a question, rearrange the sentence so that it becomes a statement.

EXAMPLE Was he the teacher?

He was the **teacher**.

Like the subject, the subject complement is never found in a prepositional phrase.

EXAMPLE The winner was **one** of my brothers.

EXERCISE. First, find the verb and its subject in each of the following sentences. (Crossing out prepositional phrases will help you.) Then draw a circle around any complement you find in the sentence and draw an arrow from it to the subject to which it refers. Three of the sentences do not have complements. (Add 10 points for each correctly marked sentence.)

EX. The tombs of ancient Egyptian pharaohs were great finds for robbers.

EX. These tombs should have been sacred.

1. However, the treasures in the tombs were irresistible to thieves.

2. Plundering became a frequent occurrence.

3. To robbers, a new royal tomb seemed an invitation for theft.

4. Where are many of those fabulous treasures today?

5. There remained few unplundered tombs.

6. One family in the Valley of the Kings were particularly notorious grave robbers.

7. Their plundering was a tradition from generation to generation.

8. One of their finds was too large and too valuable for one large haul.

9. The tomb remained the family's secret "bank" for years.

10. Eventually their illegal activities were halted by the law.

HBJ material copyrighted under notice appearing earlier in this work.

50

The Direct Object

Study the following sentences.

SUBJECT	VERB	COMPLEMENT
They	brought	the **children**.
I	remember	the **route** very well.
Marcia	built	her own **boat**.

You can easily see that these complements do not describe or explain the subject. Consequently, they can not be subject complements. They are, however, related to the verb. They name something that is affected by the action of the verb. The *children* are who were *brought;* the *route* is what was *remembered;* the *boat* is what was *built*. A complement that receives the action of the verb is called a direct object.

> The **direct object** of the verb is a noun or pronoun that receives the action of the verb or shows the result of the action. It answers the question "What?" or "Whom?" after an action verb.

Only action verbs have direct objects. The verb's action may be either physical or mental.

EXAMPLES Roy knocked the **ball** into the stands. (physical action)

You can imagine the **result**. (mental action)

Usually the direct object comes after the verb, but it may come before it.

EXAMPLE **This** I enjoy.

Like subjects and subject complements, direct objects are never found in prepositional phrases.

EXAMPLE She brought **one** of the new rackets.

Direct objects may be compound.

EXAMPLE Jack has invited **you** and **me** to his party.

EXERCISE. Underline the subject of each sentence once and the verb twice. Draw a line through any prepositional phrase. Then draw an arrow from the verb to the direct object (some objects are compound), and write the object(s) in the space to the right of each sentence. (Add 10 points for each correctly marked sentence.)

EX. Louise misspelled ten words on the test.   *words*

EX. Her failure she attributed to the teacher.   *failure*

HBJ material copyrighted under notice appearing earlier in this work.

51

1. I have already solved the first problem. . . . .

2. Last night's hail greatly damaged crops in this area. . . . .

3. How many of these have you made? . . . .

4. Four workers lifted the piano onto the stage. . . . .

5. The class elected two boys and two girls. . . . .

6. These things he left behind. . . . .

7. The huge crowd pushed Sean and me into the wrong bus. . . . .

8. Allen brought home three pheasants and a rabbit. . . . .

9. The outfielder quickly threw the ball to home plate. . . . .

10. Heavy armor protects the armadillo. . . . .

REVIEW EXERCISE. Underline the subject of each sentence once and the verb twice. Circle each complement. Then write the complement in the first space at the right, and, in the second space, write *d.o.* if the complement is a *direct object* and *s.c.* if it is a *subject complement*. (Add 10 points for each correctly marked sentence.)

1. The freshman class planned a craft fair. . . . .

2. All of the students would sell their own handcrafted objects. . . . .

3. The class would donate the proceeds to a local charity for the holiday season. . . . .

4. Naomi asked several restaurant owners for empty wine bottles. . . . .

5. Her collection was an interesting assortment of bottles of many shapes, sizes, and colors. . . . .

6. Naomi carefully cut the tops off each of the bottles. . . . .

7. Then she sanded the rough edges. . . . .

8. The old bottles became beautiful drinking goblets. . . . .

9. One green bottle with a rounded bottom was especially attractive. . . . .

10. Naomi turned this bottle into a vase. . . . .

HBJ material copyrighted under notice appearing earlier in this work.

The Indirect Object

The indirect object of the verb is a noun or pronoun that precedes the direct object and usually tells <u>to whom</u> or <u>for whom</u> (or <u>to what</u> or <u>for what</u>) the action of the verb is done.

The indirect object normally comes before the direct object.

EXAMPLES Lisa made me a <u>kite.</u> for me

                                    d.o.

                Fred sent Doris a birthday <u>present.</u> (to Doris)

In these sentences the words *me* and *Doris* are indirect objects. As shown by the phrases in parentheses, the words act as prepositional phrases. If the preposition appeared in the sentence, however, the words would be objects of the preposition, *not* indirect objects of the verb. It is the omission of the preposition that makes them indirect objects. *The indirect object is never found in a prepositional phrase.*

EXAMPLES The plumber handed the bill to me. (*Me* is the object of the preposition *to*.)
                The plumber handed me the bill. (*Me* is the indirect object of the verb *handed*.)

An indirect object may be compound.

EXAMPLE She sold Jeff and me *tickets* for the rock concert.

EXERCISE. Draw a line through each prepositional phrase. Underline each direct and indirect object and write each one in the appropriate column at the right. You will not find an indirect object in every sentence. (Add 10 points for each correctly marked sentence.)

	Indirect object	*Direct object*
EX. The event gave <u>Roger</u> an <u>inspiration</u> ~~for a story~~.	...*Roger*..	*inspiration*
1. He sold Alvin a red sweater.	. . . .	. . . .
2. Bring me the book about ghosts.	. . . .	. . . .
3. I'll give the receipt for the money to Helen.	. . . .	. . . .
4. The caller left you this message.	. . . .	. . . .

HBJ material copyrighted under notice appearing earlier in this work.

5. I threw Carmen the ball. . . . .

6. Has he read his students these stories? . . . .

7. Someone must have criticized his methods. . . . .

8. Dr. Mabie is leaving her college a valuable collection of old manuscripts. . . . .

9. Should I give the baby a bagel? . . . .

10. Shall I get it for you? . . . .

REVIEW EXERCISE. In the space at the right of each sentence, write the proper abbreviations, in order, identifying the italicized word or words: *s.c.* for subject complement; *d.o.* for direct object; *i.o.* for indirect object. Remember that subject complements follow linking verbs and that direct objects follow action verbs. (Add 10 points for each correct sentence.)

EX. Rosalie showed *me* her new *camera*. *i.o., d.o.*

EX. An egocentric person is a *bore*. *s.c.*

1. Raccoons can easily outwit *dogs*. . . . .

2. The governor granted the *prisoner* his *freedom*. . . . .

3. I may become a *veterinarian*. . . . .

4. Healthy young lions rarely attack human *beings*. . . . .

5. Ilona wrote the *lyrics* to that song. . . . .

6. Mrs. Jacklitsh teaches *trigonometry* at the high school. . . . .

7. Chita Rivera was the *star* of that Broadway show. . . . .

8. This book was the *basis* for a television series. . . . .

9. Marcy tossed *me* her fountain *pen*. . . . .

10. Are you *afraid* of high places? . . . .

HBJ material copyrighted under notice appearing earlier in this work.

Chapter Review

EXERCISE A. Cross out àll prepositional phrases. Then, in the space at the right, write each complement and its classification. Use one of these abbreviations: *s.c.* (subject complement), *d.o.* (direct object), *i.o.* (indirect object). Remember that subject complements follow linking verbs only; direct objects and indirect objects follow action verbs only. (Add 5 points for each correct line.)

EX. Ants caused me trouble ~~in my backyard.~~   *me, i.o.—trouble, d.o.*

1. They taught me the meaning of persistence.   . . . .

2. Have you ever watched ants at work?   . . . .

3. Daily I watered the lawn after school.   . . . .

4. This chore became interesting work for me.   . . . .

5. I flooded a huge ant hill with water.   . . . .

6. I thus declared war on the colony of ants.   . . . .

7. Can ants ever have committee meetings?   . . . .

8. Their subsequent action seemed sensible.   . . . .

9. These ants were unusually crafty.   . . . .

10. In fact, they eventually outwitted a human.   . . . .

11. Soon the ants built four new strongholds.   . . . .

12. They built these nests in various places.   . . . .

13. I gave all of the ants another drenching.   . . . .

14. Did defeat seem inevitable to the ants?   . . . .

15. Quickly they showed me their ingenuity.   . . . .

16. They perforated the lawn with tiny ant hills.   . . . .

17. Again I mercilessly flooded their homes.   . . . .

18. A change in strategy became necessary.   . . . .

19. The ants made a united, orderly retreat.   . . . .

20. Finally they found safety in one big happy

 ant hill—in my next-door neighbor's yard!   . . . .

EXERCISE B. The complements in the following sentences are in italics. Over each complement, write the proper one of the following abbreviations: *s.c.* for subject complement; *d.o.* for direct object; *i.o.* for indirect object. (Add 5 points for each correct answer.)

HBJ material copyrighted under notice appearing earlier in this work.

1. Tales of Sasquatch, or Bigfoot, haunted *me* throughout my childhood in the Pacific Northwest.

2. Several people traveled the mountain *trails* and brought *tales* back from their trips.

3. Some of these tales seemed *incredible*.

4. One camper told *me* a strange *story*.

5. While hiking in the backwoods, she saw large *footprints* on the trail ahead of her.

6. They appeared too *large* to belong to a human.

7. She made plaster *casts* of the footprints and gave an *anthropologist* the *casts*.

8. The unknown walker must have been a large *creature*.

9. Probably 500 pounds was its *weight* and 8 feet was its *height*.

10. It had a long, flatfooted *gait*.

11. The expert asked the *camper* a *question*.

12. Are the footprints a *hoax*?

13. Is the creature Bigfoot a *myth*, or is it a *reality*?

EXERCISE C. Write original sentences in the specified word order. Add modifiers when needed. Underline the required parts in your sentences. (Add 20 points for each correct sentence.)

EX. Subject—verb—compound direct object.

The waiter then served my father and me.

1. Subject—verb—direct object.

....

2. Subject—verb—indirect object—direct object.

....

3. Subject—verb—subject complement.

....

4. Helping verb—subject—main verb—direct object.

....

5. Subject—verb—compound subject complement.

....

HBJ material copyrighted under notice appearing earlier in this work.

Cumulative Review

A. Over each italicized word write what part of speech it is. Use these abbreviations: noun, *n.*; pronoun, *pron.*; adjective, *adj.*; verb, *v.*; adverb, *adv.*; preposition, *prep.*; conjunction, *conj.*; interjection, *int.* (Add 5 points for each correct answer.)

1 *"Wow!* Look *at* this *news* story," said Louise. "The *police* are *now*

2 using hypnosis to solve crimes."

3 *"They* are using what?" asked Sara *incredulously.*

4 "They're using hypnosis," *replied* Louise. *"Listen.* In order to find the

5 *culprit* in a hit-and-run accident, the department had the witness hypno-

6 tized *by* a doctor, *and* hypnosis *enabled* the witness to remember the

7 license plate number *of* the *hit-and-run driver's* car. *With this* information,

8 the police were able to apprehend the *guilty* party *quickly.*"

B. In the first space at the right, place an *S* if the group of words is a sentence or an *F* if it is not a sentence. If you decide that it is not a sentence, give the reason for your decision by using the letter of the appropriate reason: *a*—lacks a verb and its subject, or *b*—has a verb and its subject but is not a complete thought. (Add 10 points for each correctly marked sentence.)

EX. There are three types of matter. ......*S.* ....

EX. That have volume but no definite form. ....*F.* ...*b*.

1. A liquid is one of these types. ....

2. A liquid, taking the shape of its container. ....

3. Acting exactly as gases do. ....

4. Which is called a fluid? ....

5. Are liquids and gases both fluids? ....

6. When a liquid reaches its boiling point. ....

7. It becomes a gas. ....

8. A liquid also becomes solid. ....

9. At its freezing point, like water becoming ice. ....

10. The melting process turns ice into water. ....

C. Cross out the prepositional phrases in the sentences below. Find the base of each sentence and write the parts of the base in the appropriate columns below, after the

HBJ material copyrighted under notice appearing earlier in this work.

number of the sentence. Be sure to include all parts of compound subjects, verbs, and complements. Not all of these sentences contain complements. (Add 2 points for each correct answer.)

EX. Bill dropped his work and came with us.

	Subjects	Verbs	Complements
EX.	*Bill*	*dropped, came*	*work*

1. The Sunday afternoon sunshine faded quickly.   2. Without much warning the peaceful summer day reached a premature end.   3. A storm moved in over the lake.   4. People ran from the lake to the shelter of their cabins. 5. Dark, wind-swept sheets of rain enveloped the landscape and swallowed up the happy brightness of the day.   6. Even the bushes and trees seemed fearful and forlorn.   7. They cowered in the strange green light and huddled closer together.   8. We stood inside our cabin and looked out the window. 9. A swirling funnel emerged from a black cloud and threatened destruction and death.   10. For a while the funnel played a game of harmless leapfrog and then, like the evil witches in *Macbeth,* vanished in the stormy air.

Subjects	Verbs	Complements
1.		
2.		
3.		
4.		
5.		
6.		
7.		
8.		
9.		
10.		

HBJ material copyrighted under notice appearing earlier in this work.

Spelling: Does It End in *-ar, -er,* or *-or?*

Like many people, do you have trouble knowing whether certain common words end in *-ar, -er,* or *-or?* In referring to a physician, do you write *doct-,* and then try to decide whether the word ends in *-er* or *-or?* Difficulties like these occur because the suffix in such words is an unstressed syllable. You say *dóc tor.* Therefore, the vowel in the final syllable is reduced to the indistinct schwa sound /ə/ you learned about in Lesson 24. You cannot tell from the *sound* whether the vowel is *a, e,* or *o* in such endings.

Although you cannot use sound as a spelling clue, all is not hopeless. There are some guides that can help you decide. The suffix *-er* (and its variants *-or* and *-ar)* turns verbs into nouns. It means "one who." "One who *climbs"* is a *climber.* What is "one who buys"?

Here are some guides to the correct spelling of nouns meaning "one who":

● Only five common words in this category have the suffix spelled with *-ar.* If you can memorize these five, then you will know the important "one who" words ending in *-ar.*

      begg**ar**   li**ar**   schol**ar**   burgl**ar**   registr**ar**

● Verbs that end in *-ate* take the *-or* spelling when they are changed into nouns meaning "one who." You can therefore "test" the ending of a noun by turning it back into its verb form.

      oper**ate**   *oper**at**or*   *imitate*   *imit**at**or*

● The "one who" suffix is spelled *-or* in nouns of Latin origin. Generally, such words refer to positions of prestige, authority, or importance.

      govern**or**   profess**or**   edit**or**   act**or**

● The "one who" suffix is generally spelled *-er* in words that refer to trades or simply to situations.

      carpent**er**   plumb**er**   dream**er**   runn**er**

EXERCISE A. Write the letter *e, a,* or *o* in the blank in each of the following words. Use the four guides to help you decide. (Add 10 points for each correct answer.)

1. farm. . . .r

2. burgl. . . .r

3. ambassad. . . .r

4. nominat. . . .r

5. help. . . .r

6. imita. . . .r

7. wait. . . .r

8. bystand. . . .r

9. schol. . . .r

10. auth. . . .r

HBJ material copyrighted under notice appearing earlier in this work.

EXERCISE B. Add *e, a,* or *o* to the word containing a blank in each sentence below. Use the guides, as well as the clues in the sentences themselves. (Add 10 points for each correct answer.)

1. Being a garden. . . .r sounds like a healthy trade.

2. A person who does not tell the truth is a li. . . .r.

3. Lawy. . . .rs did not always have the prestige they have today.

4. Kate will be one of the competing swimm. . . .rs this afternoon.

5. Outside the building sat a pitiful begg. . . .r.

6. A spons. . . .r can control a TV program.

7. Who is the conduct. . . .r of the orchestra?

8. Anne Morrow Lindbergh was an airplane radio operat. . . .r.

9. A pitch. . . .r is only one member of a baseball team.

10. Maria Mitchell was an astronom. . . .r.

EXERCISE C. Be prepared to write from dictation all of the words taught in this lesson. (Add 2 points for each correctly spelled word.)

REVIEW EXERCISE. In the blank in each word below, write the vowel that correctly completes the word. Each vowel you write occurs in an unstressed syllable and will have the schwa /ə/ sound. Try to think of a "related" word to help you decide which vowel to use. (Add 10 points for each correct answer.)

1. rel. . . .tive

2. form. . . .l

3. popul. . . .r

4. cel. . . .brate

5. loc. . . .l

6. invent. . . .r

7. or. . . .gin

8. emph. . . .sis

9. civ. . . .l

10. org. . . .n

HBJ material copyrighted under notice appearing earlier in this work.

Building Vocabulary: Choosing the Right Word

English is amazingly rich in *synonyms*—words that have nearly, though never exactly, the same meaning, Often, we find one very general word like *big* surrounded by a whole cluster of words *(huge, gigantic,* and *monstrous,* for example) that have more limited and specific meanings. For effective writing and speaking, we must sort out the specific meanings of such words and fit the right word to the right context.

EXAMPLES   That store has a reputation for low prices and good service.
Julia Child has achieved renown as a gourmet cook.
The film star achieved a certain notoriety through his wild parties.

The three words printed in red mean the opinion that people have of a person or thing. *Reputation* is the most general of the three—a reputation may be good or bad, important or insignificant. *Renown* means a *good* reputation for outstanding achievement. *Notoriety* is a *bad* reputation for something harmful or scandalous. In the sentences above, it would be as wrong to speak of the movie star's *renown* as to speak of Julia Child's *notoriety*. In each case, the context shows which synonym fits.

A dictionary usually explains the differences between close synonyms. Under *big,* for example, you might find a reference to *large,* in which a list of synonyms and a discussion of their differences would be given.

EXERCISE A. Each sentence offers a choice of closely related words given in parentheses. Using a dictionary (be sure to consult lists of synonyms), decide which word fits the context best and write this word on the blank line below the sentence. After the word you have chosen, write the dictionary meaning that fits the context. (Add 10 points for each correct item.)

1. The Romans were (contemptuous, contemptible) of other nations, whom they called barbarians.

   . . . .

2. A more (intelligent, intelligible) person would have understood the problem better.

   . . . .

3. An argument that is (wise, sensible, rational) is based on logic and clear thinking rather than on an appeal to the emotions.

   . . . .

4. The new circus lion is an extremely (gentle, docile, compliant) one, and Angela finds it very easy to train.

   . . . .

HBJ material copyrighted under notice appearing earlier in this work.

5. Thornton's disposition is so (placid, sober, self-controlled) that neither happiness nor unhappiness has ever disturbed it.

. . . .

6. The accused man (stated, affirmed, alleged) that he had been in Brazil at the time of the crime, but the jury demanded proof.

. . . .

7. The toy's (breakable, frail, delicate) construction did not stand up under the hard use the children gave it.

. . . .

8. The illness was caused by a (deficiency, imperfection, lack) of the necessary vitamins and minerals in her diet.

. . . .

9. Jane Addams, recipient of the Nobel Peace Prize in 1931, was known for her (mercy, tenderness, compassion) toward the destitute.

. . . .

10. The judge's wise sentence can only (intensify, enhance, increase) her reputation for honesty and integrity.

. . . .

EXERCISE B. Write the letter of the best meaning to the left of each word. (Add 10 points for each correct answer.)

.... 1. allege, *v.*   a. quick to understand

.... 2. compassion, *n.*   b. weakness due to lack

.... 3. contemptuous, *adj.*   c. pity with desire to help

.... 4. deficiency, *n.*   d. to raise still higher

.... 5. delicate, *adj.*   e. easily taught, led

.... 6. docile, *adj.*   f. calm, untroubled

.... 7. enhance, *v.*   g. scornful

.... 8. intelligent, *adj.*   h. finely made and easily damaged

.... 9. placid, *adj.*   i. to state without proof

.... 10. rational, *adj.*   j. according to reason; logical

HBJ material copyrighted under notice appearing earlier in this work.

CHAPTER 4

Phrases and Clauses

You have learned that a sentence base consists of a subject, a verb, and (in some sentences) a complement. In addition to these three basic parts, a sentence usually contains words used as modifiers: adjectives and adverbs. A sentence may also contain groups of words which belong together and work together as single parts of speech. In this chapter you will learn more about two important word groups: phrases and clauses.

LESSON 33

The Phrase

A phrase is a group of related words that is used as a single part of speech and does not contain a verb and its subject.

EXAMPLES   He lives **in a brick house**. (phrase used as an adverb telling *where* he lives)

It is the house **with green shutters**. (phrase used as an adjective describing *house*)

A prepositional phrase is a group of words beginning with a preposition and ending with a noun or a pronoun.

EXAMPLES **at** *home*   **to** *me*   **by** *Virginia Hamilton*

Do not confuse an infinitive (*to* plus a *verb*) with a prepositional phrase. Phrases like *to go, to see,* and *to use* are the infinitive forms of verbs. Prepositional phrases end with a noun or a pronoun, *to town, to them*, not a verb.

The following words may be used as prepositions. Some may also be used as adverbs or conjunctions.

aboard	before	by	near	to
about	behind	concerning	of	toward
above	below	down	off	under
across	beneath	during	on	underneath
after	beside	except	onto	unlike
against	besides	for	over	until
along	between	from	past	up
among	beyond	in	since	upon
around	but (meaning	into	through	with
at	*except*)	like	throughout	within
				without

HBJ material copyrighted under notice appearing earlier in this work.

Some prepositions consist of more than one word: *because of, in spite of, instead of, on account of, next to, prior to.*

The noun or pronoun that ends the prepositional phrase is the object of the preposition that begins the phrase.

EXAMPLES   from my **sister**   because of **him**
               near **New York**   for **Roger Ludlow**

EXERCISE A. In each blank in the first column below, write a preposition to introduce each prepositional phrase. Do not use any prepositions twice. In the second column, complete each prepositional phrase by adding an appropriate object or objects. Correct pronoun forms used as objects of prepositions are *me, you, her, him, it, them, us.* (Add 10 points for each correct numbered item.)

1. . . . . the soup   6. beyond the . . . .

2. . . . . a magic wand   7. except . . . . and . . . .

3. . . . . them   8. during a . . . .

4. . . . . my bobsled   9. concerning . . . .

5. . . . . Janet and her   10. to . . . . and . . . .

EXERCISE B. Draw a line under each prepositional phrase in the following paragraph. Circle the object of the preposition. There are twenty-five prepositional phrases. (Add 4 points for each correctly marked phrase.)

1   Along the wharves beside the East River in the shadow of the Brooklyn

2   Bridge stands the Fulton Fish Market, perhaps the world's busiest market.

3   During the hours before dawn, the market springs into action as people

4   unload their boats and lay their wares at the feet of the world's tallest

5   skyscrapers. Buyers and sellers conduct their business in a rising

6   crescendo of noise, which by early morning exceeds the noises coming

7   from the heart of the city. Inside, the market is jammed to the ceiling with

8   crated fish from distant places, iced and ready to be distributed through

9   the city. The market is no place for the squeamish. The smell is what you

10   would expect; the sounds are deafening. On the boats there are many

11   "colorful characters," dressed for the weather, their faces made swarthy

12   by Atlantic winds. Before noon the last fish has been sent on its way, the

13   last deck has been hosed down. Fish for dinner, anyone?

HBJ material copyrighted under notice appearing earlier in this work.

The Adjective Phrase

A prepositional phrase used to modify a noun or a pronoun is called an adjective phrase.

By comparing the sentences in the following example, you will see how a phrase acts as an adjective. The first sentence contains an adjective and the second contains an adjective phrase. Notice that the adjective phrase *follows* the word it modifies.

EXAMPLE   Our Texas cousins are visiting us.

Our cousins from Texas are visiting us.

A prepositional phrase may modify the object of another prepositional phrase.

EXAMPLE   Those stamps at the front of the album are valuable.

EXERCISE A. Add an adjective phrase to each of the following nouns and pronouns. Do not use the same preposition twice. (Add 10 points for each correct answer.)

EX. a man *on a horse*

1. the highway ....
2. the one ....
3. a window ....
4. letters ....
5. a book ....

6. everyone ....
7. the girl ....
8. a necklace ....
9. a school ....
10. houses ....

EXERCISE B. Replace each adjective phrase in the following sentences with a single adjective that has the same meaning as the phrase. Underline the phrase. In the first space at the right, write the adjective that replaces the phrase. In the second space, write the noun the adjective modifies. (Add 5 points for each correct sentence.)

	Adjective	*Word modified*
EX. Tales about the West are popular.	*Western*	*tales*
1. I like stories with ghosts.	....	....
2. Winds in March often disturb me.	....	....
3. Finally I bought a chest for tools.	....	....
4. Fins on fish can injure anglers.	....	....
5. He needed words of encouragement.	....	....

HBJ material copyrighted under notice appearing earlier in this work.

6. The gentleman from Virginia
   nodded.   . . . .

7. I used a hammer with a claw.   . . . .

8. A boat for racing had sunk.   . . . .

9. Basketball is a game of action.   . . . .

10. Storms during the spring are sudden.   . . . .

11. This is a gem of value.   . . . .

12. He drives a truck with a trailer.   . . . .

13. Jeanne d'Arc is a heroine of France.   . . . .

14. This dish contains food for the turtle.   . . . .

15. The shops in Avon close early.   . . . .

16. She is a girl from France.   . . . .

17. Victoria was a queen of England.   . . . .

18. Lena wants a career in science.   . . . .

19. The store for hats was closed.   . . . .

20. The house at the corner is empty.   . . . .

EXERCISE C. Circle each adjective phrase in the following sentences. Then draw an arrow to the word it modifies. There are twenty phrases to identify. (Add 5 points for each correct answer.)

1   A liquid (like water) normally takes the exact shape of its container.

2   When water reaches a level beyond a jar's capacity, the water at the top

3   spills out. This behavior of liquids is one of the principal reasons for

4   clogged gas burners on kitchen stoves. A trick from a newspaper column

5   certainly baffled the students in my science class. The water-filled glass

6   on the teacher's desk contained a number of pennies. The water above the

7   rim was not spilling! A classmate behind me exclaimed, "Wow! The

8   water in that glass must be supernatural!" Conversation between the

9   teacher and me soon gave everyone the right key to the mystery

10   concerning the water level. The pennies in the glass had been immersed

11   carefully, thus slowly raising the level of the water. The surface tension of

12   the water prevented its spilling.

HBJ material copyrighted under notice appearing earlier in this work.

66

The Adverb Phrase

A prepositional phrase used to modify a verb, an adjective, or an adverb is called an adverb phrase.

EXAMPLES   We searched with great patience.   (phrase modifies a verb)

I am afraid of high places.   (phrase modifies an adjective)

They scored early in the game.   (phrase modifies an adverb)

Like an adverb, an adverb phrase may tell one of the following five things about the word it modifies: *how, when, where, why,* or *to what extent* (*how much* or *how often*).

EXAMPLES   She overcame evil with kindness.   (tells *how*)
During the summer, rainfall is heavy.   (tells *when*)
I jumped into the swirling water.   (tells *where*)
We collapsed from exhaustion.   (tells *why*)
We played for an hour.   (tells *how long*)

Adverb phrases may be separated by other words from the words they modify. This separation can make them a little more difficult to spot than adjective phrases, which usually come directly after the words they modify.

EXERCISE A. Each of the following sentences contains an adverb phrase. Circle each phrase and draw an arrow from the phrase to the word it modifies. In the space at the right, write what the phrase tells: *how, when, where, why,* or *to what extent.* (Add 5 points for each correct response in marking a phrase and in filling a blank.)

1. For many years people have sought the lost continent Atlantis.   . . . .

2. Some people claim it was situated off the Spanish coast.   . . . .

3. Others believe that fabled Atlantis actually existed in the Aegean Sea.   . . . .

4. They argue with certainty that a Greek island named Santorini was Atlantis.   . . . .

5. Around 1400 B.C., Santorini experienced a violent volcanic eruption.   . . . .

6. Because of this eruption, most of the island sank.   . . . .

7. Tidal waves and earthquakes occurred after the eruption.   . . . .

8. The island's flourishing civilization was lost in the disaster.   . . . .

HBJ material copyrighted under notice appearing earlier in this work.

9. Archaeologists who worked on Santorini unearthed whole towns. . . . .

10. New facts regarding Atlantis may be revealed through their research. . . . .

EXERCISE B. Circle each adverb phrase in the following sentences. Then draw an arrow from the phrase to the word it modifies. (Add 10 points for each correctly marked sentence.)

1. Luis and I have watched reruns of *Star Trek* for many years.

2. We have viewed each show with avid interest.

3. I even know the dialogue for some of the shows by heart.

4. A cult of *Star Trek* fans has developed over the years.

5. Every year they hold a *Star Trek* convention in New York City.

6. Luis and I attended the convention out of curiosity.

7. A small replica of the spaceship stood near the center of the room.

8. We examined the ship and looked inside the windows.

9. A miniature of James T. Kirk sat in the captain's chair.

10. Spock lay beneath the phaser bank, fixing the machinery.

EXERCISE C. Circle the phrase in each sentence and draw an arrow from the phrase to the word it modifies. In the space at the right tell whether the phrase is being used as an adjective or an adverb. (Add 5 points for each correct response in marking a phrase and filling a blank.)

1. The dog with the long tail is mine. . . . .

2. Pam writes with her left hand. . . . .

3. From the north came a driving snowstorm. . . . .

4. The sculpture by Augusta Savage is inspiring. . . . .

5. My book report was not copied from the book jacket. . . . .

6. Teams from twenty schools entered the tournament. . . . .

7. Buy your school supplies at Zing's. . . . .

8. We won a vacation in Florida. . . . .

9. Madame Curie's achievements in science were remarkable. . . . .

10. You must come home before midnight. . . . .

HBJ material copyrighted under notice appearing earlier in this work.

The Clause

A group of words that contains a verb and its subject and is used as a part of a sentence is called a <u>clause</u>.

The principal difference between a clause and a phrase is that a clause has both a verb and a subject, whereas a phrase does not.

PHRASES   after school (no subject or verb)
              had been stolen (a verb without a subject)

CLAUSES   when <u>school</u> <u>was</u> out (subject: *school;* verb: *was*)

              <u>which</u> <u>had been stolen</u> (subject: *which;* verb: *had been stolen*)

There are two kinds of clauses: independent clauses and subordinate clauses.

An <u>independent clause</u> expresses a complete thought and can stand by itself.

When an independent clause stands by itself, it is called a sentence.

SENTENCES   <u>Ms. Stamford</u> <u>is</u> a good driver.   <u>She</u> <u>does</u> not <u>like</u> to drive.

When these complete thoughts are combined into one sentence, they are called independent clauses, *parts* of a sentence.

             INDEPENDENT CLAUSE   INDEPENDENT CLAUSE

EXAMPLE   Ms. Stamford is a good driver, **but** she does not like to drive.

Independent clauses are usually joined by the conjunctions *and, but,* and *or.*

A <u>subordinate clause</u> by itself is only a fragment of a sentence. It must be connected with an independent clause to make its meaning complete.

SUBORDINATE CLAUSE   When Pocahontas was still young

            SUBORDINATE CLAUSE   INDEPENDENT CLAUSE

SENTENCE   When Pocahontas was still young, she helped the settlers.

Such conjunctions as *after, although, as if, because, before, if, since, though, unless, until, when, where,* and *while* are subordinate clause signals. *What, who, whom, whose, which,* and *that* can also introduce subordinate clauses.

EXAMPLES   We were fishing <u>when</u> the sun rose.
              <u>As</u> the coach had feared, our team was defeated.
              This is the man <u>who</u> helped us.
              I realized <u>that</u> the teacher had been right.

HBJ material copyrighted under notice appearing earlier in this work.

EXERCISE A. The subordinate clauses in the sentences below are italicized. Underline the subject of each subordinate clause once and the verb twice. Select the verb first; then find the subject by asking *who?* or *what?* (Add 25 points for each correctly marked sentence.)

1. *If failures do not quit,* they may eventually succeed, *as U.S. Grant did.*

2. *When Janice was ill,* she read Katherine Mansfield's "Miss Brill," *which you had recommended.*

3. *After I had overcome my stage fright,* I forgot *what my next line was!*

4. Mr. Habeeb, *who is a superb teacher,* answers questions *that the class should have asked.*

EXERCISE B. Underline the subordinate clauses in the following paragraph. (Add 5 points for each correct answer.)

1   After our class had studied various ecological systems, Mrs. Roth
2   suggested that we divide into groups. Each group would choose a project
3   that was of interest to them. The project that we chose was building a
4   woodland terrarium. Since our school is within walking distance of a park
5   with a woodland terrain, we would be able to gather the necessary
6   materials. After school was over for the day, we hiked to the park, where
7   we hunted for materials. Sheila found several flowering plants such as
8   wintergreen, whose flowers are white and bell-shaped, and pipsissewa,
9   which has leaves that are used for medicinal purposes. She put the plants
10   in cut-off milk containers whose bottoms were filled with soil so that she
11   could carry her leaves home. While I was looking for a mossy rock, I
12   found a salamander for the terrarium. Although it was quite fast, I
13   managed to catch it. We gathered our finds and went home before it got
14   dark. The next day we started work on our project. Mrs. Roth said that we
15   could use the aquarium tank from the science closet if another class wasn't
16   using it. We covered the base of the tank with gravel so that the soil would
17   have adequate drainage. Then we added a layer of woodland soil. After
18   we had placed the moss-covered rock in the terrarium, we added my
19   salamander. We planted small ferns, seedlings from spruce trees, flower-
20   ing plants, acorns, and beechnuts. When we had finished planting, we
21   placed the terrarium in a cool spot.

HBJ material copyrighted under notice appearing earlier in this work.

The Adjective Clause

Subordinate clauses, like phrases, are used as single parts of speech: adjectives, adverbs, and nouns.

An adjective clause is a subordinate clause used as an adjective to modify a noun or a pronoun.

Study the following examples to see how a subordinate clause acts as an adjective.

ADJECTIVES	ADJECTIVE CLAUSES
We saw a **hilarious** movie.	We saw a movie **which was hilarious**.
He is an **entertaining** speaker.	He is a speaker **who entertains his audience**
The **Peary** expedition explored the Arctic.	The expedition **that Peary led** explored the Arctic.

Adjective clauses are usually introduced by the relative pronouns *who, whom, whose, that,* and *which.*

EXAMPLES Ask the woman <u>who owns one</u>.

Are those the boys <u>**whom** you referred to</u>?

No one had read the stories, <u>**which** were exciting</u>.

This is the dress <u>**that** I want</u>.

This is the book <u>from **which** I took my information</u>.

Sometimes the relative pronoun is omitted.

EXAMPLES This is the dress <u>I want</u>.

Are those the boys <u>you referred to</u>?

EXERCISE A. Circle each of the ten adjective clauses in the following sentences. Draw an arrow from the clause to the word or words it modifies. (Add 10 points for each correctly marked clause.)

EX. The pony express, which was the first postal system in the West, carried

mail from Missouri to California.

1. Do you know any people who have emigrated to Israel?

2. Ynes Mexia was an explorer whose main interest was botany.

3. Last summer Mona visited Spokane, which is her birthplace.

4. Satire, which is a kind of writing, makes fun of people or actions that are

absurd.

HBJ material copyrighted under notice appearing earlier in this work.

5. Opossums that are cornered have a unique method of self-defense.

6. Betty Furness advocates consumer awareness, which is essential for good health.

7. A person whom others call "lucky" is usually an intelligent, hard worker who takes full advantage of opportunities.

8. The dog that was gnawing the bone growled at me.

EXERCISE B. Change the second sentence in each of the following pairs into an adjective clause and write the clause above the first sentence, using a caret (∧) to indicate where the clause should be inserted. In sentences 1, 2, 4, 7, and 8, you should set off the adjective clause with commas. You will learn about correct comma usage later. (Add 10 points for each correct sentence.)

EX. John Martin∧speaks Spanish fluently. *, who lived in Mexico for two years,*
   He lived in Mexico for two years.

1. My friend helped me with my serve.
   She is an excellent tennis player.

2. Joan Didion will autograph copies of her new book.
   She will be at the bookstore on Friday.

3. The gold nugget was about the size of a pea.
   The nugget set off the California gold rush.

4. That organization works to protect whales.
   They are threatened with extinction.

5. Astronomers suspect there is a planet.
   It exists beyond Pluto.

6. The firefighters will be honored by a parade.
   They rescued six children from a burning building.

7. Dogs and cats see only in black and white.
   They are colorblind.

8. Martina Arroyo sings opera around the world.
   She grew up in New York City.

9. The man has gone to North Carolina to pan for gold.
   He gave a lecture on prospecting.

10. The journalist just received the Pulitzer Prize.
    I talked to that journalist. (Use *whom*.)

HBJ material copyrighted under notice appearing earlier in this work.

The Adverb Clause

An <u>adverb clause</u> **is a subordinate clause used as an adverb to modify a verb, an adjective, or an adverb.**

An adverb clause tells *how, when, where, why, to what extent* (*how much, how long*), or *under what conditions*.

EXAMPLES   Gerald behaved **as though** he were angry. (tells *how* Gerald behaved)

We came **when** we were called. (tells *when* we came)

I will go **wherever** you send me. (tells *where* I will go)

The team lost **because** the players were tired. (tells *why* the team lost)

The girls worked harder **than** the boys did. (tells *how much* harder the girls worked)

You will pass the course **if** you pass this test. (tells *under what conditions* you will pass)

Adverb clauses are introduced by subordinating conjunctions. Some of the most frequently used subordinating conjunctions are

after	as if	before	than	when	wherever
although	as though	if	unless	whenever	while
as	because	since	until	where	

EXERCISE A. Underline the adverb clause in each sentence. Circle the subordinating conjunction. In the space at the right, put the letter that shows what the clause tells. (Add 2½ points for each correctly marked clause and each correct letter.)

a. how	c. where	e. to what extent
b. when	d. why	f. under what conditions

EX. (When) you are near a hot stove, notice the rising air.   *b.*

1. The air above the stove wiggles because heat affects air. ....

2. If air becomes hot, molecules in it quickly scatter. ....

3. Since heat causes this expansion, the hot air moves. ....

4. Hot air is lighter than cold air is. ....

5. Because it is heavy, cold air hovers near the earth. ....

6. Wherever hot and cold air come together, there is a breeze. ....

7. Air above the sea is cooler than air is above the hot beach. ....

8. When the warm air rises, the cool air rushes underneath. ....

9. Because this movement occurs, sea breezes blow inland. ....

10. Is there no wind unless the temperature of air varies? ....

HBJ material copyrighted under notice appearing earlier in this work.

11. Before you answer, you must know about prevailing winds. ....

12. Wherever the climate is hot, air rises rapidly. ....

13. Air goes downward wherever the climate is cold. ....

14. Tropical air travels toward the poles as the polar air moves
toward the equator. ....

15. Because this movement is constant, the winds prevail. ....

16. We must not act as if this is the complete picture. ....

17. Since the earth rotates, it affects wind direction. ....

18. As the earth rotates toward the east, it causes westerly winds in
the Northern Hemisphere. ....

19. Although I have read about these changes, I still want to know
more. ....

20. I will not rest until I have finished the job. ....

EXERCISE B. The following sentences contain adverb and adjective clauses.
Underline each clause and tell in the space at the right whether it is an adjective clause
or an adverb clause. (Add 5 points for each correct underlining and identification.)

	Kind of clause
EX. There's a car that looks just like ours.	adj.
1. Sally's room looks as though a tornado had hit it.	....
2. The calendar that we use today was introduced in 1582.	....
3. It was Alec and Clara who put life into that party!	....
4. I shall write when I receive your new address.	....
5. If I hear any news, I will call you.	....
6. Although taxes are unpopular, they are necessary.	....
7. Take the road that follows the coast.	....
8. Don't volunteer unless you want to work.	....
9. I saved all the money you gave me.	....
10. His arm hurts where the pitched ball struck it.	....

HBJ material copyrighted under notice appearing earlier in this work.

The Noun Clause

A <u>noun clause</u> is a subordinate clause used as a noun.

Like nouns, noun clauses may be used as subjects, subject complements, and objects.

	NOUNS	NOUN CLAUSES
SUBJECT	His **speech** alarmed us.	**What he said** alarmed us.
SUBJ. COMP.	This is our **route**.	This is **where we are going**.
DIRECT OBJECT	I know her **mother**.	I know **who her mother is**.
OBJ. OF PREP.	We will give it to the highest **bidder**.	We will give it to **whoever bids the highest**.

EXERCISE A. Underline the noun clause in each of the following sentences. In the space at the right, tell how the clause is used: *s.*(subject), *s.c.*(subject complement), *d.o.*(direct object), *o.p.*(object of preposition). (Add 5 points for each correct answer.)

EX. Do you know <u>why a photographer uses a flash</u>? *d.o.*

1. I now understand what a scratch hit is. . . . .

2. That he was safe on second seemed obvious to me. . . . .

3. Chris Evert Lloyd knows how important a good serve is. . . . .

4. I'll take whoever wants a ride. . . . .

5. This is what she gave me. . . . .

6. Whoever gets the job will have to work hard. . . . .

7. A new athletic field is what we need most. . . . .

8. I wrote about what I did last summer. . . . .

9. Where Marian went remained a secret. . . . .

10. Whoever finishes first is the winner. . . . .

EXERCISE B. Underline the subordinate clauses. In the first space, name the kind of clause, using the abbreviations *adj., adv., n.* Fill in the second space as follows:

For adjective clauses, write the noun or pronoun modified.
For adverb clauses, write what the clause tells: *how, when, where, why, extent, condition.*
For noun clauses, tell how the clause is used: *s., s.c., d.o., o.p.*
(Add 5 points for each correct sentence.)

EX. The accounts <u>that witnesses gave</u> varied greatly. *adj.* *accounts*

EX. <u>Before you decide</u>, consider all the facts. *adv.* *when*

EX. He pretended <u>that he did not know me</u>. *n.* *d.o.*

HBJ material copyrighted under notice appearing earlier in this work.

75

1. What superstitious people believe is often amazing. ....

2. Do you think that superstitions are true? ....

3. If a mirror breaks, seven years of bad luck supposedly follow. ....

4. A mirror that is broken should be buried. ....

5. The Romans were the ones who originated the superstition about mirrors. ....

6. A cat that is black might be a witch in disguise. ....

7. Be careful when a black cat crosses your path. ....

8. Do you know that spilled salt means bad luck? ....

9. Toss a pinch of salt over your left shoulder whenever you accidentally spill some. ....

10. That is what will protect you from evil. ....

11. If you walk under a-ladder, make a wish! ....

12. Some people believe that thirteen is an unlucky number. ....

13. Whoever is superstitious worries about Friday the thirteenth. ....

14. It is a day that often brings misfortune. ....

15. The person who is superstitious won't take many risks on that day. ....

16. That some buildings, in fact, have no thirteenth floor is true. ....

17. According to the Romans, bad luck might come to whoever gets married in May! ....

18. Do you know anyone who believes that? ....

19. A horseshoe is what some people keep for good luck. ....

20. Don't hang it with its prongs down, however, because the luck will spill out! ....

HBJ material copyrighted under notice appearing earlier in this work.

Chapter Review

EXERCISE A. Circle each prepositional phrase. Draw an arrow from the phrase to the word it modifies. Tell what kind of phrase it is by writing above it *adj.* or *adv.* (Add 5 points for each correctly marked phrase.)

1   Beyond a doubt, the camel is one of the strangest domesticated

2   animals. Unlike the horse or the dog, the camel has never experienced

3   affection for human beings or from human beings. A camel with a

4   grievance will often spit its cud into its owner's face. This has not created

5   good will between humans and camels. If people suddenly disappeared

6   from the earth, most domesticated animals would perish before long. The

7   camel would survive without difficulty. It has never become dependent

8   upon humans. The average camel can carry almost four hundred pounds

9   on its back without showing signs of tiring. Each camel has its own limit.

10   If the owner goes beyond the limit by even a minute amount, the camel

11   will suddenly collapse under the load from the strain and perhaps die. This

12   fact is the basis for the saying, "It was the straw that broke the camel's

13   back."

EXERCISE B. Each of the following sentences contains two subordinate clauses. Underline the clauses. In the spaces at the right, identify the clauses in order: *adjective, adverb,* or *noun.* (Add 2½ points for each correctly marked clause and correct identification.)

1. If you see Nancy, ask her about the books that I gave her. . . . .

2. Since we have no practice room, we have dropped varsity wrestling, which has always been a popular sport. . . . .

3. What I asked for was a book that had a poem by Mari Evans in it. . . . .

4. The losses that they suffered in the stock market were losses that all brokers expect. . . . .

5. When he opened the mail, he found the letter that he had been looking for. . . . .

HBJ material copyrighted under notice appearing earlier in this work.

77

6. Wherever you go, you will find people who are interesting. . . . .

7. If you like to write, include a course in creative writing among those that you elect. . . . .

8. Although I spent two hours on my home-work, I was unprepared when Mr. Horton called on me. . . . .

9. I was offered the job that I wanted, but my parents, who had other plans for me, would not let me accept it. . . . .

10. Don't repeat what she said, because she does not want to be quoted. . . . .

EXERCISE C. On the lines provided, rewrite each of the following pairs of sentences, changing the italicized sentence into a subordinate clause as directed. (Add 20 points for each correct sentence.)

1. My pen pal collects stamps. *He lives in Nigeria.* (adjective clause)

. . . .

. . . .

2. Dad cannot start the fire. *The wood is wet.* (adverb clause telling why)

. . . .

. . . .

3. That girl ought to know something about first aid. *Her mother is a doctor.* (adjective clause introduced by *whose*)

. . . .

. . . .

4. *My dog ran away.* I'll never understand it. (noun clause introduced by *why* in place of the direct object *it*)

. . . .

. . . .

5. I remembered the answer. *It was too late.* (adverb clause telling when)

. . . .

. . . .

HBJ material copyrighted under notice appearing earlier in this work.

Cumulative Review

A. Above each italicized word, write the part of speech. Use the following abbreviations: *n.* (noun); *pron.* (pronoun); *adj.* (adjective); *v.* (verb); *adv.* (adverb); *prep.* (preposition); *conj.* (conjunction); and *int.* (interjection). (Add 5 points for each correct answer.)

1　Shortly *before* the Civil War, the United States Army *imported camels*

2　*into* the Southwest for use *by* the *cavalry*. *They thought* the camels would

3　perform more *efficiently* than horses in the *hot desert* climate. *When* war

4　broke out, the *project* was abandoned, *and* the camels were turned loose.

5　*Frightened* settlers *shot* the *strange* creatures on sight. *Alas,* the animals

6　*soon* were *completely* exterminated.

B. Find the sentence base in each of the following sentences; underline the subject once, the verb twice, and circle the complement. Some sentences contain more than one complement. (Add 5 points for each correctly marked sentence.)

EX. Did Willis ever lend you that book?

1. Everyone in the audience was enthusiastic.
2. The boat at the dock belongs to Mrs. Anderson.
3. She offered me a second chance.
4. Eric and Elena are going to the picnic together.
5. Diahann takes judo lessons after school.
6. The distance from the earth to the sun is 149,000,000 kilometers.
7. Dale expected a larger reward.
8. Students and teachers were critical of the plan.
9. Mac and she took Jean and him with them.
10. The mail carrier gave Eugenio both of the letters.
11. Celia dried the first plate and then stopped.
12. In the second term, sophomores usually take either speech or creative writing.
13. The bald eagle has become an endangered species.
14. Mr. Dietz can probably give you the information.
15. During the rough weather nearly everyone on board became seasick.

HBJ material copyrighted under notice appearing earlier in this work.

16. Leave behind you the mistakes of the past.

17. Mother and Dad sent us a bushel of oranges from Florida.

18. There are several good reasons for his success.

19. In the new school Helen did not seem very happy.

20. Both the van and the car need the attention of a mechanic.

C. Underline the twenty complements in the following sentences. Above each complement write the proper identification: *d.o.*, *i.o.*, or *s.c.* Not every sentence has a complement. Remember also that a complement is never part of a prepositional phrase. (Add 5 points for each correctly marked complement.)

1. That is the best kind of bicycle.

2. Someone should have told him the truth.

3. The dog wants its dinner.

4. Where did you see my name?

5. Henry gave me half of his sandwich and kept the rest for himself.

6. She is more athletic than I.

7. Will you give the boy in the middle this information?

8. Is your father the famous musician from Kansas City?

9. I gave my little sister a book for her birthday.

10. In the morning a glittering layer of ice was on all the trees.

11. Moderate exercise can be beneficial to persons of any age.

12. Geraldine still owes me a thank-you letter.

13. Cora had already written a short note to her uncle.

14. Here are the keys to the office.

15. They were the ones with the best plans for our party.

16. Park your car in the lot behind the building.

HBJ material copyrighted under notice appearing earlier in this work.

Spelling: Three Ways of Spelling /-əl/

The sound /-əl/ is a very difficult one to spell. It appears in unstressed syllables at the end of many nouns, verbs, and adjectives. Therefore, you cannot tell by listening which vowel and consonant combination represents the sound in a particular word. The troublesome sound /-əl/ is most commonly spelled *-al, -le,* or *-el.* (It is also spelled *-ile* or *-il,* as in *hostile, fertile, evil,* and *pencil,* but since these spellings are relatively uncommon, they will not be treated here.)

How, then, do you know whether to use *-le* or *-al* or *-el?* There are no rules, but there are some guides that can help you decide. Try to memorize the guides below and the example words that illustrate them.

● The *-le* spelling is most generally used after the consonant letters *b, p, d, t,* hard *g, k, f,* and *z.*

stable	bridle	angle	rifle
staple	brittle	ankle	puzzle

● The spelling *-al* is a Latin suffix most commonly added to nouns to turn them into adjectives. The majority of such adjectives are made from words that can stand alone—without the suffix *-al.* Words ending in *-le* or *-el* can never stand alone when the *-le* or *-el* ending is removed. (As you read the words in columns 3 and 4 below, notice that a final *e* is dropped and that a final *y* is changed to *i* in the base word when *-al* is added.)

origin	original	fate	fatal
accident	accidental	bride	bridal
profession	professional	bury	burial
music	musical	secretary	secretarial

Note: Some adjectives (and a few nouns) ending in *-al* have entered English directly from Latin or French, and thus have no separate noun form that can stand alone in English. Here are some of the more common of these words: Memorize them.

frugal	legal	moral	rural	annual	dental	animal	hospital

● The *-el* spelling is used in most other words to which the two guides above do not apply. Among these *-el* words are:

kennel	vessel	quarrel	parcel	tunnel	channel	barrel	gavel

EXERCISE A. Using the guides you have learned, spell correctly the /-əl/ sound omitted from each word or word part on page 82. Write *-le, -al,* or *-el* in the short blank. Then write the complete word, correctly spelled, in the longer blank. Remember the rules about changing *y* to *i* and dropping final *e.* The meaning of each word you are to write is given in parentheses. (Add 10 points for each correctly spelled word.)

HBJ material copyrighted under notice appearing earlier in this work.

EX. parent. *al.* ...*parental*... (having to do with parents)

1. logic..... .... (according to the rules of logic)

2. simp..... .... (plain, unadorned)

3. matrimony..... .... (pertaining to marriage)

4. midd..... .... (halfway between)

5. pick..... .... (a cucumber aged in brine)

6. flann..... .... (a fabric much used in pajamas)

7. baff..... .... (to perplex)

8. caram..... .... (a chewy candy)

9. catt..... .... (cows, steers, bulls)

10. universe..... .... (pertaining to the universe)

EXERCISE B. Study the guides and all of the words taught in this lesson, and be prepared to write the words from dictation. (Add 4 points for each correctly spelled word.)

REVIEW EXERCISE. Write the letter *a, e,* or *o,* whichever is correct, in the blank in each word. (Add 10 points for each correct answer.)

1. bystand....r

2. profess....r

3. burgl....r

4. auth....r

5. begg....r

6. carpent....r

7. schol....r

8. lawy....r

9. govern....r

10. operat....r

HBJ material copyrighted under notice appearing earlier in this work.

Building Vocabulary: Words to Learn

administrator /ad mín is trắ tər/ *n.* A person responsible for managing the affairs of a business, government body, or other organization: *An administrator does not always have a voice in deciding the policies that are carried out.*—**administer**, *v.*

agile /áj əl/ *adj.* Light, quick, and sure in movement: *A high jumper must be extremely agile. An agile mind moves quickly from one idea to the next without making mistakes.*—**agility** /ə jíl ə tē/ *n.*

aspiration /ás pə rắ shən/ *n.* A deep longing for something higher or better than one has or is: *The scientist's highest aspiration was to find a cure for cancer.*

faction /fák shən/ *n.* A group within a political party, legislature, or other organization, often used unfavorably: *A faction within the party is opposed to the bill and will stop at nothing to prevent its passage.*

glamorous /glám ər əs/ *adj.* Attractive and exciting but also deceptive, unreal, like magic: *Acting is considered a glamorous career, but teaching, which may be exciting and rewarding, is not usually thought of as glamorous.*—**glamour**, *n.*

grotesque /grō tésk/ *adj.* Strange and fantastic in shape or appearance; absurdly misshapen: *The clowns wore grotesque costumes. Their sense of humor was grotesque.*

heedless /héd lis/ *adj.* Paying no attention; ignoring advice, a warning, etc.: *The sign said "Danger! Road Under Construction," but the heedless man drove on without even slowing down.*

sulk /sulk/ *v.* To be cross and ill-humored, refusing to be cheered up: *When Sean could not have his own way, he sulked for an hour.*—**sulky**, *adj.*

supersede /sū pər sḗd/ *v.* To take the place of something because it is in some way better: *Beginning in the 1920's, talking pictures gradually superseded the old silent films.*

valid /vál id/ *adj.* Based on evidence that can be supported; true and significant: *Sickness is a valid reason for staying out of school.*—**validity** /və líd ə tē/ *n.*

EXERCISE. Fill each blank with the word from this lesson that makes the best sense in the context. In some cases, a verb may need to change form to agree with the rest of the sentence. (Add 10 points for each correct answer.)

1. Because they earn large sums of money and often live in beautiful homes, movie stars seem to lead . . . . lives.

2. A small . . . . within the club was determined to raise the dues, regardless of what the rest of us thought.

3. Large jet airplanes have . . . . most other forms of trans-Atlantic transportation.

4. With a(n) . . . . leap, the monkey cleared the top of the fence and escaped.

5. At the party, the prize for the most . . . . costume went to the boy who came dressed as a gorilla.

6. A school principal must be an able . . . . as well as a trained educator.

HBJ material copyrighted under notice appearing earlier in this work.

7. A person's . . . . in life should reach higher than merely having a well-paying job and a comfortable home.

8. Aaron said over and over that he thought we were mistaken, but in fact he gave no . . . . reasons for his opinion.

9. I don't believe Coreen is the . . . . sort of person who would ignore such an obvious danger.

10. Even if you don't get your own way, you don't need to . . . . about it.

REVIEW EXERCISE. In the space to the left of each sentence, write the letter of the word that could best fill the blank. (Add 10 points for each correct answer.)

a. deficiency	d. diminutive	g. fragile	j. placid
b. degenerate	e. enhance	h. inertia	k. rational
c. depict	f. ensue	i. inference	l. rebate

. . . . 1. He slammed on the brakes, but the car's ____ carried it off the road.

. . . . 2. The novel ____ life on a Western ranch a hundred years ago.

. . . . 3. The dishes are handsome, but they are too ____ for everyday use.

. . . . 4. A scientist makes logical ____ from known facts.

. . . . 5. Paula carried the ____ dog around with her like a toy.

. . . . 6. The British continued to disregard American rights, and the War of 1812 ____ .

. . . . 7. This coupon entitles you to a 10 percent ____ on your next purchase of our product.

. . . . 8. This movie is not likely to ____ the star's reputation.

. . . . 9. The children's bickering would upset even the most ____ disposition.

. . . . 10. The sickly lion cubs suffered from a vitamin ____ .

HBJ material copyrighted under notice appearing earlier in this work.

CHAPTER 5

Completeness in the Sentence

There are two things that you need to know in order to make your sentences complete. You must know what a sentence is, and you must know where it ends. If you know what a sentence is, you will never punctuate a piece of a sentence—a sentence fragment—as if it were a whole sentence. If you know where a sentence ends, you will always put a suitable end mark after it so that you do not string sentences together to make run-on sentences.

Phrase Fragments

A phrase is a fragment of a sentence. It must not be written by itself as a sentence.

You know that a phrase is a group of words used as a single part of speech, and you should be able to recognize and avoid prepositional phrase fragments. You should also be on your guard against four other kinds of phrases from which careless writers make sentence fragments by treating them as if they were complete sentences.

The Participial Phrase. A participle is a word formed from a verb and used as an adjective. A present participle, indicating present time, is formed by adding *-ing* to the verb. A past participle, indicating past time, is formed in various ways, but most often by adding *-ed* to the verb.

FRAGMENT   Jody robbed a beehive. *Filled with honey.* (phrase fragment made from a past participle)

SENTENCE   Jody robbed a beehive filled with honey

FRAGMENT   He plunged into a stream. *Thus avoiding the angry bees.* (phrase fragment built around a present participle)

SENTENCE   He plunged into a stream, thus avoiding the angry bees

The Appositive Phrase. An appositive phrase is a group of words that explains or identifies the noun or pronoun it follows. It is set off by commas.

FRAGMENT   I met Mr. Seton. *The owner of the beehive.* (phrase fragment made from an appositive)

SENTENCE   I met Mr. Seton, the owner of the beehive

HBJ material copyrighted under notice appearing earlier in this work.

85

The Gerund Phrase.   A gerund is a verb form ending in *-ing* that is used as a noun.

FRAGMENT   Pat decided to give up.   *Running the marathon race.*   (phrase fragment made from a gerund)
SENTENCE   Pat decided to give up running the marathon race

The Infinitive Phrase.   An infinitive is made up of *to* plus a verb: *to strive, to seek, to find, to yield.* An infinitive phrase begins with an infinitive.

FRAGMENT   Mr. Seton told me.   *To leave his bees alone.*   (phrase fragment made from an infinitive)
SENTENCE   Mr. Seton told me to leave his bees alone

EXERCISE. Some of the items in this exercise contain phrase fragments and others contain only complete sentences. In the space to the left of each item, write *S* for complete sentences. Identify each sentence fragment by writing in the space at the left one of the following abbreviations: *prep.* (prepositional phrase fragment); *part.* (participial phrase fragment); *app.* (appositive phrase fragment); *inf.* (infinitive phrase fragment).; *ger.* (gerund phrase fragment). For all fragments, cross out the incorrect period and capital letter. You will not be marked for commas that may be needed. (Add 10 points for each correctly marked item.)

.... 1. The blizzard paralyzed the city. Causing the mayor to proclaim a state of emergency.

.... 2. We spent the night in Easton. A city in eastern Pennsylvania.

.... 3. Mr. Mohan told me how hard the job would be. Then he offered me more money than I had expected.

.... 4. You will drive farther but reach home sooner if you take this route. Following side roads to avoid crowded highways.

.... 5. He finally finished. Taking the math test yesterday.

.... 6. Delores decided to go to the jazz festival. To hear Ella Fitzgerald and Wynton Marsalis perform.

.... 7. We watched Julia try. Stunt-riding on the pinto pony.

.... 8. The entertainment committee scored its greatest success last night. With its humorous skit and an exhibition by the band.

.... 9. Nancy asked me to come to her house this evening. She wants me to help her with some back assignments in algebra.

.... 10. She lives in the town's oldest house. A beautiful colonial home.

HBJ material copyrighted under notice appearing earlier in this work.

Subordinate Clause Fragments

A <u>subordinate clause</u> is a fragment of a sentence. It must not be written by itself as a sentence.

Like a phrase, a subordinate clause does not express a complete thought. It must always be attached to the sentence of which it is a part, rather than left by itself with a capital letter at the beginning and a period at the end.

SENTENCE The earthquake occurred because of a fault.
FRAGMENT *Which is a break in the crust of the earth.*
SENTENCE The earthquake occurred because of a fault, <u>which is a break in the crust of the earth.</u>

SENTENCE Our government maintains scores of seismograph observatories.
FRAGMENT *Because seismographs record both the location and the intensity of an earthquake.*
SENTENCE Our government maintains scores of seismograph observatories <u>because seismographs record both the location and the intensity of an earthquake.</u>

Subordinate clauses can usually be identified by the words with which they begin. The following words commonly begin subordinate clauses:

who (whose, whom)	although	because	than	whenever
which	as	before	unless	where
that	as if	if	until	wherever
after	as though	since	when	while

EXERCISE A. Some of the items below are sentence fragments. Others consist of a complete sentence and a sentence fragment. Rewrite the incorrect items, joining fragments to their sentences or supplying a new independent clause to go with a fragment. Do nothing with any item that is correct as it stands. (Add 20 points for each correctly treated item.)

1. Shirley Temple Black, who was ambassador to Ghana. . . . .
. . . .

2. If your car skids on ice, don't use the brakes. . . . .
. . . .

3. If you break a string in your tennis racket. Get it restrung without delay.
. . . .
. . . .

HBJ material copyrighted under notice appearing earlier in this work.

4. I would like to read that book. Which is an exciting mystery. ....

....

....

5. Larry drove off in the camp truck. Leaving the rest of us without food.

....

....

EXERCISE B. There are ten uncorrected sentence fragments in the paragraph below. Join each to a sentence by crossing out the unnecessary period and replacing the incorrect capital letter with a small letter. (Add 10 points for each corrected fragment.)

1   At our school, everyone looks forward to Clean-up Day. Even though it
2   means hard work for all of us. All ninth-grade classes are excused for the
3   afternoon on Clean-up Day. Which is observed every spring. Members of
4   the student council supervise the work. After they have met previously to
5   decide the area for which each class will be responsible. Some students
6   are equipped with rakes and spades. That are loaned by trusting parents
7   who are interested in the project. Trash baskets, wheelbarrows, bushel
8   baskets, hedge clippers, and even lawn mowers are rushed into action.
9   When the time for work arrives at the beginning of the sixth period. After
10   Clean-up Day ninth-graders are naturally interested in keeping the
11   grounds neat. Because they have worked hard to get them that way. They
12   don't want to see them littered with paper. You don't dare throw a gum
13   wrapper or a lunch bag anywhere but in the trash baskets. Unless you want
14   to have trouble with ninth-graders. Almost everyone enjoys Clean-up
15   Day. Probably because most of us like to get out of going to classes.
16   There are always some loafers. Who are more interested in getting out of
17   work than in helping. Even the loafers, however, get busy. When they see
18   how seriously most of the students take the work.

HBJ material copyrighted under notice appearing earlier in this work.

Correcting Fragments

EXERCISE. Some of the following items are complete sentences. Others contain fragments of sentences. Write *S* before those which are complete sentences. Write *F* before those which contain fragments. Cross out punctuation and replace capital letters with small letters so that each fragment will be part of a sentence. You need not consider commas in this exercise. (Add 5 points for each correctly marked item.)

.... 1. As civilizations developed, people realized the need for systems of measurement. That would allow them to trade among themselves.

.... 2. Linear measurements are measurements of length. Among early civilizations measurements of the body provided the most convenient basis for linear measurements.

.... 3. Among the first groups to develop a system of measurement were the Egyptians. Who were using measuring devices as early as 3000 B.C.

.... 4. The Egyptian unit of measure for length was the cubit. Which equaled the length of the arm from the elbow to the fingertips.

.... 5. The need for a standard unit of measure was recognized. Since a cubit could differ from one person to another.

.... 6. Based on the length of the pharaoh's forearm, a cubit stick was used. In much the same manner as a ruler is used today.

.... 7. The accuracy of the cubit stick can be judged by considering the dimensions of the pyramids. The sides of the Great Pyramid of Giza vary by no more than .05 percent.

.... 8. The Romans kept their standards for length and weight in the temple. By decree of law, people were required to use weights and measures exactly like the standards.

.... 9. As they were conquered by Rome, other lands were forced to adopt the Roman standards for weights and measures. To allow for convenient trade between the parts of the empire.

.... 10. The Roman unit of measure for length was the foot, which was divided into twelve *uniciae,* or inches. Weight was measured in *librae.*

HBJ material copyrighted under notice appearing earlier in this work.

.... 11. Rome forced a period of unification on Western Europe. When Rome fell, much of the unity of Europe collapsed with it.

.... 12. Failing communication between the various parts of the empire finally broke down. The standardizing of weights and measures that the Romans had accomplished.

.... 13. Although medieval Europe retained the system of weights and measures inherited from the Romans. Many regional differences developed.

.... 14. At the beginning of the ninth century. Charlemagne tried to reunite parts of the former Roman Empire.

.... 15. One of his reforms was to try to impose standards of weights and measures. Since so many variations had crept into the old Roman system. In fact, almost every town had its own system.

.... 16. Though Charlemagne's efforts met with little success. Some degree of uniformity was imposed by the great trade fairs. Held during the twelfth and thirteenth centuries.

.... 17. Merchants had to conform to the standards of the fairs. In order to participate in them.

.... 18. As England grew as a separate nation, its rulers established an English system of measurement. And imposed it on the people throughout its realm.

.... 19. Recognizing the need for standard units. Henry I defined the yard as the distance from the point of his nose to the end of his thumb.

.... 20. An inch was defined as the length of three dry barleycorns placed end to end. While a pound was established as the weight of 7,680 grains of wheat.

HBJ material copyrighted under notice appearing earlier in this work.

More Practice in Correcting Fragments

EXERCISE A. The following paragraph contains several phrases and subordinate clauses incorrectly used as though they were complete sentences. By crossing out end marks and replacing capital letters with small letters, change the paragraphs so that there are no fragments. You will not be graded on your use of commas. (Add 10 points for each corrected fragment.)

1   In 1670 Gabriel Mouton made a radical suggestion. The adoption of a
2 totally new system of weights and measures for France. This new system
3 would use measurements of the earth as a basis for defining units. Rather
4 than measurements of the body. Which had provided the previous
5 standards. Each unit would be based on a multiple of 10. The prefixes
6 attached to the unit would indicate the multiple. Mouton's proposal was
7 argued for about 120 years. Before any concrete action was taken on it.
8 After the fall of the Bastille, the National Assembly attempted to
9 modernize the French government. It was a time of radical ideas, and
10 Talleyrand revived Mouton's radical proposal. Declaring the need for a
11 more efficient system that all people could easily learn.

12   In 1795 the metric system was officially adopted. Making the meter the
13 standard for length, the gram for mass, and the liter for volume. Different
14 prefixes were added to the root words to indicate larger or smaller units.
15 So that it was readily apparent that one *kilo*gram equaled 1,000 grams and
16 one *centi*meter equaled one one-hundredth of a meter. Certainly a system
17 in which units are multiples of 10 is easier to use than the English system.
18 Where twelve inches equal one foot, three feet equal one yard, and 5,280
19 feet equal one mile. As Napoleon conquered other nations, he forced them
20 to adopt the metric system. Just as the Romans had forced conquered
21 nations to adopt the Roman system.

22   Today the metric system is used in most of the major nations throughout
23 the world. Sometimes its adoption followed revolution. As in the cases of
24 France, the U.S.S.R., and China. Sometimes it followed political reform
25 and modernization. In any case, a system of measurement in international
26 use has aided trade of both goods and ideas throughout the world.

HBJ material copyrighted under notice appearing earlier in this work.

EXERCISE B. Follow the directions given for Exercise A. (Add 5 points for each corrected fragment.)

1   Every afternoon the playground is filled with boys and girls. Who are
2   getting rid of their stored-up energy. As soon as they get out of the
3   cafeteria. They head for the play areas. Which are behind the school
4   building. It isn't long before the children are playing a dozen different
5   games. Such as soccer, volleyball, handball, and basketball. There are
6   usually several softball games. Because there are three diamonds laid out
7   on the playground. Sometimes the three games get mixed. With the
8   outfielders running into each other. Occasionally one of our outfielders
9   will be surprised. When the ball from another game hits the player in the
10 back. Once I saw a left fielder on one diamond stop a ball. Which had
11 been hit by a batter on another diamond. I watched to see what he did with
12 the ball. To my surprise he looked over at the other game. Saw the
13 situation over there. And threw the runner out at second base. This act
14 brought on an argument. Which was soon settled. When the umpire
15 declared the runner safe. As soon as everyone understood what had
16 happened. They applauded the umpire's decision. As I watched this
17 incident, I thought it would be fun to lay out three diamonds. So that they
18 would have the same outfield. An arrangement that would make life
19 exciting for the fielders. Who would have to play in three games at the
20 same time. In a professional game, the outfielders would have to get three
21 times their normal pay. Because they would do three times as much work.
22 Of course team owners would not like this arrangement. Unless the games
23 could draw three times as many fans. In such a layout there would be
24 many other exciting possibilities. Which you can easily imagine. If you
25 know anything about baseball.

HBJ material copyrighted under notice appearing earlier in this work.

Using End Marks

In preparation for your study of the run-on sentence, the second major error in writing complete sentences, you may need a review of the punctuation marks used at the end of a sentence. This lesson will give you a quick review of these end marks.

A sentence is followed by an appropriate end mark (period, question mark, exclamation point).

1. A sentence that makes a statement is followed by a period.

EXAMPLES   Eleanor Roosevelt was an outstanding humanitarian.
She was twice a delegate to the United Nations.

2. A sentence that asks a question is followed by a question mark.

EXAMPLES   What shall we do?
Where are you going?

3. An indirect question that is part of a statement is not followed by a question mark.

EXAMPLES   We asked the teacher what we should do.
I asked the girls where they were going.

4. An exclamation is followed by an exclamation point.

EXAMPLES   What good luck we had!
The roof is falling in!

5. A sentence that expresses a request or a command may be followed by either a period or an exclamation point, depending upon the purpose of the sentence.

EXAMPLES   Take this note to Miss Fredericks, please.
Look out, Jim!

EXERCISE A. Place the proper end mark after each of the following sentences. In this exercise, when an end mark and quotation marks come together, place the end mark *inside* the quotation marks. (Add 10 points for each correct answer.)

1. What did I say in my note to Celia

2. I asked her what animal uses its nose for an arm

3. How quickly she wrote the answer, an elephant

HBJ material copyrighted under notice appearing earlier in this work.

4. Celia's note to me said, "Try to stump me again"

5. Imagine our surprise when we saw Mr. Baker behind us

6. Why do Celia and I always get caught

7. Mr. Baker said gruffly, "Tell me why tears come to your eyes when you are peeling an onion"

8. After a moment of silence, he asked, "What is the difference between an onion and an apple"

9. Stalling for time, Celia exclaimed, "An onion and an apple"

10. "Pay attention to today's lesson, and learn the answer to my riddle," Mr. Baker advised sternly

EXERCISE B. Change each of the following sentences as directed and use appropriate end marks. Add or omit words when necessary. (Add 10 points for each correct sentence.)

The game starts at two o'clock.

EX. *Direct question:* Does the game start at two o'clock?

EX. *Command:* Start the game at two o'clock!

That fumble will cost us the game.

1. *Direct question:* ....

2. *Exclamation:* ....

Mario should leave at once.

3. *Direct question:* ....

4. *Command:* ....

Was that road dangerous?

5. *Statement:* ....

6. *Exclamation:* ....

You told him what I said.

7. *Direct question:* ....

8. *Exclamation:* ....

The rug should be cleaned right away.

9. *Direct question:* ....

10. *Command:* ....

94

HBJ material copyrighted under notice appearing earlier in this work.

Correcting the Run-on Sentence

Failure to use an end mark when you have completed a sentence is a serious error in writing. Another serious error is placing a comma at the end of a sentence. A comma is not an end mark. Sentences that are not followed by an end mark *run on* into the following sentence. They are therefore called *run-on sentences*.

RUN-ON   Virginia was busy campaigning for her favorite candidate she passed out pamphlets to all the people in her apartment building one day a week she worked at the candidate's office downtown. (No end marks are given. Each sentence runs on into the next.)

CORRECTED   Virginia was busy campaigning for her favorite candidate. She passed out pamphlets to all the people in her apartment building. One day a week she worked at the candidate's office downtown.

RUN-ON   Ken liked shop best of all his classes, he was good at making things with his hands, last year he made some beautiful pieces of furniture for his room at home. (Commas have been used in place of end marks. Each sentence runs on into the next.)

CORRECTED   Ken liked shop best of all his classes. He was good at making things with his hands. Last year he made some beautiful pieces of furniture for his room at home.

EXERCISE. Read the following groups of sentences. End marks have been omitted. Insert proper end marks in the right places and put a capital letter at the beginning of each sentence. (Add 4 points for each corrected run-on.)

1. The guests pushed their chairs back from the table when they were through eating Helen's father set up his movie projector on the table and showed some pictures he had taken during his recent trip on the white wall of the dining room the pictures showed up very well.

2. Mr. Solomon had coached Morgantown's football teams for twenty years in that time he had had five undefeated teams and ten championships when he retired, the whole town turned out to pay homage to him.

3. Jackie Barnes, who lives next door, has been taking cornet lessons every evening after supper she practices sitting in our living room, we struggle through every exercise with her our muscles grow tense and our nerves jump as Jackie slurs her way up to a high note will she make it will she muff it when she has either succeeded or failed, we relax until the next effort.

HBJ material copyrighted under notice appearing earlier in this work.

4. Do you know how to dance the limbo it's really quite easy two people hold a pole four feet from the ground the limbo dancers sway to the strong rhythm of the music as they bend their knees and go under the pole if the dancers touch the pole, they are out the pole is lowered bit by bit until only one dancer is left.

5. The ancient Chinese believed in an ultimate spirit, called the *Tao* this spirit was divided into two opposing forces. The yin was the negative force. It was receptive, absorbing, and passive the yang was the positive force it was penetrating, creative, and active although the yin and yang were opposites, the root of each was found in the other when they were in harmony, the world was at peace when they were in a state of imbalance, there was strife.

6. Historians have shown that many of the characters of the Wild West fell quite short of their legends most of us are used to seeing Wyatt Earp portrayed as a gallant marshal in fact he broke the law as often as he upheld it during his lifetime he was a horse thief, a stagecoach robber, and a coldblooded killer perhaps the most disappointing fact of all is that at one time he worked as a bill collector.

HBJ material copyrighted under notice appearing earlier in this work.

Chapter Review

EXERCISE A. The following paragraph is composed of run-on sentences. Some of the commas have been incorrectly used as end marks. Decide where the sentences end and insert the proper end marks. Begin each sentence with a capital letter. Be careful not to create any fragments. (Add 10 points for each corrected run-on.)

1　A blizzard is a novelty in the South, where many children have never
2　seen a heavy snow, everyone at school was excited about the six inches of
3　snow that fell yesterday in the classrooms teachers had difficulty keeping
4　our attention. Of course, I, too, was very excited, as soon as school was
5　out, I dashed home, put a new film in my camera, and spent an hour
6　taking twelve snapshots, since I wanted to send unusual pictures to my
7　pen pal in south Texas, I took pictures at various angles of our new house
8　to capture the beauty of the snow-laden shrubs. I also took superb action
9　shots of my dogs scuffling in deep drifts, then I snapped sparrows pecking
10　at scraps of bread on the picnic table, which had deep snow on top of it,
11　after building a snowman, I took a close-up of it. Delighted at the
12　prospect of sending the twelve pictures to my friend as quickly as
13　possible, I decided to take the film immediately to a studio in order to
14　have the pictures developed, before I did so, however, I remembered that
15　when I had snapped each picture, the camera had clicked, but that the
16　click had sounded unusual, I thought, "Could my camera be out of
17　order?" Holding the unloaded camera up to the light, I pushed the button,
18　heard the click, but saw no flash of light, the shutter was not working, not
19　one ray of light had reached the film!

EXERCISE B. The following story is confusing because it contains fragments and run-on sentences. Make the story clear by changing the punctuation and capital letters so that there will be no fragments or run-on sentences. (Add 4 points for each corrected fragment or run-on.)

A FISHY STORY

1　Captain Bill Atkins, a Brooklyn fisher, brought his cruiser to the
2　cod-fishing grounds off Ambrose Lightship about 11:30 one morning last
3　spring. Planning to catch a few cod. He baited some lines and tossed them

HBJ material copyrighted under notice appearing earlier in this work.

4   over Harry, the only other member of the crew, busied himself in a
5   similar manner By the middle of the afternoon. They had collected a good
6   catch and had just decided to call it a day. When there came a huge tug on
7   one of the lines. Indicating that an especially big one had taken the bait,
8   Captain Atkins and Harry heaved mightily on the line. Finally the fish
9   broke above the surface, one look was enough for Harry. Who dropped
10 the line and headed for the most remote spot on the boat, near Captain
11 Atkins lay a two-by-four. Which the undaunted captain seized and
12 brought down on the head of his catch. In a few moments the fish lay
13 panting heavily on the deck. Giving Captain Atkins and Harry a chance to
14 inspect it.

15   This was the first time either man had ever seen such a monster. On its
16 head were four horns and an antenna a foot long in its mouth, which was
17 the size of a football, were five rows of vicious teeth the monster
18 measured four-and-a-half feet in length and weighed seventy pounds
19 while Harry and Captain Bill were gazing at this unknown caller, they
20 were horror-struck when the "fish" shook off the effects of the blow and
21 began to walk across the deck toward them. On its *feet!* Harry departed in
22 haste Captain Atkins seized a hammer and advanced to do battle
23 following a brief scuffle the fish lay still again, and the bewildered captain
24 turned his ship toward home.

25   The captain's fish story went the rounds in Brooklyn as fast as the
26 captain could spread it about the details there could be no argument.
27 Because, after all, there was the fish to be seen by anyone who wanted to
28 see it, authorities at the American Museum of Natural History informed
29 Captain Atkins that his monster was known by various names. The
30 "angler fish" or the "goose fish" or the "fishing frog" fish of this kind
31 usually do not swim but walk on the floor of the ocean. Waving their
32 antennae to lure other fish Captain Atkins accepted this information,
33 showing no interest in going to the bottom to get proof.

HBJ material copyrighted under notice appearing earlier in this work.

Cumulative Review

A. In the spaces to the right of each sentence, name in order the part of speech of the italicized words in the sentence. Use abbreviations. (Add 5 points for each correct answer.)

1. *In* 1867 the United States *bought* Alaska for $7,200,000. ....

2. People thought we *had* paid *too* much. ....

3. They called *it* "Seward's *icebox*." ....

4. The price *actually* works out to about a dollar *and* a ....

   quarter per *square mile*. ....

5. *Alaskan* minerals alone have *grossed at* least a *billion* ....

   dollars! ....

6. *After almost* a century had passed, Alaska was admitted to ....

   statehood. ....

7. The biggest state *then* advocated *kindness* to all *unhappy* ....

   Texans. ....

B. In the spaces to the right, give the subject and verb in each sentence. Select the verb first and write it in the second column. Be sure to give all parts of the verb. (Add 5 points for each correct answer.)

	Subject	*Verb*
1. Has either of you ever bitten into a green persimmon?	....	....
2. Some of the fuses are not good.	....	....
3. Splashing among the rocks was a school of lively fish.	....	....
4. Can Sam or Clarissa cook quail?	....	....
5. Saturday I watered the lawn and spaded the flower beds.	....	....
6. There have been few objections to the new schedule.	....	....
7. To the pitcher went full credit for the victory.	....	....
8. Linda's collection of old comic books will be on display.	....	....

HBJ material copyrighted under notice appearing earlier in this work.

9. Where is your book report? . . . .

10. Do not waste your money. . . . .

C. In the first space at the right, copy the complement(s) in each sentence. In the second space identify the complement, using these abbreviations: subject complement, *s.c.;* direct object, *d.o.;* indirect object, *i.o.* (Add 5 points for each correct answer.)

	Complement	*Kind*
1. Some employees fear automation.	. . . .	. . . . . .
2. Define an obtuse angle.	. . . .	. . . . . .
3. What ancient peoples built pyramids?	. . . .	. . . . . .
4. Our sandwiches became soggy.	. . . .	. . . . . .
5. That we did not foresee.	. . . .	. . . . . .
6. The police gave them valuable information.	. . . .	. . . . . .
7. No one would believe me.	. . . .	. . . . . .
8. Mr. Silver told us the answers to the test.	. . . .	. . . . . .
9. Our new car is a station wagon.	. . . .	. . . . . .
10. Regina reached second base safely.	. . . .	. . . . . .

D. Each of the following sentences contains a phrase or a subordinate clause. Underline each phrase and clause. In the first space at the right, state whether the underlined group of words is a phrase or a clause. In the second space tell whether it is used as an adjective or an adverb or a noun. (Add 5 points for each correct answer.)

	Phrase or clause	*Use*
1. The audience roared when the ventriloquist outfrowned his dummy.	. . . .	. . . .
2. Near the wigwam stood a totem pole.	. . . .	. . . .
3. The palm is the symbol of victory.	. . . .	. . . .
4. What you said makes no sense.	. . . .	. . . .
5. Mark Twain enjoyed portraying Southern life in his stories.	. . . .	. . . .
6. This is a time for action.	. . . .	. . . .
7. Who is going with you?	. . . .	. . . .
8. He remembered the egg in his pocket.	. . . .	. . . .
9. Mom asked where you were.	. . . .	. . . .
10. At the end of her speech, Ms. Sandlov demanded action.	. . . .	. . . .

HBJ material copyrighted under notice appearing earlier in this work.

Spelling: Using *-ent* and *-ence*

Among the trickiest words to spell are those that end in *-ent* and *-ence* or *-ant* and *-ance*. Because each of these suffixes is an unstressed syllable, the vowel becomes the indistinct schwa sound /ə/. How then can you tell whether a word ends in *-ent* or *-ant; -ence* or *-ance*?

Unfortunately, there are few generalizations that are really helpful. Mostly, words with these endings have to be memorized. Since they are so easily confused, they will be taught separately: *-ent* and *-ence* in this lesson, *-ant* and *-ance* in Lesson 60.

Here are the only useful guides available for words ending in *-ent* and *-ence:* (Memorize the words given as examples.)

● The suffix *-ent* (which is the more common form) is added to a verb to make it an adjective, as in list *1* below. Sometimes there is no separate verb in English, as in list *2*. Only the adjective form (derived from a Latin verb) exists.

	1	*2*
confide	confident	prominent
depend	dependent	violent
insist	insistent	innocent
differ	different	obedient
revere	reverent	eminent
emerge	emergent	permanent

● Many adjectives ending in *-ent* have related nouns that end in *-ence*. If you can spell one, you can spell the other.

Here are the noun forms of the *-ent* adjectives given under the first guide above:

confident	confidence	prominent	prominence
dependent	dependence	violent	violence
insistent	insistence	innocent	innocence
different	difference	obedient	obedience
reverent	reverence	eminent	eminence
emergent	emergence	permanent	permanence

EXERCISE A. Add the suffix *-ent* to each of the following verbs to change the verb to an adjective. Write the adjective in the blank. Remember the rule about dropping final *e* before adding a suffix beginning with a vowel. (Add 10 points for each correct answer.)

EXAMPLE   exist + ent = *existent.*

1. consist + ent = ...

2. indulge + ent = ...

3. reside + ent = ...

4. inhere + ent = ...

5. diverge + ent = ...

6. precede + ent = ...

HBJ material copyrighted under notice appearing earlier in this work.

7. cohere + ent = ...   9. persist + ent = ...

8. converge + ent = ...   10. urge + ent = ...

EXERCISE B. For each adjective below, write the corresponding noun form ending in *-ence*. (Add 5 points for each correctly spelled word.)

EX. convenient *convenience* ....

1. lenient ....   11. indulgent ....

2. absent ....   12. recurrent ....

3. irreverent ....   13. violent ....

4. competent ....   14. excellent ....

5. evident ....   15. present ....

6. magnificent ....   16. impudent ....

7. silent ....   17. penitent ....

8. independent ....   18. patient ....

9. diligent ....   19. adolescent ....

10. prominent ....   20. intelligent ....

EXERCISE C. Be ready to write from dictation all of the words taught in this lesson. (Add 2 points for each correctly spelled word.)

REVIEW EXERCISE. Complete each word by writing in the blank *-le, -al,* or *-el,* whichever is correct. (Add 10 points for each correct answer.)

1. dent ....   6. ank ....

2. origin ....   7. annu ....

3. quarr ....   8. kenn ....

4. stab ....   9. barr ....

5. hospit ....   10. puzz ....

HBJ material copyrighted under notice appearing earlier in this work.

Building Vocabulary: Analyzing Words

When chemists analyze a chemical compound, they break it down into its parts to see what it is made of. You do much the same thing when you analyze words. By breaking a new word down into its parts, you can often see that its root, or main part, is a word whose meaning you already know. If you know the meaning of a few common prefixes and suffixes, you can usually form a good idea of the meaning of the new word.

EXAMPLE   An **ungovernable** temper is a serious fault.

The word printed in red consists of three main parts: the prefix *un-*, the root *govern*, and the suffix *-able*. *Govern*, of course, means "to rule" or "control." Combined with the prefix *un- (not)* and the suffix *-able (able, capable)*, it means "not capable of being controlled," hence "wild, unruly, violent."

Usually, a suffix changes the part of speech of the word to which it is added (*-able* turns the verb *govern* into an adjective). A prefix, on the other hand, usually does not change the part of speech (*governable* and *ungovernable* are both adjectives). Study the meanings of these common suffixes and prefixes and try to think of words in which they are used.

PREFIXES un- (in-, il-, im-, ir-) *meaning* not—**un**necessary
re- *meaning* back, again, backward—**re**make

SUFFIXES -able (-ible) *meaning* able, capable—us**able**
-al (-ial) *meaning* concerning, pertaining to, according to—sensation**al**

EXERCISE A. Without using a dictionary, divide the following words into prefix, root, and suffix, as in the example. Then write a short definition that shows how the prefix or suffix discussed in this lesson affects the root meaning of the word. Afterward, check your answers in a dictionary. You will not be scored on this exercise. Note that some words have both a prefix and a suffix.

EX. im|mater|ial /ím ə tír ē əl/ *adj.* *not pertaining to matter*

1. controversial /kón trə vúr shəl/ *adj.* ....
....

2. incompetent /in kóm pə tənt/ *adj.* ....

3. managerial /mán ə jír ē əl/ *adj.* ....

4. inadequate /in ád ə kwit/ *adj.* ....

5. cultural /kúl chər əl/ *adj.* ....

6. unintelligible /ún in tél ə jə bəl/ *adj.* ....
....

HBJ material copyrighted under notice appearing earlier in this work.

7. reconcile /rék ən sīl/ v. ....

....

8. inflexible /in flék sə bəl/ *adj.* ....

9. unpalatable /un pál it ə bəl/ *adj.* ....

....

10. refrain /ri frān/ *v.* ....

EXERCISE B. In the space to the left of each sentence, write the letter of the following definition that best explains the italicized word. (Add 10 points for each correct answer.)

a. Subject to argument and strong disagreement.
b. Having to do with things that show mental and artistic refinement.
c. Not enough; insufficient.
d. Lacking the strength, training, or other qualifications for an activity.
e. Firm, unyielding, rigid.
f. Like a manager; reflecting the skills, abilities, and outlook of a trained business executive.
g. To bring back into harmony persons or ideas that have been opposed.
h. To hold back from doing something.
i. Impossible to understand.
j. Not pleasing to the taste.

.... 1. The constant discussion in the newspapers has made the new school policy an extremely *controversial* matter.

.... 2. *Incompetent* drivers are as dangerous to others as to themselves.

.... 3. Maggie Lena Walker's *managerial* skills made her a successful insurance and banking executive.

.... 4. You can't do your best work with *inadequate* food and sleep.

.... 5. Most large cities offer far greater *cultural* opportunities than do small towns.

.... 6. Even today, Einstein's theories are *unintelligible* to all but a few highly trained mathematicians.

.... 7. We hoped to *reconcile* the former enemies after the war.

.... 8. The Senator's *inflexible* opposition has prevented the bill from passing.

.... 9. A bad cold may make ordinary food seem quite *unpalatable*.

.... 10. Please *refrain* from whispering while I am talking.

HBJ material copyrighted under notice appearing earlier in this work.

CHAPTER 6

Capital Letters

What is the distinction in meaning between *girl* and *Pam,* between *school* and *Stewart School,* between *river* and *Missouri River?* If you understand the differences between the words in each of these pairs, you understand the basic rule governing the use of capital letters. The words without capitals refer to *any* girl, *any* school, *any* river. They are *common* nouns. Those words with capitals name a *particular* girl, school, and river. They are *proper* nouns. The basic rule is that you use a capital letter when you write a proper noun, one that singles out a particular person, place, or thing. An adjective formed from a proper noun is a proper adjective. Proper adjectives are also capitalized: English (from England); American (from America); African (from Africa). Of course, whether the noun or adjective is proper or common, the first letter is always capitalized for any word that begins a sentence. This chapter will call your attention to the various kinds of proper nouns and adjectives and give you practice in recognizing and capitalizing them.

LESSON **54**

Capitals for Geographical Names

Capitalize geographical names.

CITIES AND TOWNS   Carson City, Centerville
COUNTIES AND TOWNSHIPS   Sussex County, Warren Township
STATES   Illinois, New Hampshire, Florida
COUNTRIES   Brazil, United States of America
CONTINENTS   Africa, Asia
ISLANDS   Long Island, the Virgin Islands
BODIES OF WATER   Fern Lake, Trout Creek, Red River, Atlantic Ocean
MOUNTAINS   Ozark Mountains, Whitestone Mountain
STREETS   Canfield Avenue, Thirty-fourth Street
PARKS   Blue Lake State Park, Penny Park
SECTIONS OF THE COUNTRY   the North, the Far West

1. Capitalize words like city, street, lake, river, park, mountain, and ocean when they are part of a proper name.

EXAMPLES   Whitefish Lake, Green Mountain, Oklahoma City

HBJ material copyrighted under notice appearing earlier in this work.

2. Capitalize <u>east</u>, <u>west</u>, <u>north</u>, and <u>south</u> when they name a section of the country. Do not capitalize <u>east</u>, <u>west</u>, <u>north</u>, and <u>south</u> when they name directions.

EXAMPLES   I have lived in the *West* longer than in the *South*. (sections of the country)
Go *south* to the hospital and turn *east*. (directions)
The *east* wind brought rain. (direction)

3. Do not capitalize a common noun modified by a proper adjective unless it is part of a name.

EXAMPLES   a Spanish *city*   New York *City*
a Minnesota *lake*   Pine *Lake*

EXERCISE. Find the twenty-five incorrect items and add capital letters where they are needed. (Add 4 points for each corrected item.)

EX. Kildare *road*

EX. a *swiss* town

1. the Ohio river
2. a Chicago firm
3. los angeles freeway
4. Hingham county residents
5. the Rocky Mountains
6. the atlantic ocean
7. Pigeon river national forest
8. great salt lake
9. a Cherokee leader
10. the canadian ambassador
11. the south side of nineteenth street
12. the capital of north carolina
13. the spanish people
14. a new england village
15. a seneca lake resort
16. long island, new york
17. crater lake national park
18. seventh avenue
19. a city in the middle west
20. the nations of Europe and Asia
21. a Chinese village
22. Main street runs north and south.
23. an african country
24. the sahara desert
25. nations of the far east
26. the pacific northwest
27. Mount Katahdin
28. an ocean beach
29. San Diego county
30. Myrtle beach
31. a college in the East
32. Nassau boulevard
33. two miles east
34. a french restaurant

HBJ material copyrighted under notice appearing earlier in this work.

Capitals for Special Groups and Events

Capitalize words like club, corporation, hotel, building, theater, high school, **and** college **when they are part of a proper noun.**

PART OF A PROPER NOUN	COMMON NOUN
Hi-Y *Club*	a school *club*
Margate Building *Corporation*	a large *corporation*
Statler *Hotel*	a new *hotel*
Dupont *Building*	a tall *building*
Century *Theater*	an air-conditioned *theater*
Altoona *High School*	a *high school* in Altoona
Middlebury *College*	a New England *college*

Capitalize names of special events and calendar items (days of the week, months, and holidays).

EXAMPLES   Battle of Waterloo   Thanksgiving Day
                French Revolution   Monday, July 1

Capitalize names of races and religions.

EXAMPLES   a Baptist, a leader of the Jews, a Polynesian

Do not capitalize seasons, school years, or school subjects except languages and the names of specific courses.

EXAMPLES   summer, fall, spring, winter
                freshman, sophomore, junior, senior
                English, French, algebra, history (*but:* History I)

EXERCISE A. Change each proper noun below to a corresponding common noun. Change each common noun to a corresponding proper noun. (Add 10 points for each correct item.)

EX.   Future Scientists Club   *a club for future scientists*

EX.   sometime next spring   *on Thursday, May 14*

1. Parent-Teacher Association   ....

2. a hospital in the city   ....

3. two holidays   ....

4. my school   ....

5. the Civil War   ....

HBJ material copyrighted under notice appearing earlier in this work.

6. a war involving the world   . . . .

7. Algebra I   . . . .

8. two foreign languages   . . . .

9. on Main Street   . . . .

10. a native of this country   . . . .

EXERCISE B. Draw a line through any word that begins incorrectly. Write the word correctly in the blank to the right of the line. If there is no error in a line, write *C* (for *correct*) in the blank. (Add 5 points for each correct answer.)

EX. Last fall during ~~thanksgiving~~, Kim and her family took   *Thanksgiving*

     a ~~Vacation~~ in ~~florida~~.   *vacation, Florida*

EX. They stayed at the King ~~hotel~~ on Jackson Street.   *Hotel*

1   miami is probably. the best-known resort in Florida, a   . . . .

2   popular vacation spot in the south. Located at   . . . .

3   Florida's southern tip, Miami beach is actually a   . . . .

4   narrow island in the atlantic Ocean. It is separated   . . . .

5   from the rest of Miami by Biscayne bay. When   . . . .

6   tourists tire of sunning, they can visit the historic   . . . .

7   cape Florida Lighthouse, which was built in 1825.   . . . .

8   People interested in art might enjoy a visit   . . . .

9   to the Dade county Art Museum, which was once the   . . . .

10   home of james Deering. (Don't go on Christmas.   . . . .

11   The Building will be closed!) For nature   . . . .

12   enthusiasts, the Everglades National park   . . . .

13   is so rich in wildlife that a visit there in the summer   . . . .

14   is like a fresh-air classroom or nature 101.   . . . .

15   Other parts of Florida have attractions of their own.   . . . .

16   For example, there is the Chassahowitzka National   . . . .

17   wildlife Refuge near Homosassa. Chassahowitzka is a   . . . .

18   Native american word that means "pumpkin   . . . .

19   opening place." Central Florida is known for its   . . . .

20   beautiful lakes and, of course, for Walt disney World.   . . . .

HBJ material copyrighted under notice appearing earlier in this work.

Capitals for Titles

Capitalize titles of persons when used before the person's name.

EXAMPLES   Captain Brown, Superintendent Ieradi, Judge Hanlon

Do not capitalize titles used alone or after the person's name unless they are titles of current high government officials.

EXAMPLES   The *President* lives in the White House.
Mr. Herbert Cameron, *vice-president* of the bank, is in his office.
Reporters interviewed the *Secretary of Agriculture*.

Capitalize <u>mother</u>, <u>father</u>, <u>sister</u>, **etc., when they are used as names.**
Do not capitalize <u>mother</u>, <u>father</u>, <u>sister</u>, **etc., when they are preceded by a possessive:** <u>his</u>, <u>her</u>, <u>my</u>, <u>John's</u>, **etc.**
Capitalize words of family relationship preceding a name.

USED AS NAMES   I will ask M*other* for her permission.
Hello, F*ather*.

NOT USED AS NAMES   The *mother* of the children was away from home.
This is my *mother*.   (preceded by a possessive)

TITLES PRECEDING NAMES   We visited G*randmother* Owen and my A*unt* Jane.

Modern usage does, however, permit the writing of *mother, father, sister,* etc., without a capital even when they are used as names. Hence either way is acceptable, but most writers follow the rule given here.

Capitalize the first word and all important words in titles of books, magazines, poems, stories, movies, and works of art.

EXAMPLES   *The House on the Strand*   (book)
the San Francisco Chronicle   (newspaper)
Apartment Life   (magazine)
The Empire Strikes Back   (movie)

Note: Within a sentence the word *the* before the title of a magazine or newspaper is not capitalized. At the beginning of book and art titles *the* is always capitalized.

Capitalize nouns and pronouns referring to God.

EXAMPLE   The congregation prayed to G*od*, asking for H*is* blessing.

Note: Do not capitalize words referring to the gods of primitive religions and ancient mythologies.

EXAMPLE   The ancient Greek g*ods* interfered in the affairs of mortals.

HBJ material copyrighted under notice appearing earlier in this work.

EXERCISE A. Correct the capitalization in the following paragraph by inserting capitals where they should be and by drawing a slanting line through capitals that should be small letters. (Add 5 points for each correct answer.)

1   As an assignment for latin class, we read the tale of Orpheus and

2   Eurydice in Robert Graves's book, *the Greek myths*. I enjoyed the story of

3   the musician from thrace, who charmed Hades, the God of the under-

4   world, with his music. The god was persuaded to allow Orpheus' Wife,

5   Eurydice, to return to life. But hades set one condition. If Orpheus looked

6   back to see if his Wife was behind him before they both reached the upper

7   world, Eurydice would have to return to the land of the dead. On the brink

8   of the upper world, the Master Musician looked back, and Eurydice was

9   lost to him forever. Our Teacher played parts of Gluck's opera, *orpheus*

10   *and eurydice*. She arranged for us to obtain discount tickets to a film by

11   the french director Jean Cocteau. His film *orpheé* was based on the

12   ancient legend. It seems the tale has influenced many artists. Last night,

13   uncle Ernest showed me a print of a Mosaic by an unknown roman artist,

14   entitled *Orpheus charming the beasts*.

EXERCISE B. Write a brief sentence using each word below correctly (and *not* at the beginning of the sentence). (Add 10 points for each correct sentence.)

EX. *General:* The NATO commander was General Norstad.

EX. *general:* John Pershing was a general.

1. *God:* ....

2. *god:* ....

3. *President:* ....

4. *president:* ....

5. *Father:* ....

6. *father:* ....

7. *Captain:* ....

8. *captain:* ....

9. *Aunt:* ....

10. *aunt:* ....

HBJ material copyrighted under notice appearing earlier in this work.

Practice with Capital Letters

EXERCISE A. Correct the capitalization in the following sentences by inserting capitals where they should be and by drawing a slanting line through capitals that should be small letters. (Add 2 points for each correct answer.)

1. Members of the baptist Training Union went as a group to see *King of kings;* the Manager of the palace theater had made special arrangements for presenting this Classic during the easter holidays.

2. Today monuments erected by Historical Societies mark the oregon trail, which began at independence, missouri, and crossed kansas, south dakota, wyoming, idaho, and northern oregon.

3. Benét's *John brown's body* gives a vivid account of the Attack on Harpers Ferry.

4. In 1862 president Lincoln issued the emancipation proclamation, officially freeing all slaves on january 1, 1863.

5. Clara Barton was the First President of the american Red Cross.

6. Robert Millikan, a former Professor at the university of California, won the nobel prize because of his contributions to Science; he is remembered especially for his investigation of Cosmic Rays.

7. Mrs. Kittridge, Head of the English department, discovered that book reports on such classics as Brontë's *Wuthering heights* and Eliot's *Silas marner* were based on the *Cliff's notes* sold in Haley's stationery store.

8. Laura Bohannan, an american anthropologist, is best known for her study of the tiv tribe in West Africa.

9. *Current,* a painting by Bridget Riley, hangs in the museum of modern art in New york City.

10. Martin Luther King, Jr., who believed in nonviolent protest, was head of the Southern Christian leadership conference.

EXERCISE B. Insert the necessary capital letters in the following paragraphs. (Add 2 points for each correct answer.)

1   After we had finished reading selections from dante's *the divine comedy*

2   in english class last wednesday, ms. portinari asked us to write a

HBJ material copyrighted under notice appearing earlier in this work.

3   composition. She said that most religions, whether current or past, have

4   some concept of an afterlife. Our assignment was to compare dante's idea

5   of an afterlife with one found in another religion or in mythology. I did

6   my spanish and history assignments quickly. Then I spent most of the

7   evening working on this task for english. It was the most thought-

8   provoking assignment I had had since entering martin luther king Jr. high

9   school.

10   I decided to investigate the ideas found in buddhism. My aunt, who

11 teaches a course in philosophy and religion at the university of hawaii in

12 honolulu, told me that although buddhism is largely an oriental religion,

13 its ideas and dogmas are quite familiar to people living in the occidental

14 world. This religion was an outgrowth of hinduism. Gautama siddhartha

15 became the buddha when he received enlightenment after meditating in a

16 forest near the town of varanasi. Followers of buddhism believe that

17 people experience a series of reincarnations. According to aunt Sylvia,

18 buddhists feel that people control their destinies. The good or evil they do

19 in this life controls the type of life they will have in their next

20 reincarnation. Since buddhists consider life to be full of suffering, their

21 ultimate goal is to end the series of reincarnations. This state is called

22 *nirvana*.

23   Actually, the ideas of dante and the ideas of buddhists are very far

24 apart. While the italian master presented a world in which good and evil

25 were rewarded or punished after death, the buddhists present a world in

26 which people are compensated for their actions in their next life. In

27 dante's christian philosophy, the good are rewarded with paradise. For

28 buddhists, the good are rewarded by ceasing to exist.

29   Last night father brought home a copy of a novel by a german writer,

30 hermann hesse. His novel, *siddhartha,* is based on the life of the buddha.

31 Both mother and father saw a movie version of *siddhartha* last july at the

32 beekman theater.

HBJ material copyrighted under notice appearing earlier in this work.

Chapter Review

EXERCISE A. Write the letter of the correct form *(a or b)* in the blank. (Add 4 points for each correct answer.)

a. EX. a. Seneca Lake   b. Seneca lake

.... 1. a. the Virgin Islands   b. the Virgin islands

.... 2. a. a State Park   b. a state park

.... 3. a. the aim of the South   b. the aim of the south

.... 4. a. a mile North of here   b. a mile north of here

.... 5. a. the Mississippi River   b. the Mississippi river

.... 6. a. a City in Kansas   b. a city in Kansas

.... 7. a. Salt Lake City   b. Salt Lake city

.... 8. a. next Sunday   b. next sunday

.... 9. a. next Spring   b. next spring

.... 10. a. a few Sophomores   b. a few sophomores

.... 11. a. our English teacher   b. our english teacher

.... 12. a. courses in Mathematics   b. courses in mathematics

.... 13. a. taking Geometry I   b. taking geometry I

.... 14. a. a Polynesian dance   b. a Polynesian Dance

.... 15. a. Redlands High School   b. Redlands high school

.... 16. a. Standard Oil Company   b. Standard Oil company

.... 17. a. for my Father   b. for my father

.... 18. a. a mythic God   b. a mythic god

.... 19. a. faith in God   b. faith in god

.... 20. a. *The Diary of Anne Frank*   b. *the Diary of Anne Frank*

.... 21. a. Twenty-First Street   b. Twenty-first Street

.... 22. a. the Norman Conquest   b. the Norman conquest

.... 23. a. the President of the club   b. the president of the club

.... 24. a. the U.S. President   b. the U.S. president

.... 25. a. several Catholics   b. several catholics

HBJ material copyrighted under notice appearing earlier in this work.

EXERCISE B. If a sentence below contains no errors in capitalization, write *C* (for *correct*) in the blank. If a sentence contains a word or words with an incorrect capital or small letter, draw a line through the error and write the word or words correctly in the blank. (Add 5 points for each correctly marked item.)

EX. I am learning a great deal about the/Physical/Sciences. *physical sciences*

1. The title of Professor Katakura's speech was "the Importance of Erosion." . . . .

2. He delivered it to new members of the Future Farmers of America. . . . .

3. First he showed us Seniors some pictures of the Grand Canyon. . . . .

4. "The Colorado river has cut into these rocks," he said. . . . .

5. He continued, "You High-school students know this." . . . .

6. Then he told us how water changes the land. . . . .

7. The Mountains in New Hampshire show effects of erosion. . . . .

8. Water has stripped the White mountains of enough rock to take more than six kilometers off their height! . . . .

9. Heavy Spring rains wash topsoil into rivers. . . . .

10. Each week the Mississippi River carries millions of tons of land to the gulf of Mexico. . . . .

11. That friday night my father and I went to the Tower Theater. . . . .

12. On the screen, pioneers were moving Westward. . . . .

13. I was still thinking about the Professor's lecture. . . . .

14. The story of early Western life did not interest me. . . . .

15. I liked, however, scenes of the ocean and the rockies. . . . .

16. "The Pacific ocean," I said, "is like an investor." . . . .

17. Later my father asked me to explain my odd comparison. . . . .

18. An investor puts money into a Company to make money. . . . .

19. By evaporating, the ocean puts water into land. . . . .

20. This water, or "principal," eventually returns to the Ocean and brings valuable land, or "interest." . . . .

114

HBJ material copyrighted under notice appearing earlier in this work.

Cumulative Review

A. The questions below each italicized sentence refer to words and word groups in the sentence. Answer the questions in the spaces provided. (Add 4 points for each correct answer.)

The Red River often changes the northern boundary of Texas.

1. The subject is: . . . .
2. The verb is: . . . .
3. The complement is: . . . .
4. What kind of complement is it? . . . .
5. What part of speech is *boundary?* . . . .
6. What part of speech is *northern?* . . . .
7. What part of speech is *often?* . . . .
8. Write the prepositional phrase. . . . .
9. What word does the phrase modify? . . . .
10. Is it an adjective or an adverb phrase? . . . .

The rise and the fall of the Red River are important because Texas claims only the south bank.

11. The compound subject of the main clause is: . . . .
12. The verb of the main clause is: . . . .
13. The complement of the main clause is: . . . .
14. What kind of complement is it? . . . .
15. What part of speech is *south?* . . . .
16. What part of speech is *rise?* . . . .
17. Write the first and last words of the subordinate
    clause. . . . .
18. Is it an adjective or an adverb clause? . . . .
19. Write the prepositional phrase. . . . .
20. Is it an adjective or an adverb phrase? . . . .

In the spring, the rising river may cover the exposed south riverbed, may enlarge Oklahoma, and may shrink Texas.

HBJ material copyrighted under notice appearing earlier in this work.

115

21. The compound verbs are ...., ..., and

....

22. What kind of complement is *Oklahoma?* ....

23. What kind of complement is *riverbed?* ....

24. What kind of complement is *Texas?* ....

25. Is *In the spring* an adjective or an adverb phrase? ....

B. Place an *S* before the items which are complete sentences. Place an *F* before those which are or contain fragments. (Add 20 points for each correct answer.)

.... 1. Have you done the problems? The ones in today's assignment?

.... 2. The train roared through the night. Thundering over bridges, shouting through tunnels, hooting at every village and crossroad.

.... 3. By staying in tourist houses and cabins instead of hotels, we saved money. As a result we had enough money for a trip into Mexico.

.... 4. The old house that had remained vacant for years.

.... 5. The entire neighborhood was covered with smoke. As the tire warehouse down the street burned out of control for hours.

C. Change the punctuation and capital letters in the following paragraph to remove all fragments and run-on sentences. (Add 10 points for each corrected fragment or run-on.)

1 Have you ever heard a jug band? These bands are composed of
2 instruments. You can make yourself. From items commonly found around
3 the house. The next time you buy cider. Save the jug it produces a bass
4 throb when the player blows across the top of it. Providing the horn
5 section for the band. A comb covered with tissue also produces interesting
6 music. Central to the jug band is an old-fashioned washboard. With a few
7 tin plates and cups attached to the side of it. Washboards are played with
8 metal thimbles used as picks. Metal washtubs can be used as drums this
9 versatile item can also be played as a string instrument. Simply turn the
10 washtub upside down. And attach a pole to its side. Make a hole in the
11 center of the tub. For a string to go through. The top of the string attaches
12 to the top of the pole. So that the pole, string, and tub assume a triangular
13 formation. Then get your friends together and play.

HBJ material copyrighted under notice appearing earlier in this work.

Spelling: Using *-ant* and *-ance*

In this lesson, you will study words that end in *-ant* and *-ance,* the other forms of the endings *-ent* and *-ence* that you learned in Lesson 52.

Here are some guides for the use of *-ant* and *-ance:* (Memorize the example words.)

● The suffix *-ant* is usually added to a verb to form an adjective, as in list *1.* The words in list *2* have no separate English verbs. (Note the dropping of the final *e* and the changing of *y* to *i* in some of the words.)

	1		*2*
resist	resistant		arrogant
assist	assistant		elegant
defy	defiant		vigilant
ignore	ignorant		abundant
rely	reliant		distant
attend	attendant		exuberant

● Many adjectives ending in *-ant* have related nouns which end in *-ance.* Knowing how to spell either form means you can spell the other.

Here are the noun forms of the adjectives above:

resistant	resistance	arrogant	arrogance
assistant	assistance	elegant	elegance
defiant	defiance	vigilant	vigilance
ignorant	ignorance	abundant	abundance
reliant	reliance	distant	distance
attendant	attendance	exuberant	exuberance

● The suffixes *-ant* and *-ance* are added to verbs ending in *-ate.* This is one group of words that is easy to remember. The *a* in *-ate* is your clue to use *-ant* and *-ance*—all three endings have an *a* in the last syllable.

radiate	radiant	radiance
tolerate	tolerant	tolerance
dominate	dominant	dominance

EXERCISE A. Add the suffix *-ant* to each of the following verbs to change the verb to an adjective. Write the adjective in the blank. Remember the rules about final silent *e* and *y*. (Add 20 points for each correct answer.)

1. observe + ant = ...   4. please + ant = ...

2. pend + ant = ...   5. comply + ant = ...

3. exult + ant = ...

HBJ material copyrighted under notice appearing earlier in this work.

EXERCISE B. For each verb ending in -ate below, write the related -ant form. (Add 10 points for each correct answer.)

EXAMPLE irritate *irritant*

1. stimulate ....
2. resonate ....
3. lubricate ....
4. stagnate ....
5. vibrate ....

6. luxuriate ....
7. participate ....
8. vacate ....
9. immigrate ....
10. celebrate ....

EXERCISE C. For each word below, write the related form ending in -ance. (Add 10 points for each correct answer.)

1. fragrant ....
2. significant ....
3. reluctant ....
4. repugnant ....
5. brilliant ....

6. instant ....
7. important ....
8. entrant ....
9. repentant ....
10. recalcitrant ....

EXERCISE D. Be ready to write from dictation all of the words taught in this lesson. (Add 10 points for each correctly spelled word.)

REVIEW EXERCISE. For each word below, write the corresponding adjective form in the blank. (Add 10 points for each correctly spelled word.)

EXAMPLE indulge *indulgent*

1. consist ....
2. converge ....
3. confide ....
4. reside ....
5. cohere ....

6. depend ....
7. inhere ....
8. urge ....
9. insist ....
10. precede ....

HBJ material copyrighted under notice appearing earlier in this work.

Building Vocabulary: Words to Learn

atrocious /ə trṓ shəs/ *adj.* Savage, extremely cruel, wicked: *The prisoner was found guilty of an atrocious crime and sentenced to life imprisonment.*

contagion /kən tā́ jən/ *n.* The spreading of a disease from person to person through physical contact; hence, any disease spread in this way: *The government controls entrance into the country in order to combat contagion.*—**contagious,** *adj.*

denounce /di noúns/ *v.* To state strongly that someone is deserving of blame; also, to give information against someone. *The newspapers have denounced the mayor for not carrying out his election promises.*—**denunciation** /di nún sē ā́ shən/ *n.*

discreet /dis krḗt/ *adj.* Careful; showing forethought and good judgment: *Lawyers must be very discreet in discussing their clients with others.*

impact /ím pakt/ *n.* The forceful striking together of two objects: *The impact of the bullet knocked the tin can fifty feet.*

insoluble /in sól yə bəl/ *adj.* Impossible to solve or explain: *How the robber got into the bank vault remains an insoluble mystery.*

pessimism /pés ə míz əm/ *n.* A tendency to look on the dark side of things; lack of hope that things will turn out well: *The team's pessimism about their chances today is due to the fact that they have lost the last three games.*—**pessimist,** *n.*—**pessimistic,** *adj.*

recuperate /ri kū́ pə rāt/ *v.* To get well again after an illness, accident, etc.: *It will be a week before Jerry recuperates fully from his operation.*

subsist /səb síst/ *v.* To have enough food to keep alive but no more; to live: *People can subsist on a thousand calories per day, but their health may suffer.*

vivacious /vi vā́ shəs/ *adj.* Lively and spirited: *Mark's vivacious personality makes him a pleasant and amusing companion.*

EXERCISE. Fill each blank with the word from this lesson that makes the best sense in the context. In some cases, a verb may need to change form to agree with the rest of the sentence. (Add 10 points for each correct answer.)

1. When the ship struck the iceberg, the . . . . knocked most of the passengers off their feet.

2. Even after leaving the hospital, Mike still did not . . . . fully from his pneumonia for at least two more weeks.

3. It was hardly . . . . of Willis to boast to the police officer that he had never been caught speeding before.

4. We do not think that the problem is . . . . , but it will need all our efforts to overcome it.

5. To prevent . . . . , the doctor washed her hands thoroughly after examining the patient.

6. The legislature . . . . the governor's plans to impose a state income tax.

7. The man's . . . . crimes horrified the entire community.

8. Maria is an extremely . . . . person who is the center of attention at every party.

HBJ material copyrighted under notice appearing earlier in this work.

9. While traveling, the Plains Indians were able to . . . . on a diet of dried meat and berries.

10. Sandra was only expressing her usual . . . . when she said that she had probably flunked the examination.

REVIEW EXERCISE. In the space to the left of each sentence, write the letter of the word from the following list that could best fill each blank. (Add 10 points for each correct answer.)

a. agile	e. degenerate	h. faction	l. supersede
b. aspiration	f. delicate	j. heedless	m. unintelligible
c. contemptible	g. ensue	k. reconcile	n. valid
d. controversial			

. . . . 1. Garry's first enthusiasm for the plan will ____ into indifference when he realizes how much work it will involve.

. . . . 2. It was ____ to take the smaller child's books and throw them in the mud.

. . . . 3. A person in ____ health should not take up mountain climbing as a hobby.

. . . . 4. The ____ little dog leaped through the paper-covered hoop and then hopped out of the ring on its hind legs.

. . . . 5. Youth should be a time of deep dreams and high ____.

. . . . 6. The revised schedule of lunch hours will ____ the one that is now in effect.

. . . . 7. A subject as ____ as politics is not usually a good one for conversation with strangers.

. . . . 8. Liz and Ella were not on speaking terms for weeks, but we have at last been able to ____ them.

. . . . 9. The Latin oration at my brother's college graduation was ____ to nearly everyone in the audience.

. . . . 10. ____ of our warnings, Gabby went right on tugging at the drawer until he broke it.

HBJ material copyrighted under notice appearing earlier in this work.

CHAPTER 7

Punctuation

This chapter will teach you the correct use of three marks of punctuation—the comma, quotation marks, and the apostrophe. You have already learned the use of end marks (period, question mark, and exclamation mark) in your study of sentence completeness in Chapter Five.

The Comma: In Series

Use commas to separate items written in a series.

EXAMPLES   You will be required to read short stories, plays, poems, and essays. (series of nouns)

That is a long, childish, uninteresting book. (series of adjectives)

We stumbled into the hall, bumped into the chair, turned on the light, and laughed in relief. (series of predicates)

I did not know where you were, how you were, or when you would return. (series of clauses)

When the last two items in a series are joined by *and*, you may omit the comma before *and* if the comma is not needed to make the meaning clear.

COMMA NOT NECESSARY   The turnpike connects Harrisburg, Philadelphia and Pittsburgh. (A comma before *and*, while perfectly correct, would not affect the meaning of the sentence.)

COMMA AFFECTS MEANING   For lunch we served soup, tomato juice, ham and cheese sandwiches. (Without a comma before *and,* the sentence suggests that we served only three items: soup, juice, and sandwiches.)

For lunch we served soup, tomato juice, ham, and cheese sandwiches. (With a comma before *and,* the sentence says that we served four items.)

Follow your teacher's directions concerning the use of the comma before *and*. Some teachers may prefer that you always use it because it is almost always correct, and using it may prevent your writing unclear sentences.

Do not use a comma (1) between an adjective and the noun it modifies or (2) before an adjective which is thought of as part of the noun.

HBJ material copyrighted under notice appearing earlier in this work.

A good rule to follow when punctuating a series is to use a comma between words when you can logically put the word *and* (or *or*) in place of the comma.

INCORRECT   This part of Boston is full of narrow, winding, crowded, streets. (Illogical: "narrow and winding and crowded *and* streets." The noun *streets* is not a part of the series.)

CORRECT   This part of Boston is full of narrow, winding, crowded streets. (Logical: "narrow *and* winding *and* crowded streets.")

INCORRECT   Sam is an alert, left guard. (Illogical: "alert *and* left guard." The adjective *left* is thought of as part of the noun *guard*.)

CORRECT   Sam is an alert left guard.

If all items in a series are joined by <u>and</u> or <u>or</u>, do not use commas.

EXAMPLES   You will read <u>short stories</u> and <u>plays</u> and <u>poems</u> and <u>essays</u>.

Should assemblies be planned by <u>students</u> or <u>teachers</u> or a <u>committee</u> of students and teachers?

EXERCISE.   Insert commas where they are needed in the following sentences. (Add 10 points for each correctly marked sentence.)

1. Janet Susan and I use various remedies for insomnia.

2. When she can't get to sleep, Janet takes a relaxing bath drinks hot chocolate or reads a telephone book.

3. To fall asleep quickly, Susan requires three things: fresh air and soft music and complete darkness.

4. Not concerned about baths and food dull reading and soft music lighting and ventilation, I use my imagination to go to sleep.

5. I visualize something that is quiet pleasant and peaceful.

6. I often imagine that I am an astronaut touring the vast mysterious universe an explorer all alone in the silence of a huge untouched forest or an aborigine quietly enjoying the beauties of nature.

7. Sitting near my cave door and watching a beautiful sunset, I am not disturbed by such noises as a neighbor's blaring television set or a loud ambulance siren or noisy highway traffic.

8. Sometimes I try to discover for myself ways of taming animals raising crops or inventing a language.

9. I grow weary and fall asleep as I try to invent my own alphabet sign language and smoke signals.

10. The sound symbols I devise are far cruder than those found in the early Chinese Egyptian or Semitic languages.

HBJ material copyrighted under notice appearing earlier in this work.

The Comma: Appositives

Use commas to set off expressions that interrupt the sentence.

In this lesson and in the next two lessons, you will learn how to punctuate various kinds of expressions that interrupt the sentence. The kind of interrupter you will study in this lesson is the appositive. An *appositive* is a noun or a pronoun, often with modifiers, used to explain or identify another noun or pronoun. It usually follows the word it explains or identifies.

Appositives with their modifiers are set off by commas.

EXAMPLES Dickinson, a superb poet, wrote her poems in seclusion.
Next on the program was Big Tex, a rodeo clown.

A short appositive, especially if it is a single word, may be so closely related to the noun preceding it that it need not be set off by commas.

EXAMPLES My friend Mrs. Silver   The play *Macbeth*
Your sister Fran   The author Welty

EXERCISE A. Insert commas where they are needed in the following sentences. (Add 10 points for each correctly marked sentence.)

1. When Alfred Hitchcock the well-known director died in 1980, people mourned the loss of this master of suspense.

2. In one movie *Strangers on a Train* an innocent man becomes involved in a bizarre murder plot.

3. The climax of this movie a scene at a carousel thrills audiences.

4. Two things clever plots and unusual camera angles always add surprises to any Hitchcock film.

5. Hitchcock frequently used two devices the chase and the case of mistaken identity to build suspense in his films.

6. He didn't always write his own stories but used books such as *Rebecca* the romantic suspense story by Daphne du Maurier.

7. Who can forget the scene in *Rebecca* where Mrs. Danvers the sinister housekeeper stands at the window, engulfed in flames?

8. Hitchcock's peers other members of the film community admired both his talent and his sense of humor.

HBJ material copyrighted under notice appearing earlier in this work.

9. When tempers flared during filming, Hitchcock a master of psychology would say, "It's only a movie."

10. One Hitchcock movie *North by Northwest* remains a classic the norm against which many similar movies of suspense are measured.

EXERCISE B. By using correctly punctuated appositives, revise the following sentences to eliminate wordiness. (Add 10 points for each correct sentence.)

1. The entire truckload spilled onto the middle of Halleck Turnpike. The truckload consisted of four tons of gravel. ....

....

2. Ike blew the fuses again. He is one of our scientific geniuses. ....

....

3. Mr. Nevins discovered the cause of the million-dollar blaze. He is the chief of the fire department. ....

....

4. I am working on Unit Five. The title of the unit is "The Westward Movement." ....

....

5. I saw Judy on the train. Judy is my cousin. ....

....

6. The class read "Second Nature." Diana Chang wrote this poem. ......

....

7. The house was built in 1860. It is an ornate mansion. ....

....

8. Mr. Ahmed asked us to ride in the plane. It was a tiny Piper Cub. ....

....

9. Do you remember Sue? She is the girl I told you about. ....

....

10. Aunt Kate arrived on Friday and asked Mom to accept a job in Portland. It was the day after Thanksgiving. ....

....

....

HBI material copyrighted under notice appearing earlier in this work.

The Comma: Direct Address; Introductory Words

Words used in direct address are set off by commas.

EXAMPLES   Bob, do you know my sister?
                Please come here a minute, Marcia.
                Now, my son, tell me the truth.

Words such as well, yes, no, and why are followed by a comma when they are used to introduce a sentence or remark.

EXAMPLES   No, you may not go out tonight.
                Why, what a surprise!

EXERCISE. Insert commas where they are needed in the following sentences. Not every sentence requires commas. Be able to explain your punctuation. (Add 5 points for each correctly marked sentence.)

1. Yes air pressure can be tremendously important.
2. Suppose Clara that you fell out of a high-flying airplane.
3. Well air is very thin fifteen miles up.
4. Why the air pressure inside your body would cause death.
5. Seriously Clara you can test this principle in your kitchen.
6. Does a pressure cooker have a safety valve Clara?
7. I did a research paper on air pressure last year Teresa.
8. Changes in pressure can be quite dangerous.
9. Oh then you know about the problems faced by divers.
10. Yes flyers experience relatively slow changes in pressure compared to divers.
11. One of the first places a diver feels pressure changes Teresa is the eardrum.
12. Rapid changes in pressure can cause the drum to burst.
13. I've heard Clara that divers hold their noses and blow when they start to feel pain in their ears.
14. Yes swallowing also helps to equalize pressure.
15. Do you know Clara why your ears pop when you go up a mountain?

HBJ material copyrighted under notice appearing earlier in this work.

16. Why I think it's a result of the pressure on the inner ear equalizing the pressure on the outer ear.

17. Why is it better for a diver to have perfect teeth than teeth with fillings Teresa?

18. Well I don't think I know the answer to that question.

19. Really Teresa it's a serious problem.

20. Air pressure exerts a different force on the filling than on the tooth, and Teresa under severe conditions it can cause a tooth to collapse.

REVIEW EXERCISE. Insert commas where needed in the following sentences. In the blank at the left of each number write the letters, *in order,* of the appropriate reason for each comma used. (Add 10 points for each correctly marked sentence.)

a. in series   c. with words in direct address
b. with appositives   d. after introductory words

.... 1. Oh I know the definition of *espirit de corps* a French phrase meaning "team spirit."

.... 2. In your class Mr. Melton I have learned that a good explanatory paragraph has more than one sentence develops a central idea and presents specific details.

.... 3. The new shortstop a fellow named Ted Anderson boasted that he could catch pitch and play first base better than we could.

.... 4. No this machine a recent model does not use so much electricity oil and water as the older models.

.... 5. School-building alterations a large item in the budget are necessary because of the present inadequate cafeteria facilities the crowded classrooms and the undersized auditorium.

.... 6. Amelia Earhart a famous flyer made a solo flight across the Atlantic.

.... 7. Yes this graceful towering pine tree a village landmark faces destruction.

.... 8. On Saturday Angelo Santi our best trumpet player rehearsed with the school band in the morning marched with the band at the game in the afternoon and played in a dance orchestra at night.

.... 9. For lunch we had trout green beans fried potatoes and hot rolls.

.... 10. Yes in late January a series of arctic blasts hit Europe and the United States and set new records for all-time low temperatures.

HBJ material copyrighted under notice appearing earlier in this work.

The Comma: Parenthetical Expressions; Dates and Addresses

Parenthetical expressions are set off by commas.

A parenthetical expression interrupts the main thought of a sentence to make a side remark that adds information or relates ideas. Expressions commonly used parenthetically are *I believe* (*think, hope, etc.*), *on the contrary, on the other hand, of course, in my opinion, for example, however, to tell the truth, nevertheless, in fact, generally speaking*. Because it is not essential to the sentence, a parenthetical expression is always set off by commas.

EXAMPLES   The majority, on the other hand, voted for Ruth.
This book is, I believe, the best book I have ever read.

EXERCISE A. Insert commas where needed in the following sentences. (Add 10 points for each correctly marked sentence.)

1. In my opinion most people in the Western world have an intrinsic dislike of snakes.

2. Westerners in fact use the expression "a snake in the grass" to describe a treacherous person.

3. Snakes of course are often portrayed as embodiments of evil in Western literature.

4. However in many Eastern cultures the snake is revered.

5. The Hindus for example venerate the snake.

6. Generally speaking they see snakes as protecting rather than harming humans.

7. Snakes also figure predominantly I believe in the myths of the Cretans.

8. Several Minoan goddesses were in fact actually snake goddesses.

9. On the other hand Native Americans also placed high value on the snake.

10. In times of famine for example snake dances were performed.

In a date or address consisting of two or more parts, put a comma after every part—except, of course, when the finial part comes at the end of a sentence.

Note: Each of the following is considered *one* part of a date or address:

March 15 (the month followed by the day)

HBJ material copyrighted under notice appearing earlier in this work.

757 Third Avenue (the street number and street name)
New York (the city)
New York 10017 (the state followed by the zip code)

EXAMPLES   A letter addressed on May 10, 1986, to Mr. Leonard Hudspeth, 155 Dutchess Avenue, Dayton, Ohio 45420, was lost. (Notice that the comma after the man's name is needed because the address interrupts the sentence.)

EXERCISE B. Insert commas where needed in the following sentences. (Add 20 points for each correctly marked sentence.)

1. On October 2 1985 you may have seen the New York Yankees play the Milwaukee Brewers at Yankee Stadium.

2. Jan wrote to the General Electric Company Schenectady New York to obtain information about the engines of atomic submarines.

3. Mr. Van Dunk may be reached at 1120 Four Brooks Road Stamford Connecticut 06903 or at 420 Main Street White Plains New York 10601.

4. The letter addressed to 1425 Ocean Drive Long Beach was forwarded to Tucson Arizona after a delay of several days.

5. The letter from Springfield Illinois was dated December 1 1985.

REVIEW EXERCISE. Write brief, correctly punctuated sentences containing answers to the questions. (Add 20 points for each correct sentence.)

1. When and where were you born? ....
   ....

2. What are three of your favorite foods? ....
   ....

3. When was the Declaration of Independence signed? ....
   ....

4. What states border the state you live in? ....
   ....

5. On what date does Christmas vacation begin and end? ....
   ....

HBJ material copyrighted under notice appearing earlier in this work.

The Comma: Compound Sentences

A <u>compound sentence</u> is a sentence composed of two or more independent clauses joined together, but not containing any subordinate clauses.

Use a comma before <u>and</u>, <u>but</u>, <u>or</u>, <u>for</u>, <u>so</u>, or <u>nor</u> when it joins independent clauses in a compound sentence.

EXAMPLES   At the airport check your suitcases, and Frank will help you carry the packages.

No one knew the route, but Bob thought he could figure it out.

Do not confuse a sentence in which two *verbs* are joined by a conjunction with a compound sentence, in which two *independent clauses* are joined by a conjunction.

EXAMPLE   Darlene limped off the field and collapsed on the players' bench.

The second verb phrase, "collapsed on the players' bench," is not an independent clause because it shares its subject with the first verb phrase, "limped off the field." The subject of *collapsed* is *Darlene; Darlene* is also the subject of the first verb *limped*. Two or more verbs having the same subject are called a *compound verb*. Do not use a comma between parts of a compound verb.

EXAMPLE   The clerk wrote down my order and handed me a receipt.

In the following examples, the first sentence has a compound verb and does not need a comma. The second sentence is a compound sentence composed of two independent clauses, and it does need a comma.

COMPOUND VERB   We met Alex and asked him to go with us. (no comma)

COMPOUND SENTENCE   We met Alex, and Ed asked him to go with us. (comma)

EXERCISE. Insert commas where needed in the following sentences. Do not be misled by compound verbs. Not all sentences require commas. (Add 10 points for each correctly marked sentence.)

1. Christopher always does the cooking and his roommate cleans up.

2. The hero kissed the heroine and her jealous dog bit him.

3. The logs will be hauled by truck or they will be floated down the river.

4. Tomás does not fear lightning nor do tornadoes frighten him.

5. Most of us thought that the movie was dull but Abby liked it.

HBJ material copyrighted under notice appearing earlier in this work.

6. The crowd swarmed onto the field and carried off the goal posts.

7. You must obey the rules of the school or suffer the consequences.

8. Put covers on all your textbooks and they will stay clean.

9. Our small vessel weathered every storm and brought us safely into port.

10. Father believes everyone but Mother is more cautious.

REVIEW EXERCISE. Insert commas where needed in the following story. Give the reason for your punctuation by writing at the end of each corrected line the letter of the comma use it illustrates. (Add 5 points for each correctly marked line.)

a. in series
b. with appositives
c. in direct address
d. with parenthetical expressions

e. after introductory words
f. with dates and addresses
g. with main clauses
h. no comma necessary

On June 16 1985 my family left Wheeling and moved to   1. ....

2915 Mockingbird Lane Tarrytown. I was very lonesome in my   2. ....

surroundings for a while but soon I became acquainted with   3. ....

Bud my next-door neighbor. We have already found a number   4. ....

of interesting amusing things to do together.   5. ....

Last Saturday night for instance Bud exclaimed, "I'd like a   6. ....

large ripe juicy watermelon right now!" He added that Mr.   7. ....

Heston a nearby farmer had a patch full of "wonderful"   8. ....

melons. "Are you game Phil?" he asked me slyly.   9. ....

We quickly left town crossed a cornfield and invaded   10. ....

the melon patch. Oh what a grand time we had thumping   11. ....

and grabbing melons! Before long however I saw a   12. ....

flashlight glint in Mr. Heston's hand. "Run Bud! Run!"   13. ....

I yelled. We carried our booty only one melon on our   14. ....

fast retreat. Mr. Heston did not yell run or follow us.   15. ....

All that he did in fact was stand there and laugh at us.   16. ....

At last we reached my quiet safe backyard. We cut into the   17. ....

bitter smelly melon and knew we had stolen a "wine melon"   18. ....

the unsavory cousin of the watermelon. We realized of course   19. ....

that we deserved what had happened to us.   20. ....

HBJ material copyrighted under notice appearing earlier in this work.

The Comma: Introductory Phrases and Clauses

An introductory expression begins, or *introduces* the sentence.

Use a comma after an introductory adverb clause.

EXAMPLES   If the weather is bad, commencement exercises will be held indoors.

Because the school is overcrowded, double sessions will be necessary.

Introductory adverb clauses usually begin with one of the following words:

after	as though	since	whenever
although	because	unless	where
as	before	until	wherever
as if	if	when	while

Use a comma after an introductory phrase containing a participle.

EXAMPLES   Expecting the worst, we armed ourselves. (introductory phrase containing a present participle)

Badly broken by its fall, the lamp could not be repaired. (introductory phrase containing a past participle)

Use a comma after a succession of introductory prepositional phrases.

EXAMPLES   Behind the small table in the corner, the dog had hidden its favorite toys.

At the edge of the woods near the school, there is a small pond.

EXERCISE. Insert commas where needed in the following sentences. Not all sentences require a comma. Before each corrected sentence write the letter of the comma use it illustrates. (Add 10 points for each correctly marked sentence.)

a. after an introductory adverb clause
b. after an introductory participial phrase
c. after two or more introductory prepositional phrases

.... 1. Since water is deeper than it looks good spear fishers shoot below rather than at their apparent target.

.... 2. If a fish underwater sees you on a pier you probably look as though you are higher than you really are.

.... 3. By explaining refraction I can give sensible reasons for these strange appearances.

HBJ material copyrighted under notice appearing earlier in this work.

.... 4. Although she is our best tennis player Sally is out for the year.

.... 5. While I was working at the gas station I learned a lot about cars.

.... 6. Complete your homework assignments before you go home.

.... 7. Chasing a fly ball in center field Armand stepped in a hole and sprained his ankle.

.... 8. Angered by her brother's remarks Jan stamped out of the room.

.... 9. A display of school spirit often helps the team to play better.

.... 10. If people object to my suggestion let them state their reasons.

REVIEW EXERCISE. Insert commas where needed in the following paragraphs. (Add 4 points for each correct answer.)

WEST DRESSED

1 In the first half of the 1980's Western wear the traditional clothes of the
2 cowhand became high fashion. Yes boots dungarees, and hats appeared on
3 city streets as well as on Texas plains. Outfitted from head to toe city
4 slickers it seemed had taken to wearing clothes from the American West.
5 They bought the clothes ''weathered'' them until they looked appropriate-
6 ly worn, and then treated them with respect!

7 Available in a wide range of styles Western boots became very popular.
8 Many people had their boots custom made and some pairs definitely
9 reflected individual tastes. Toes could be rounded squared, or needle
10 sharp. Heels too came in a variety of styles. The Dallas Cowboys football
11 players for example still wear custom-designed boots of silver blue, and
12 white.

13 Although dungarees were originally designed for cowhands miners and
14 farmers the pants serve a more fashionable purpose today. In nearly every
15 town in the country people from all walks of life now wear these
16 comfortable durable pants.

17 Do you ever wonder how today's cowhands descendants of the
18 originators of Western wear feel about the widespread interest in their
19 style of clothes? In all likelihood they view it as just a passing fad a
20 temporary obsession.

HBJ material copyrighted under notice appearing earlier in this work.

Quotation Marks

Use quotation marks to enclose a direct quotation—a person's exact words. Do not use quotation marks to enclose an indirect quotation—not a person's exact words.

EXAMPLES   Dorothy said, "I'd like to go with you." (Direct quotation. The words enclosed by quotation marks are Dorothy's exact words.)

Dorothy said that she'd like to go with us. (Indirect quotation. The sentence tells what Dorothy said but not in her exact words.)

A direct quotation begins with a capital letter.

EXAMPLE   She said, "Turn to the back of the book."

When one quoted sentence is divided into two parts by such interrupting expressions as *he said* and *I replied,* the second part begins with a small letter.

EXAMPLE   "This book," she said, "was written by two reporters for the *Washington Post.*"

Of course, if an expression like *he said* or *I replied* comes at the end of a sentence, the following sentence must begin with a capital letter.

EXAMPLE   "We're late," whispered Phyllis. "The show has already begun."

A direct quotation is set off from the rest of the sentence by commas, a question mark, or an exclamation mark.

Commas and periods are always placed *inside* closing quotation marks. Question marks and exclamation points are placed inside when the *quotation* is a question or an exclamation. Otherwise they are placed outside.

EXAMPLES   "The first prize," the announcer said, "goes to Setsu Uchiyama."
"Where have you been?" she asked.
"Look out!" we cried.
Did you hear him say, "Get out"?

In a quotation of several sentences, do not put quotation marks around each sentence, but only at the beginning and end of the entire quotation.

INCORRECT   Terry said, "If you do not join, you will not be supporting school activities." "You will have to pay twice as much for tickets to games and plays." "The whole activity program will be hindered."

CORRECT   Terry said, "If you do not join, you will not be supporting school activities. You will have to pay twice as much for tickets to games and plays. The whole activity program will be hindered."

HBJ material copyrighted under notice appearing earlier in this work.

When you write dialogue (a conversation), begin a new paragraph every time the speaker changes.

EXAMPLE "What time is it, Mother?" called Frances.
"It's almost six o'clock by my watch," her mother answered.
"Do you think we can catch the 6:10 bus?" Frances asked.
"You're the only reason we can't," replied Mrs. Stevens. "Hurry, will you?"

EXERCISE A. Correctly punctuate the following dialogue. (Add 4 points for each correct answer.)

1 One of the great unsolved mysteries Chris said is the strange disappear-
2 ance of the crew of a ship called the *Mary Celeste*. According to the story,
3 the crew of another ship found the *Mary Celeste,* totally abandoned, in the
4 Atlantic in 1872.

5 Where was its crew asked Jenny. Was anyone on board

6 Well Chris explained no one was on board, but there was no evidence
7 that the ship had had any serious trouble. Everything was dry and in its
8 place, and there was plenty of food. All of the lifeboats were gone, but
9 none of the people were ever found

10 Perhaps Jenny said new evidence will turn up.

EXERCISE B. Change each indirect quotation below to a direct quotation, and change the punctuation accordingly. (Add 20 points for each correct sentence.)

EX. I asked Tom to paint the trellis.
"Tom, will you paint the trellis?" I asked.

1. Gabriella announced that she knew that Billy would apologize.

. . . .

2. Dad wondered where we were going and when we would return.

. . . .

3. The coach advised us to keep our heads up.

. . . .

4. Wanda shouted that she did not want to watch television.

. . . .

5. Sue asked me why I had not kept my promise to her.

. . . .

HBJ material copyrighted under notice appearing earlier in this work.

The Apostrophe to Form Possessives

The apostrophe is used for two important purposes: (1) to form possessives, and (2) to show where letters have been left out in contractions.

To form the possessive of a singular noun add an apostrophe s ('s).

EXAMPLES   one boy's coat, the boss's job, Jim's dog (one boy, one boss, one Jim)

To form the possessive of a plural noun ending in s, add only an apostrophe (s').

EXAMPLES   birds' nesting ground (nesting ground of many *birds*)
boys' voices (voices of many *boys*)

Most plural nouns end in *s*. A few, however, do not end in *s: children, men, women, people,* etc. These few words are made possessive in the same way that singular nouns are made possessive.

To form the possessive of a plural noun not ending in s, add an apostrophe s ('s).

EXAMPLES   a men's club, children's games, people's government

When you are deciding how to make a word possessive, you must ask yourself whether the word is singular or plural; that is, whether it refers to one person or thing or to several persons or things. A good way to decide is to substitute in your mind a prepositional phrase.

EXAMPLES   a boy's coats (coats *of a boy*—*boy* is singular)
several boys' coats (coats *of several boys*—*boys* is plural)

Do not use an apostrophe in plurals unless they are possessive.

EXAMPLES   Her **pupils** respect her.   (*pupils* is simply plural, no apostrophe)
Her **pupils'** respect pleases her.   (*pupils* is possessive).

To form the plurals of letters, numbers, signs, and words used as words, add an apostrophe s ('s).

EXAMPLES   a's, z's, 2's, 1980's, ?'s, +'s
There are no *if*'s, *and*'s, or *but*'s about it.

EXERCISE A.   Each group of words below shows possession. In Column *A*, rewrite the words to include a prepositional phrase beginning with *of.* In Column *B*, write *S* or *P* to indicate whether the object of the preposition *of* is singular or plural. In Column *C*, write the object of the preposition (the possessive word) with the apostrophe in place to indicate whether the possessive word is singular or plural. (Add 5 points for each correct line.)

HBJ material copyrighted under notice appearing earlier in this work.

	A	B	C
EX. Bills friends	*friends of Bill*	(S)	*Bill's* friends
EX. the dogs tails	*tails of the dogs*	(P)	*dogs'* tails
1. a friends family	....	( )	.... family
2. friends families	....	( )	.... families
3. the girls locker room	....	( )	.... locker room
4. Guss hat	....	( )	.... hat
5. the boys gym	....	( )	.... gym
6. the babys playpen	....	( )	.... playpen
7. Margaret Walkers poems	....	( )	.... poems
8. the Presidents speech	....	( )	.... speech
9. the cars front bumpers	....	( )	.... bumpers
10. the cars front bumper	....	( )	.... bumper
11. an employees welfare	....	( )	.... welfare
12. all employees welfare	....	( )	.... welfare
13. many trees branches	....	( )	.... branches
14. a trees branches	....	( )	.... branches
15. an officers uniforms	....	( )	.... uniforms
16. some officers uniforms	....	( )	.... uniforms
17. Vics brother	....	( )	.... brother
18. Willies sister	....	( )	.... sister
19. several voters opinions	....	( )	.... opinions
20. Mexicos history	....	( )	.... history

EXERCISE B. Insert apostrophes where needed in the following paragraph. (Add 20 points for each correct answer.)

1   Harry Houdinis most popular feat was his escape from the water torture
2   cell. The cells steel frame seemed to make escape impossible, but even
3   steel couldn't foil this masters attempt. Fans cheers followed this stunt.
4   Although one movie claimed Houdini died doing this escape, he didn't.
5   The escape artists death was the result of peritonitis.

HBJ material copyrighted under notice appearing earlier in this work.

The Apostrophe in Pronouns and Contractions

The possessive pronouns, <u>his</u>, <u>hers</u>, <u>its</u>, <u>ours</u>, <u>yours</u>, <u>theirs</u>, and <u>whose</u> do not require an apostrophe.

EXAMPLES This campaign button is **hers**
I like **its** color.
Theirs are better than **ours**

To form the possessive of indefinite pronouns like <u>one</u>, <u>everyone</u>, and <u>anybody</u>, add an apostrophe <u>s</u> ('s).

EXAMPLES <u>Everyone's</u> answers were incorrect.
Has <u>anybody's</u> invitation been sent?

Use an apostrophe to indicate where letters have been left out in a contraction.

When you combine two words into one word by omitting one or more letters, you are forming a *contraction*.

EXAMPLES should not = shouldn't they have = they've
I will = I'll   it is = it's

Note: Its (without an apostrophe) is the possessive form of *it. It's* (with an apostrophe) is a contraction of *it is.* Never put an apostrophe in *its* unless you mean *it is.*

EXAMPLES The French Club enlarged **its** treasury by giving a bake sale.
It's a good way to make money.

EXERCISE. In the blank spaces, write contractions of the words at the left. (Add 5 points for each correct answer.)

1. we have	. . . .	9. do not	. . . .
2. is not	. . . .	10. let us	. . . .
3. you are	. . . .	11. who is	. . . .
4. does not	. . . .	12. it is	. . . .
5. she will	. . . .	13. must not	. . . .
6. were not	. . . .	14. he would	. . . .
7. cannot	. . . .	15. we will	. . . .
8. he is	. . . .	16. they are	. . . .

HBJ material copyrighted under notice appearing earlier in this work.

17. Dominic is . . . .   19. will not . . . .

18. they had . . . .   20. I shall . . . .

REVIEW EXERCISE. Circle any word below that should have an apostrophe and write the word correctly in the blank to the left of the line. If there is no error in a line, write *C* (for *correct*) in the blank. (Add 4 points for each correctly marked line.)

DOG TALES

1. . . . .   In one of Thomas Mertons books, there is a brief

2. . . . .   reference to a dog and its apparent unfriendliness.

3. . . . .   Actually, its not really the fault of the dog at all.

4. . . . .   Theres a great deal of truth in the old saying that

5. . . . .   dogs reflect their owners habits! The story told in

6. . . . .   Mertons book is about one of the visitors who likes

7. . . . .   dogs and asks the owner what his dogs name is. The

8. . . . .   owner, whos fond of playing practical jokes on every-

9. . . . .   one, promptly replies, "His names Rex." But when the

10. . . . .   visitor calls the dog, the dog just sits. Naturally, no

11. . . . .   self-respecting dogs going to come when someone calls

12. . . . .   it by another dogs name! It makes me laugh when

13. . . . .   I think of the poor visitors dismay at what seems to be

14. . . . .   the dogs unfriendliness. I have forgotten the real name

15. . . . .   of the dog, but its certainly not Rex!

16. . . . .   I also like that story of Murrays, the one about his

17. . . . .   aunts, whose dog is thoroughly confused. The dogs

18. . . . .   called Snick, but his aunts often say to it, "Snick, theres

19. . . . .   a dog! Chase it away from here." Snick, an obedient

20. . . . .   dog, promptly obeys the aunts order. However, when the

21. . . . .   aunts are talking to Snick at other times, they often say,

22. . . . .   "Youre a nice little dog."

23. . . . .   Snick doesnt realize who they are talking about and

24. . . . .   looks around for a dog to chase. The trouble is, Snick

25. . . . .   thinks shes a snick, not a dog!

HBJ material copyrighted under notice appearing earlier in this work.

Chapter Review

EXERCISE A. Insert punctuation marks where needed in the following sentences. (Add 2 points for each correct answer.)

1. Theres one in every class said Mr. Papas as Nick came in late without his notebook textbook, or pencil.

2. Arnold Freiberg captain of the gray team tells me that hes confident of victory in tonights meet.

3. No Im afraid youre wrong about that Dan I said Its hard to get people to change their minds.

4. When you approach a green light dont go too fast If youre going fast you wont be able to stop if the light changes

5. If youd show a little more patience said Mrs. Chambers people would like you better and your friends wouldnt drift away from you.

6. At yesterdays track meet in Bloomfield our opponents excelled in almost every event but the relays were very closely contested.

7. On May 1 1985 her address was 68 Park Terrace Houston Texas 77017.

8. At Alans party we had Mrs. Kings potato chips Mr. Bauers pretzel nuggets, and Nancys punch

EXERCISE B. Insert punctuation marks where needed in the following passage. (Add 2 points for each correct answer.)

1   Does the popcorn man still visit city neighborhoods on summer
2   evenings Few people I think remember his irregular visits exciting
3   moments in the lives of small fry. Unexpectedly almost mysteriously, he
4   would appear at the usual corner anchor his high glass-enclosed pushcart
5   at the curb light its wavering gas burner and proceed with the ritual of
6   popping corn. A small, purring jet burner beneath the pot of melting
7   butter lighted the vendors face with a warm ruddy glow as he stood beside
8   his cart an island of light in the darkening street. Families interrupted
9   their front-porch visiting and children gathered from blocks around to
10 patronize this cheerful salesman.

HBJ material copyrighted under notice appearing earlier in this work.

11   "A bag of popcorn, please." Then came the deft scoop into the snowy
12   pile the shaking down of the bag before the second scoop, and the
13   professional, swirling dip of the butter can usually an old enamel
14   coffeepot over the overflowing bag. A dash of salt was the finishing
15   touch. Well my friends that warm aromatic bag of popcorn was surely a
16   taste of heaven.

17   Today's children however know a different kind of neighborhood
18   traveling vendor. The new vendors have gleaming, mobile "stores" with
19   posters splashed across them, advertising the latest flavors: pineapple
20   banana coconut chocolate tropical fruit, and butter crunch. These
21   "stores" may be pushcarts motor scooters, or small trucks. They are
22   refrigerators on wheels and these people sell ice cream. Theres nothing
23   quiet hidden, or mysterious about them. As they jingle loudly down the
24   blocks the streets come to life. Children burst from backyards cellars
25   vacant lots, and front doors. Parents dig into pocketbooks purses, and
26   trouser pockets for coins. Each time the truck stops the driver wearing a
27   crisp white uniform swings open the thick door. Digging into the frosty
28   interior, the vendor brings out the requested delicacies. Everyones
29   familiar with the shrill screams of Johnny Merkle our local three-year-old
30   as he races after the truck. Hes always afraid hes going to be late but
31   Johnnys not one to be left behind. Got any lemon-orange today?" he asks
32   every time as he holds out a fist full of moist pennies.

33   For five minutes the childrens games are stopped and parents activities
34   are interrupted. The ice cream provides a bit of relief on a hot summer day
35   but in my opinion it cant equal the popcorn vendors wares.

HBJ material copyrighted under notice appearing earlier in this work.

Cumulative Review

A. Below each italicized sentence in this exercise there are questions about parts of the sentence. Write the answer to each question in the space at the right. (Add 5 points for each correct answer.)

A song of universal popularity is "Happy Birthday to You."

1. What is the subject of the sentence? . . . .

2. What is the verb in this sentence? . . . .

3. What part of the sentence is "Happy Birthday to You?" . . . .

4. What part of speech is *popularity?* . . . .

5. Is *of universal popularity* a phrase or clause? . . . .

6. What word does *of universal popularity* modify? . . . .

7. Is *of universal popularity* used as an adjective or an adverb? . . . .

Did astronauts once sing us this song from space?

8. What is the subject of the sentence? . . . .

9. What is the verb in the sentence? . . . .

10. What part of the sentence is *us?* . . . .

11. What part of speech is *us?* . . . .

12. What part of speech is *this?* . . . .

13. What part of the sentence is *song?* . . . .

14. What part of speech is *once?* . . . .

15. What does *from space* modify? . . . .

Although the song is universally popular today, an earlier version of the same song under a different title had no success.

16. What is the subject of the independent clause? . . . .

17. What is the verb in the independent clause? . . . .

18. What part of the sentence is *success?* . . . .

19. What word introduces the subordinate clause? . . . .

20. Is the subordinate clause used as an adjective or an adverb? . . . .

HBJ material copyrighted under notice appearing earlier in this work.

In the following paragraphs, punctuation marks and capital letters have been either omitted or used incorrectly. Correct the paragraphs by inserting punctuation and capitals in the proper places and removing those which are incorrect. (Add 2 points for each correct answer.)

1   When Mr. Coleman the principal of Garfield high school, asked Earl
2   the reason for his eight tardinesses this month Earl explained about his
3   alarm clock. Determined not to be late to school this year he had bought
4   the clock from Mr. Stephenson. Proprietor of Stephensons American
5   secondhand emporium on First street. The alarm had worked very well.
6   Until the day Earl knocked the clock off the windowsill. From that day on,
7   however, he had had trouble. Because he could not longer set the alarm
8   properly. The clock survived its fall into the bushes outside Earls window
9   but the alarm indicator had been shifted. As the clocks owner explained.
10   He couldn't tell how the alarm was set.

11   Earl had he believed figured out a solution. He waited until the alarm
12   went off, then he checked with his wristwatch. When the indicator on the
13   clock pointed to 7:00 the alarm went off at 2:15. Making use of this
14   information Earl set the clock for 12:15. Expecting it to ring at 7:30 the
15   time he had to get up. This careful figuring did not help the clock rang at
16   8:30, leaving him no time for eating breakfast and getting to school. The
17   next day he set the alarm for 11:15. Which was one hour earlier. He was
18   awakened at 9:00.

19   Finally Earl decided to push the clock out the window again, In the
20   hope that the second crash would knock the alarm back into working
21   order. The second tumble changed everything. By completely breaking
22   the clock.

23   "Now, said principal Coleman you had better give in and buy another
24   clock." He sent Earl to the Fixit clock hospital, where Earl bought
25   another secondhand model.

26   I dont think Ill keep this one on the windowsill, Mr. Coleman"
27   declared Earl. As he displayed his purchase. Itll be safer on the table."

HBJ material copyrighted under notice appearing earlier in this work.

Usage: Avoiding "Is when," "Being as," and "Had ought"

Do not use <u>is when</u> or <u>is where</u> in writing a definition.

NONSTANDARD   A catboat is *where a boat has* one mast and no jib.
STANDARD   A catboat is **a boat with** one mast and no jib.

NONSTANDARD   An anthology is *when a book contains* many selections.
STANDARD   An anthology is **a book containing** many selections.

Do not use being as or being that for since or because.

NONSTANDARD   *Being* as I am a new student, I have few friends here.
STANDARD   **Since** (or *because*) I am a new student, I have few friends here.

Do not use had with ought.

NONSTANDARD   We *had ought* to start.
STANDARD   We **ought** to start.

NONSTANDARD   You *hadn't ought* to do it.
STANDARD   You **ought** not to do it.

EXERCISE. If a sentence below contains one or more usage errors, write *I* (for *incorrect*) in the blank, cross out the error, and write your correction above it. (If a word or letter is unnecessary, merely cross it out.) If a sentence is correct, write *C* (for *correct*) in the blank. (Add 5 points for each correctly marked sentence.)

....   1. Someone had ought to tell her the truth.

....   2. You had ought to learn to play backgammon.

....   3. That fire must be somewhere near here!

....   4. A satellite is when a small planet goes around a larger one.

....   5. Since a hurricane was approaching, we left the island.

....   6. Being as Joan is only twelve, she doesn't understand irony.

....   7. A dune is where a sandhill has been formed by the wind.

....   8. An air-cooled engine is where a radiator is not needed.

....   9. If you have nothing to do, you can take this note to Mrs. James.

.... 10. You hadn't ought to complain.

.... 11. We did the work badly, being as we were in a hurry.

.... 12. She had ought to do as well as Ana.

HBJ material copyrighted under notice appearing earlier in this work.

.... 13. Being that the weather looked bad, we postponed our trip.

.... 14. When you come back from town, please bring my mail.

.... 15. Why didn't you bring the supplies with you when you came?

.... 16. If you come in the morning, bring your lunch.

.... 17. An I-beam is where a beam is shaped like a capital *I*.

.... 18. Being as she is older, she should set a good example.

.... 19. They had ought to remember what you said.

.... 20. I didn't want to hurt his feelings, being as he's so new.

REVIEW EXERCISE. Select the correct one of the two words in parentheses and copy it in the space at the right. Cross out the incorrect word. (Add 5 points for each correct answer.)

1. We were playing fairly (good, well) in the first half. ....

2. May I (bring, take) this home? ....

3. Someone (ought, had ought) to bring refreshments. ....

4. May I (bring, take) this paper down to Miss du Boise? ....

5. Charlie pitches (good, well) in a tight spot. ....

6. (Being, Because) I am tall, I tend to slouch. ....

7. She did not perform so (well, good) in the rehearsal. ....

8. In the store I asked her to (take, bring) the meat home. ....

9. How (well, good) they sing the songs. ....

10. We (hadn't ought, ought not) to copy. ....

11. Go to the office and (take, bring) your books with you. ....

12. She (ought not, hadn't ought) to be so critical. ....

13. I'll run over to Ann's and (bring, take) her this book. ....

14. Someone (ought, had ought) to find out the truth. ....

15. Mary did (good, well) in math. ....

16. I often (bring, take) an extra blanket when I go camping. ....

17. You (ought, had ought) to pay your debts promptly. ....

18. Would you mind (bringing, taking) me the newspaper? ....

19. Because of his cold, Don did not play very (good, well). ....

20. She will (bring, take) us a surprise when she comes. ....

144

HBJ material copyrighted under notice appearing earlier in this work.

Spelling: The Four Forms of *in-*

The common prefix *in-* (meaning "not") has three other forms: *im-*, *il-*, and *ir-*. Look at the following lists of words, which illustrate all four forms of *in-*, and see if you can decipher any patterns or rules concerning when to use which form of this prefix.

(Hint: Look at the letter immediately following the prefix in each work.)

1	*2*	*3*
inappropriate	imbalance	illegal
inefficient	impolite	illiterate
inimitable	impossible	illogical
inoffensive	impartial	
incorrect	imperfect	*4*
indecent	immortal	irregular
inhuman	immoderate	irreligious
insane	immodest	irresponsible

Here are some rules concerning the forms of the prefix *in:*

Change *in-* to *im-* before words beginning with *b, p,* or *m.*

Change *in-* to *il-* before words beginning with *l.*

Change *in-* to *ir-* before words beginning with *r.*

Keep the *in-* form before words beginning with any letter other than those covered in the first three rules above.

The process in which a sound in a word tends to become like the sound that follows it is known as **assimilation**. It is often difficult to say the /n/ sound in *in-* when the very next sound is /b/, /p/, or /m/. The lips begin to form the /p/ in *possible,* for example, before they finish saying the /n/ of *in-*.

Knowing that *in-, im-, ir-,* and *il-* mean "not," and keeping in mind the rules concerning assimilation, you can add these prefixes to such words as *movable, regular,* and *rational* and come up with the correctly spelled (two consonants) "new" words: *immovable, irregular,* and *irrational.* On the other hand, you will never be tempted to put two *n*'s at the beginning of *inefficient,* for example, because you know that this word is made up of the prefix *in-* plus *efficient,* and means "not efficient."

EXERCISE A. Join the prefix *in-, im-, il-,* or *ir-* to each word below to make a new word meaning "not" plus the meaning of the word given. (Add 5 points for each correct answer.)

HBJ material copyrighted under notice appearing earlier in this work.

1. ....mortal
2. ....comparable
3. ....legible
4. ....personal
5. ....material
6. ....reconcilable
7. ....numerable
8. ....exact
9. ....passable
10. ....sanity

11. ....liberal
12. ....patient
13. ....active
14. ....mature
15. ....reducible
16. ....practical
17. ....formal
18. ....legitimate
19. ....resolute
20. ....mobile

EXERCISE B. Write five words (other than those taught in this lesson) that contain the *im-* form of *in-* (meaning "not"); five that contain the *il-* form; five that contain the *ir-* form; five that contain the original *in-* form. (Add 5 points for each correct answer.)

im-	*il-*	*ir-*	*in-*
1.	1.	1.	1. ....
2.	2.	2.	2. ....
3.	3.	3.	3. ....
4.	4.	4.	4. ....
5.	5.	5.	5. ....

EXERCISE C. Be ready to write from dictation the words taught in this lesson. (Add 2 points for each correctly spelled word.)

REVIEW EXERCISE. In the blank, write the related *-ant* form of each word below. (Add 10 points for each correctly spelled word.)

1. reluctance ....
2. defy ....
3. distance ....
4. stagnate ....
5. fragrance ....

6. comply ....
7. vacate ....
8. ignore ....
9. rely ....
10. instance ....

HBJ material copyrighted under notice appearing earlier in this work.

Building Vocabulary: How Words Are Defined

To define a word is simply to explain what it means. You can sometimes accomplish this by giving one or more close synonyms. More often, you must follow a formal, two-step process in defining a word—the same method by which most dictionary definitions are written.

To define a word, first relate it to other words that are close in meaning. Then show how it differs in meaning from these words.

Both steps are important. To use words accurately, you must know not just their general meaning but how they differ from near synonyms. For example, how would you use the two-step method to define *felony* as it is used in the following sentence.

EXAMPLE   She was guilty of a **felony** and was given a long prison sentence.

Clearly, *felony* must have the general meaning of "crime." How does its meaning differ? A definition naturally falls into two parts:

DEFINITION   A felony is   (1) a crime   (2) of a serious nature, punishable by imprisonment

Now see if you can work out a definition for the verb *to mar* in the same way—by thinking of a synonym and showing how the meanings differ.

EXAMPLES   That hot dish has **marred** the finish on the dining table.
Ken's pleasing personality is **marred** by his occasional faultfinding.

To mar must have the general meaning of "to damage." But the damage, while real and troublesome, does not go too deep. The marred table is still usable. Ken's personality is usually pleasing except for his faultfinding.

DEFINITION   To mar is   (1) to damage   (2) superficially

Notice that a good definition can usually be substituted in the original context for the word defined. When you explain a word, test your definition in this way.

EXAMPLES   The prisoner was guilty of a **crime of a serious nature**
The hot dish **damaged** the finish on the dining table **superficially**

EXERCISE.   Study the context in which each italicized word is used. Then read the definitions of these words and analyze them in this way: circle the broad, general synonyms that classify the meaning of each word; underline the rest of the definition that tells how the meaning of the word differs from that of its synonyms. (Add 10 points for each correctly marked definition.)

HBJ material copyrighted under notice appearing earlier in this work.

1. "I have long *advocated* a tax reform," said the senator, "and I am happy to see that my views have at last become law."

2. The children often *bicker* among themselves, but no one takes it very seriously.

3. "If you don't get out of here this very minute," *blustered* Mr. Willing, "I'm going to call the police!"

4. The eruption of Mt. Vesuvius, which destroyed Pompeii, was perhaps the greatest *cataclysm* of ancient times.

5. After I had been waiting for a quarter of an hour, the salesperson at last *condescended* to notice that I was there.

6. The news commentator took lessons in *elocution* to improve his delivery on radio and television.

7. Sitting by the fire, the elderly woman often *laments* the day of her youth and prosperity.

8. The family is notable for its *piety*. They never miss church on Sunday and always begin their meals by saying grace.

9. When soldiers seized the palace, they said that they were protecting the queen, but this was merely a *pretext*.

10. It is absurd even to suggest that a person of such *rectitude* as Judge Wylie would ever accept a bribe.

DEFINITIONS

1. **advocate** /ád və kāt/ *v.*   To speak or declare oneself in favor of an idea or action.
2. **bicker** /bík ər/ *v.*   To quarrel or argue in a petty, fussy way.
3. **bluster** /blús tər/ *v.*   To talk in a noisy, bullying, foolish way.
4. **cataclysm** /kát ə klíz əm/ *n.*   A disaster; any large and violent upheaval or natural change.
5. **condescend** /kón di sénd/ *v.*   To behave toward a supposed inferior in a lofty or superior manner.
6. **elocution** /él ə kyū shən/ *n.*   The art of reading aloud or speaking clearly, effectively, and correctly.
7. **lament** /lə mént/ *v.*   To grieve deeply and openly.
8. **piety** /pí ə tē/ *n.*   Reverent respect shown toward God or toward one's parents or country.
9. **pretext** /prḗ tekst/ *n.*   A false reason or explanation for an action, stated in order to conceal the real one.
10. **rectitude** /rék tə tūd/ *n.*   Moral uprightness; virtuous behavior, in accordance with clear standards of right and wrong.

HBJ material copyrighted under notice appearing earlier in this work.

CHAPTER 8

Making Words Agree

Number is the grammatical term for the distinction between words that mean "one" and words that mean "more than one." Words that refer to one (single) thing are said to be *singular* in number. Words that refer to more than one thing are said to be *plural* in number.

For a sentence to be grammatically correct, certain parts of it must agree in number. If one of these parts is singular, other parts must be singular also. If one is plural, others must be plural. The parts of a sentence that must agree with one another are the subject and verb, and pronouns and their antecedents (the words the pronouns refer to). Most of the time in your speaking and writing you automatically keep these parts in agreement, but there are certain constructions that present special problems. This chapter will tell you what these constructions are and give you practice in using them correctly.

LESSON 76

Agreement of Subject and Verb

A verb agrees with its subject in number.

In the following examples, notice how the verb changes in number when the subject changes in number. This change is necessary to keep the verb and its subject in agreement.

EXAMPLES The style has changed.

Styles have changed.

A satellite in orbit travels five miles a second.

Satellites in orbit travel five miles a second.

Using a singular verb with a plural subject or a plural verb with a singular subject is a grammatical error in agreement.

NONSTANDARD   The *children was* unusually quiet that night.
STANDARD   The children were unusually quiet that night.

NONSTANDARD   There *has been* many *complaints* about the proposed tax law.
STANDARD   There have been many complaints about the proposed tax law.

HBJ material copyrighted under notice appearing earlier in this work.

In most cases, an *s* added to the end of a noun makes the noun plural. However, an *s* added to the end of a verb makes the verb singular.

SINGULAR   This pen   *look*s expensive.
           This pen   *ha*s a ball point.
           This pen   *write*s under water.

PLURAL   These pen*s*   *look* expensive.
           These pen*s*   *have* ball points.
           These pen*s*   *write* under water.

EXERCISE A. After each of the following verbs, write *S* if the verb is singular, *P* if the verb is plural. Think of the verbs as they would be if used with the subjects *it* or *they*. (Add 5 points for each correct answer.)

1. walks	8. was	15. carries ....
2. tries	9. shine	16. fly ....
3. make	10. lies	17. goes ....
4. wishes	11. takes	18. lose ....
5. has	12. go	19. ask ....
6. are	13. give	20. exists ....
7. have	14. leave	

EXERCISE B. Some of the subjects and verbs paired in the following list agree in number; some do not agree in number. Write *C* (for *correct*) before those that agree and *I* (for *incorrect*) before those that do not agree. For those which do not agree, cross out the verb and write after it the correct form. (Add 5 points for each correct item.)

.... 1. planes fly	.... 11. houses has ....
.... 2. pupils thinks	.... 12. woman write ....
.... 3. motor runs	.... 13. mountains stands ....
.... 4. cities is	.... 14. guard waits ....
.... 5. child asks	.... 15. cats jump ....
.... 6. players have	.... 16. dentist advise ....
.... 7. horse looks	.... 17. people was ....
.... 8. tree grows	.... 18. Liz give ....
.... 9. flowers are	.... 19. desk sits ....
.... 10. dresses seems	.... 20. girls risk ....

HBJ material copyrighted under notice appearing earlier in this work.

Subjects Followed by a Phrase

The number of a subject is not usually changed by a prepositional phrase following the subject.

Sentences like the following sometimes cause an error in agreement because the speaker carelessly makes the verb agree with a word in the phrase instead of with the subject of the verb.

EXAMPLES One of the children was absent. (*One* was, not children were)

This book of short stories is interesting. (*book* is, not stories are)

Mr. Auburn, with his sons, has gone shopping. (*Mr. Auburn* has gone *with his sons*, not sons have gone)

Members of the council enjoy special privileges. (*Members* enjoy, not council enjoys)

The following common pronouns are singular: *each, either, neither, one, everyone, everybody, no one, nobody, anyone, anybody, someone, somebody.*

EXAMPLES Each of the players was examined by a doctor.

Neither of the twins has been tardy all year.

The following common words are plural: *several, few, both, many.*

EXAMPLES Few of the apples are ripe enough to eat.

Both of the lawyers have been highly recommended.

Some, any, none, all, and *most* may be either singular or plural, depending on the meaning of the sentence. These are subjects whose number may be affected by a word in a following phrase.

EXAMPLES Some of the food was good.   All of the money is gone.

Some of the meats were good.   All of the pennies are gone.

EXERCISE A. In each sentence below, cross out the prepositional phrase, find the subject, and select the appropriate verb from the choice in parentheses. Then write the subject and verb in the space provided. (Add 10 points for each correct sentence.)

...*One was*... EX. One of the paper cups (was, were) leaking.

.... 1. Cosmic rays in this room (is, are) striking us right now.

.... 2. The cause of her troubles (was, were) apparent.

.... 3. Each of you (has, have) heard this legend.

.... 4. (Do, Does) either of the girls own a bicycle?

HBJ material copyrighted under notice appearing earlier in this work.

151

.... 5. Everyone in my class (knows, know) that!

.... 6. The fibers of the wood (is, are) then crushed.

.... 7. Neither of the girls (plays, play) the piano.

.... 8. A few of your friends (were, was) here.

.... 9. The length of these boats (are, is) twenty feet.

.... 10. (Is, Are) one of these notebooks yours?

EXERCISE B. Underline the subject and the verb in each of the following sentences. If the verb agrees in number with the subject, place a *C* (for *correct*) before the sentence. If the verb does not agree with the subject, place an *I* (for *incorrect*) before the sentence and correct the verb. (Add 5 points for each correctly marked sentence.)

.... 1. Merchandise on the lower shelves was damaged by flood water.

.... 2. Neither of the reports are clearly written.

.... 3. Not one of the bills were counterfeit.

.... 4. Both sentences in the paragraph say the same thing.

.... 5. A few members of the band was not in uniform.

.... 6. Neither of the rugs lie flat.

.... 7. Every one of these planes carries fifty passengers.

.... 8. Only one of us have a catcher's mitt.

.... 9. All of our supplies were bought at the supermarket.

.... 10. Cora, along with the other freshmen, take gym three times a week.

.... 11. Some members of the team have played professionally.

.... 12. Each of us were acting selfishly.

.... 13. Some kinds of shellfish tastes delicious.

.... 14. Each of the organizations have a faculty sponsor.

.... 15. Frank, along with the other students, enjoys this kind of work.

.... 16. Has some of the students already returned?

.... 17. Traffic on the parkways seems heavy today.

.... 18. Empty seats on the bus is rare.

.... 19. The works of this writer have always been popular.

.... 20. One of those days was rainy.

HBJ material copyrighted under notice appearing earlier in this work.

The Compound Subject

A compound subject consists of two or more connected words. The words are usually connected by *and* or *or*.

EXAMPLES   A tree and a telephone pole were lying across the road.
Ed or his brother has to stay at home.

Most compund subjects joined by and are plural and take a plural verb.

EXAMPLES   Sally and Marie are in my class.   (two people are)
The engine and one car were derailed.   (two things were)

If a compound subject names only one person or thing, then the verb must be singular.

EXAMPLES   The medical director and chief surgeon is Doctor Church.   (one person is)
Bacon and eggs is my favorite Saturday lunch.   (the one dish is)

Singular subjects joined by or or nor are singular and take a singular verb.

EXAMPLES   Either the captain or the mate is aboard.   (one, not both)
Paul or Carl has your notebook.   (one, not both)

When a singular subject and a plural subject are joined by or or nor, the verb agrees with the subject nearer the verb.

EXAMPLES   Neither the dogs nor the cat is licensed.
Neither the cat nor the dogs are licensed.

Plural subjects joined by or or nor are, of course, plural.

EXAMPLES   Neither the students nor the teachers are enthusiastic.
The juniors or the seniors have won the trophy.

EXERCISE. The following sentences contain compound subjects. In some of the sentences the verb and subject agree. In others, they do not agree. Place a C (for *correct*) before the correct sentences and an *I* (for *incorrect*) before the incorrect sentences. Then cross out each incorrect verb and write the correct form above it. (Add 10 points for each correctly marked sentence.)

.... 1. Either Felicia or Ellen is planning a barbecue.

.... 2. Both Dot and Avery have suggested good ideas.

HBJ material copyrighted under notice appearing earlier in this work.

.... 3. Harry or Beatrice always lead our class discussions.

.... 4. Either Jan or Alison are going to meet us.

.... 5. Have either Andrea or Edna spoken to you?

.... 6. The winner and new champion is Lynn Contrucci!

.... 7. The team and the coach has already left.

.... 8. Franks and beans is a popular Saturday night meal.

.... 9. Bob and Glenda probably has the directions.

.... 10. Neither her books nor her papers was recovered.

REVIEW EXERCISE. Underline the subject in each sentence below. Then circle the correct one of the two verbs in parentheses (Add 5 points for each correct answer.)

1. One of the most popular literary forms (is, are) the mystery story.

2. The first mysteries in English (was, were) written by Wilkie Collins.

3. *The Moonstone*, the most successful of Collins' novels, (was, were) written in 1868.

4. Its plot complications and involvements (is, are) fascinating to readers.

5. Edgar Allan Poe, author of short stories, poems, and essays, (is, are) credited with developing the character of the modern detective.

6. The solution to the crimes (is, are) found by M. Dupin through ratiocination, or the process of logical thinking.

7. Neither the stories of Collins nor those of Poe (is, are) as widely read as those of Arthur Conan Doyle.

8. The facts of the case (presents, present) an elementary solution to his clever detective, Sherlock Holmes.

9. (Has, Have) either England or the United States produced a current mystery writer as popular as Conan Doyle?

10. (Is, Are) there anyone who has not read or seen a movie version of at least one mystery by Agatha Christie or Dorothy Sayers?

HBJ material copyrighted under notice appearing earlier in this work.

Subjects That Follow Verbs; Collective Nouns

When the subject follows the verb, as in sentences beginning with <u>here</u>, <u>there</u>, and <u>where</u>, be careful to find the subject and make the verb agree with it.

NONSTANDARD	There *is* several *routes* available.
STANDARD	There are several <u>routes</u> available.
NONSTANDARD	Here *is* your *papers*.
STANDARD	Here are your <u>papers</u>.

When the sentence is a question, the position of the verb may change.

EXAMPLES   The apples <u>are</u> in the bag.

Are the <u>apples</u> in the bag?

You must be especially careful not to use the contracted forms *here's,* *there's,* and *where's* with a plural subject.

NONSTANDARD	Where's your *friends*?
STANDARD	Where are your <u>friends</u>?

EXERCISE A. In the following sentences the subject comes after *here, there,* or *where.* Underline the subject and notice whether it is singular or plural. If the verb agrees with the subject, place a *C* (for *correct*) before the sentence. If the subject and verb do not agree, place an *I* (for *incorrect*) before the sentence. Then cross out the incorrect verb and write the correct form above it. (Add 10 points for each correctly marked sentence.)

.... 1. Where's Sheila and Julia?

.... 2. Here are the girls.

.... 3. There are numbers on all the parts to be cleaned.

.... 4. Here's some more parts that must be numbered.

.... 5. Where's that yellow chalk?

.... 6. Where are the gasoline and clean rags?

.... 7. There's the rags on that shelf.

.... 8. Where is the bolt that fits here?

.... 9. There's no numbers on these cleaned parts!

.... 10. Here's the reason.

HBJ material copyrighted under notice appearing earlier in this work.

Collective nouns may be either singular or plural.

A *collective noun* names a group of persons or objects. A collective noun may be used with a plural verb when the speaker is thinking of the individual parts of the group; it may be used with a singular verb when the speaker is thinking of the group as a unit.

EXAMPLES   The committee <u>was</u> appointed by the president. (Committee is thought of as a unit.)

The committee <u>have</u> been discussing the problem among themselves. (Committee members are thought of as individuals.)

The team <u>is</u> a strong one.

The team <u>do</u> not agree about their chances in the game today.

The following list gives several commonly used collective nouns:

army	committee	flock	squadron
audience	crowd	group	swarm
class	faculty	herd	team
club	fleet	jury	troop

EXERCISE B. The subjects in the following sentences are collective nouns. Think about the meaning of each sentence. Ask yourself whether the collective noun is thought of as a unit or as individuals. Then draw a line under the correct verb. (Add 10 points for each correct answer.)

1. A squadron of navy planes (were, was) flying overhead.

2. Our herd of Ayrshire cattle (is, are) the largest in the state.

3. The class (was, were) not in their seats when the bell rang.

4. The flock of wild geese flying above us (were, was) a beautiful sight.

5. Behind closed doors the jury (were, was) arguing among themselves.

6. The committee (was, were) angered by our refusal of its offer.

7. The faculty (are, is) not in agreement with one another.

8. The club (meet, meets) every Friday.

9. The entire team (has, have) been declared ineligible.

10. A group of pilots (was, were) discussing the weather among themselves.

HBJ material copyrighted under notice appearing earlier in this work.

Reviewing Agreement of Verb and Subject

EXERCISE A. In the spaces at the right of each sentence, write the subject and the correct one of the two verbs given in parentheses. (Add 2½ points for each correct answer.)

	Subject	*Verb*
1. Both of the meals (look, looks) good.	. . . .	. . . .
2. Neither Al nor Peg (dance, dances).	. . . .	. . . .
3. One of the players (is, are) hurt.	. . . .	. . . .
4. This collection of poems (look, looks) interesting.	. . . .	. . . .
5. The crowd (was, were) angrily shouting at one another.	. . . .	. . . .
6. (There's, There are) only twelve students in the class.	. . . .	. . . .
7. Each of those jackets (costs, cost) too much.	. . . .	. . . .
8. Bread and butter (is, are) a fattening combination.	. . . .	. . . .
9. (Where's, Where are) the hammer or the ax?	. . . .	. . . .
10. The rash on her hands (is, are) probably poison ivy.	. . . .	. . . .
11. Kathy, along with her sister, (has, have) chicken pox.	. . . .	. . . .
12. (Where's, Where are) Malcolm or Maria?	. . . .	. . . .
13. Every one of the actors (needs, need) another rehearsal.	. . . .	. . . .
14. After their defeat the team (was, were) wearing gloomy expressions.	. . . .	. . . .
15. (Is, Are) Quentin or Bea going to type my paper?	. . . .	. . . .
16. A ring of towering mountain peaks (enclose, encloses) the valley.	. . . .	. . . .

HBJ material copyrighted under notice appearing earlier in this work.

157

17. Jack or Isaac (is, are) awake. . . . .

18. A pound of tomatoes (costs, cost) eighty-nine cents right now. . . . .

19. (Here's, Here are) the bulbs. . . . .

20. Wires on the wing (discharges, discharge) static electricity. . . . .

EXERCISE B. Underline the subject of the independent clause in each sentence. In some of the sentences, the verb and subject agree. In others, they do not agree. Place a C (for *correct*) before the correct sentences and an *I* (for *incorrect*) before the incorrect sentences. Then cross out the incorrect verb and write the correct form above it. (Add 5 points for each correctly marked sentence.)

. . . .   1. My science class has been experimenting with dry ice.

. . . .   2. Does Al or Fern know why radium glows in the dark?

. . . .   3. The reporters on this newspaper belongs to the Newspaper Guild.

. . . .   4. There are both tin and steel in a tin can.

. . . .   5. Disintegrating atoms of uranium gives off dangerous particles.

. . . .   6. With a magnifying glass, each of them have seen a fly's eyes.

. . . .   7. Everyone in the class was to give a report.

. . . .   8. There's two sides to that question.

. . . .   9. Have either Teresa or Vera ever told you what happened?

. . . .   10. Some of us has been studying electricity.

. . . .   11. The best game of the season was the last.

. . . .   12. Lila, along with Sharon and Larry, have hall duty first period.

. . . .   13. Where's those tickets I ordered?

. . . .   14. Neither sophomores nor juniors are eligible.

. . . .   15. Bread and milk doesn't make a good supper.

. . . .   16. How was the main dish and dessert today?

. . . .   17. The cut of her clothes are always just right.

. . . .   18. Both Susan and Bernardo play a good game.

. . . .   19. The color of the drapes contrast with the plaid furniture.

. . . .   20. Do either of them know how to swim?

HBJ material copyrighted under notice appearing earlier in this work.

Agreement of Pronoun and Antecedent

A pronoun agrees with its antecedent in number.

EXAMPLES   1. Our <u>pitcher</u> was sure that he would win.
2. Each <u>girl</u> took her turn at bat.
3. A <u>few</u> of the students had brought their own lunches.
4. Several <u>teachers</u> expressed their opinions.

In the first two sentences above, the antecedents *pitcher* and *girl* are singular. Notice that the pronouns *he* and *her* (printed in red), which refer to these antecedents, are also singular. The pronouns, therefore, agree with their antecedents in number.

In sentences 3 and 4, the antecedents *few* and *teachers* are plural. The pronouns *their* and *their* (printed in red), which refer to *few* and *teachers*, are also plural. They, therefore, agree with their antecedents.

As you learned in your study of agreement between verb and subject, the following words are singular: *each, either, neither, one, everyone, everybody, no one, nobody, anyone, anybody, someone, somebody*. Use singular pronouns when referring to these words.

Note: In ordinary conversation we often hear *their* instead of *his* or *her* when referring to *everyone, everybody, anybody* because these words strongly suggest more than one person. However, in formal writing and in doing the exercises in this book, use the singular pronouns (*his, hers, its*, etc.) in referring to these words. In your own writing, you can, if you wish, avoid the problem of agreement with *everyone* by making the subject plural. For example, instead of saying *Everyone brought his lunch*, you could say *All brought their lunches*.

Two or more antecedents joined by <u>and</u> should be referred to by a plural pronoun.

EXAMPLE   <u>Rachel and Pat</u> gave their speeches in class.

Two or more singular antecedents joined by <u>or</u> or <u>nor</u> should be referred to by a singular pronoun.

EXAMPLE   <u>Neither Rachel nor Pat</u> gave her speech in class.

HBJ material copyrighted under notice appearing earlier in this work.

In the sentences in this exercise, the pronouns and their antecedents are printed in italics. Draw a line through each pronoun that does not agree with its antecedent and write the correct pronoun above it. (Add 10 points for each correctly marked sentence.)

1. If you see *either* of my sisters, ask *them* to call me.

2. Remember to correct the *pronouns* that do not agree with *their* antecedents.

3. Neither *student* has completed *their* assignment.

4. *Everyone* wore *their* costume to the party.

5. *Not one* of my friends asked *his* parents.

6. *Each* of the dogs was looking for *its* trainer.

7. *Anyone* who thought that deserved what *they* got.

8. *Neither* of them would lend me *their* book.

9. A *student* should accept *her* responsibilities.

10. *Nobody* in the class has done *their* assignment very well.

EXERCISE B. Fill in the blank in each of the following sentences with a pronoun that will agree with its antecedent. Draw a line under the antecedent. (Add 10 points for each correct sentence).

EX. <u>Everyone</u> brought ..... *his* ... skates.

EX. Only <u>one</u> of the girls brought ..... *her* .... tennis racket.

1. Many of the parents voiced .... opinions.

2. No one wanted .... name mentioned in the paper.

3. Each student was given a locker for .... equipment.

4. If everyone had .... way, we'd never get anything done.

5. Both Mrs. Larson and Mr. Feldman took .... classes on a trip.

6. Everybody said what .... thought.

7. Neither wanted to have .... picture taken.

8. Some of the group expressed .... opinions quite frankly.

9. Both the carpenter and the welder finished .... work yesterday.

10. A person should be careful of .... English.

HBJ material copyrighted under notice appearing earlier in this work.

Chapter Review

EXERCISE A. Circle the subject of each verb in parentheses; then select the correct verb within the parentheses and write it in the space at the left. (Add 5 points for each correct answer.)

Does EX. (Does, Do) (anybody) know the seven wonders of the ancient world?

.... 1. There (is, are) only one wonder that still stands.

.... 2. Everyone in Egypt (is, are) proud of the ancient Pyramid of Cheops.

.... 3. Either Joanna or Helga (say, says) that four huge cathedrals could fit inside this pyramid.

.... 4. Several of the wonders (was, were) destroyed by earth-quakes.

.... 5. One of the wonders (was, were) sold for scrap metal.

.... 6. Jeremy and Angelo (is, are) building a model of the Hanging Gardens of Babylon.

.... 7. A committee (is, are) deciding on seven new wonders.

.... 8. Anyone with a suggestion (has, have) the right to submit it.

.... 9. Many tall buildings in this country (is, are) being considered.

.... 10. There (is, are), many modern creations that would qualify.

EXERCISE B. Circle the antecedent(s) in each sentence. Then select the correct pronoun from the pair in parentheses and write it in the space provided. (Add 5 points for each correct answer.)

his EX. (Everyone) there offered (his, their) help.

.... 1. Nan and Aretha bought (her, their) own tickets.

.... 2. She or Sally will lend you (her, their) books.

.... 3. One of the men forgot to bring (his, their) tools.

.... 4. The head of the detective team proposed (her, their) solution.

.... 5. Each new student has a guide assigned to (him, them).

.... 6. Both of the girls had (her, their) notes handy.

HBJ material copyrighted under notice appearing earlier in this work.

.... 7. Neither of the boys finished (his, their) job.

.... 8. All citizens should accept (his, their) responsibilities.

.... 9. Few boys on the team did (their, his) best.

.... 10. Anybody can pass this course if (he, they) will work.

EXERCISE C. Write *C* (for *correct*) before each correct sentence; write *I* (for *incorrect*) before each sentence containing an error in agreement. Correct each error by crossing it out and writing the correct form above it. (Add 5 points for each correctly marked sentence.)

..*C*. EX. Neither of the boys played his best game.

..*I*. EX. One of the boys lost ~~their~~ *his* money.

.... 1. A person is always pleased when you laugh at their jokes.

.... 2. Neither of the children know how to swim.

.... 3. Each of Cicely Tyson's roles is demanding.

.... 4. Ask Lisa and Francesca for their opinions.

.... 5. Only a brave person would risk their life in such a heavy sea.

.... 6. The trial of the three suspects has been postponed.

.... 7. Neither Lee nor Bob would reveal their plans.

.... 8. I think nobody could do this job by themselves.

.... 9. Some of the motorists want a change in the driving laws.

.... 10. Here's some ballots that have not been counted.

.... 11. Bread and cheese was a customary noon meal.

.... 12. Each of her grandparents live alone.

.... 13. One of her daughters looks exactly like her.

.... 14. Both women, when challenged, showed their true character.

.... 15. Every one of the games were close.

.... 16. Anybody can build their own boat with this kit.

.... 17. Do either Carmen or Norma have a driver's license?

.... 18. The bottom of these cans is made of steel.

.... 19. Jill or Peg will bring her record player.

.... 20. We learned not to ask either of the nurses about her war experiences.

HBJ material copyrighted under notice appearing earlier in this work.

Cumulative Review

A. In one of the paired items in columns A and B, punctuation and capitalization are correct. In the space to the right, write the letter (A or B) of the column containing the correct item. (Add 5 points for each correct answer.)

	A	*B*	
1.	Its almost midnight.	It's almost midnight.	....
2.	On May 1, 1981, we moved.	On May 1, 1981 we moved	....
3.	We'll win today's game.	We'll win todays game.	....
4.	I live on Oak street.	I live on Oak Street.	....
5.	I said she was wrong.	I said, "she was wrong."	....
6.	a new baseball, bat	a new baseball bat	....
7.	a clear, beautiful day	a clear beautiful day	....
8.	the President of the club	the president of the club	....
9.	I asked who it was.	I asked who it was?	....
10.	They worshiped god	They worshiped God.	....
11.	in the early spring	in the early Spring	....
12.	*To the Lighthouse*	*To The Lighthouse*	....
13.	"Stop," he yelled!	"Stop!" he yelled.	....
14.	Is his nickname "The Bug?"	Is his nickname "The Bug"?	....
15.	She said, "I win."	She said, "I win".	....
16.	a History course	a history course	....
17.	my English teacher	my english teacher	....
18.	I stumbled, and fell.	I stumbled and fell.	....
19.	Who's turn is it?	Whose turn is it?	....
20.	Who's pitching, Rebecca?	Who's pitching Rebecca?	....

B. Correct all errors in the following passage: capital letters, punctuation, fragments, and run-on sentences. (Add 2 points for each correct answer. Each corrected fragment or run-on counts as one answer.)

CHOOSE YOUR CHEW

1   Please put your chewing gum into the wastebasket John says the english

2   teacher in the class and a dozen other students abruptly stop chewing shift

HBJ material copyrighted under notice appearing earlier in this work.

3   their gum, and try to look innocent. Yes gum-chewing one of Americas
4   most popular habits frequently causes strained pupil-teacher relations in
5   some schools its forbidden. Although now and then they may enjoy a stick
6   themselves, high-school teachers object to gum-chewing in class. Teach-
7   ers objections of course do not always discourage the rows of contented
8   jaw-wagging faces. School custodians furthermore frown upon gum, they
9   are tired of cleaning it off desks, chairs, and floors. Especially after its
10 hardened.

11   The craze all started when Santa Anna the mexican dictator fled to
12 Staten island New York in 1875. Bringing with him a strange elastic
13 substance which he would break into pieces, put into his mouth, and chew
14 Thomas Adams an amateur inventor asked Santa Anna about this queer
15 chewy substance. And learned that it was chicle a gum of the sapodilla
16 tree, a tree native to Mexico and guatemala. Adams tried first to develop it
17 as a rubber substitute but he failed in this attempt, then he made the first
18 chewing gum in America.

19   After getting his familys reaction to the product Adams put it on sale in
20 a local store. Because it sold well he invented a machine to manufacture it
21 in stick form and he was soon shipping it all over the country. As the
22 gums success attracted other manufacturers various flavors were tried out.
23 Among them balsam pepsin, and Adams own licorice, Americas favorite
24 flavor, however, has always been mint.

HBJ material copyrighted under notice appearing earlier in this work.

Spelling: The Many Forms of *ad-* and *sub-*

How often have you misspelled such words as *accurate* and *support* because you neglected to write two *c*'s or two *p*'s? The knowledge you acquired in Lesson 74 concerning assimilation can help you to spell correctly such words as *accurate* and *support*. As you recall, *assimilation* is the tendency for a sound to become like the sound that immediately follows it. For example, you remember that when the prefix *in-* is added to the word *legal*, the *n* changes to an *l* and the world becomes *illegal*. The *n* is said to have been "assimilated."

The process of assimilation occurs in a great many words that contain the prefixes *ad-* (meaning "to, toward") or *sub-* (meaning "under, beneath"). The final consonant in each of these two prefixes tends to change and become the same as the beginning consonant of the root to which it is added.

Examine the words below, all of which contain an assimilated form of the *d* in *ad-*:

ad	+	cept	=	accept
ad	+	ford	=	afford
ad	+	gravate	=	aggravate
ad	+	leviate	=	alleviate
ad	+	nounce	=	announce
ad	+	ply	=	apply
ad	+	rive	=	arrive
ad	+	sert	=	assert
ad	+	tend	=	attend

As you see, *ad-* may change to *ac-, af-, ag-, al-, an-, ap-, ar-, as-,* or *at-*. If you learn to recognize the prefix in such words as those above, you will remember to include a double consonant where the prefix joins the root.

Now look at some words in which the *b* in the prefix *sub-* has become assimilated:

sub	+	cess	=	success
sub	+	fix	=	suffix
sub	+	pose	=	suppose

EXERCISE A. Combine the prefix *ad-* with each root to make a new word. Write the new word, correctly spelled, in the blank. (Add 5 points for each correct answer.)

EXAMPLE   ad + tract = *attract* . . . .

1. ad + cuse = ...   5. ad + gressive = ...

2. ad + proach = ...   6. ad + point = ...

3. ad + flict = ...   7. ad + nulment = ...

4. ad + tract = ...   8. ad + liance = ...

HBJ material copyrighted under notice appearing earlier in this work.

9. ad + rest = ...

10. ad + sume = ...

11. ad + fection = ...

12. ad + tempt = ...

13. ad + nexation = ...

14. ad + sist = ...

15. ad + rayed = ...

16. ad + cording = ...

17. ad + fair = ...

18. ad + luring = ...

19. ad + cident = ...

20. ad + prove = ...

EXERCISE B. Combine the prefix *sub-* with each root below to make a new word. Write the new word, correctly spelled, in the blank. (Add 10 points for each correct answer.)

1. sub + fering = ...

2. sub + press = ...

3. sub + ported = ...

4. sub + ply = ...

5. sub + fice = ...

6. sub + ceeding = ...

7. sub + focate = ...

8. sub + cessful = ...

9. sub + plant = ...

10. sub + cumb = ...

EXERCISE C. In the blanks, write five words (other than those taught in this lesson) in which the prefix *ad-* has become assimilated, and five words in which *sub-* has become assimilated. (Add 10 points for each correct answer.)

ad-	*sub-*
1.	1. ....
2.	2. ....
3.	3. ....
4.	4. ....
5.	5. ....

REVIEW EXERCISE. In the blank in front of each word, write *in-*, *im-*, *il-*, or *ir-*, whichever form of the prefix *in-* is correct for that word (Add 10 points for each correct answer.)

1. .....personal

2. .....legible

3. .....efficient

4. .....responsible

5. .....mortal

6. .....polite

7. .....regular

8. .....active

9. .....mobile

10. .....literate

HBJ material copyrighted under notice appearing earlier in this work.

Building Vocabulary: Words to Learn

adornment /ə dáurn mənt/ *n.* Anything that adds beauty and value to that to which it is attached, often in a mental or spiritual sense: *Honesty is among the chief adornments of a good character.*—**adorn,** *v.*

arduous /ár jū əs/ *adj.* Difficult because requiring hard, steady work to accomplish: *Tearing down a building is usually an arduous task. The climbers had chosen the most arduous route to the top of the mountain.*

beset /bi sét/ *v.* To attack from all sides: *Many difficulties beset the politician who tries to keep election promises. The poet's life was beset with grief.* Note that *beset* does not change when used with the helping verbs *to be* and *to have.*

intercept /ín tər sépt/ *v.* To catch something and keep it from getting where it is going: *The coast guard ship intercepted the smugglers before they could land.*

invincible /in vín sə bəl/ *adj.* Incapable of being conquered or overcome: *After winning eight straight games, the team seems invincible.*

isolate /í sə lāt/ *v.* To separate or keep by itself; to cut off from outside contact: *Heavy snowdrifts on the roads isolated the town for a week.*

query /kwír rē/ *v.* To ask questions; to question or cast doubt on the truth or accuracy of something: *Several committee members queried Wilma about her plans for the subscription campaign.*

sloth /slōth/ *n.* Great habitual laziness: *Mark said that he did not have time to do his homework, but the real reason was simply his usual sloth.*—**slothful,** *adj.*

slovenly /slúv ən lē/ *adj.* Sloppy in appearance or in manner of doing things: *The many erasures of the page showed it was done in a slovenly manner.*

succumb /sə kúm/ *v.* To give up or give in to; often, to die of something. *Twenty years ago, people often succumbed to pneumonia.*

EXERCISE. Fill each blank with the word from this lesson that makes the best sense in the context. (Add 10 points for each correct answer.)

1. Tired of city life, the woman had sought to . . . . herself in a tiny cabin in the wilds of northern Minnesota.

2. Only by the most . . . . efforts did the explorers succeed in fording the raging river.

3. Mr. Winstanley finally . . . . when offered a piece of pumpkin pie with whipped cream, and that was the end of his diet.

4. Shakespeare's genius would have been the . . . . of any age.

5. I'm sorry to have to . . . . your conclusions, but I believe you've made a mistake somewhere.

6. Karen's . . . . is so great that we have given up expecting her to be of any help in our project.

7. Napoleon must have seemed . . . . to the frightened people of Europe before he began his disastrous invasion of Russia.

8. Fortunately, the Allies . . . . the message to the Axis troops in Normandy.

HBJ material copyrighted under notice appearing earlier in this work.

9. How can you live in such a(n) .... fashion, with the bed unmade and dirty clothes lying on the floor?

10. With her pockets full of money, the girl was .... by many temptations.

REVIEW EXERCISE. In the space at the left, write the letter of the best meaning for the italicized word. (Add 5 points for each correct answer in the first group and 10 points for each correct answer in the second group.)

.... 1. *profound* interest   a. disease spread by contact

.... 2. a *rational* plan   b. to speak strongly against

.... 3. an efficient *administrator*   c. to speak in favor of

.... 4. *inadequate* help   d. deep, serious

.... 5. dangerous *contagion*   e. not enough

.... 6. *denounce* a criminal   f. reasonable or logical

.... 7. overcome by *pessimism*   g. reverent respect

.... 8. *advocate* a plan   h. a manager

.... 9. *piety* toward parents   i. to grieve deeply for

.... 10. *lament* a past mistake   j. gloomy lack of hope

To the left of each sentence, write the letter of the word that could best fill the blank.

.... 11. It was hardly ____ to make faces at that police officer.
   a. grotesque   b. prudent   c. placid

.... 12. A small ____ stands in the way of the bill's passage.
   a. elocution   b. pretext   c. faction

.... 13. After several failures, we decided the problem was ____.
   a. insoluble   b. inflexibile   c. incompetent

.... 14. A bully may ____ at someone in order to be frightening.
   a. sulk   b. bicker   c. bluster

.... 15. Phyllis said the restaurant's food was ____ and sent it back.
   a. immaterial   b. valid   c. unpalatable

HBJ material copyrighted under notice appearing earlier in this work.

CHAPTER 9

Using Verbs Correctly

As you study the verbs printed in red in the sentences below, notice how the basic forms (or principal parts) of the verb *see* are used to express various times.

PRINCIPAL PARTS OF THE VERB *see*

Present	*Present Participle*	*Past*	*Past Participle*
see	seeing	saw	(have) seen

1. I **see** the point now.   (present)
2. He **is seeing** double.   (present)
3. Yesterday she **saw** the President.   (past)
4. I **had seen** Gwen before then.   (past)
5. She **will see** a circus tomorrow.   (future)

It is important to remember that the past participle of a verb must always have a helper: *have seen, has seen, had seen, was seen.* The present participle (a principal part of the verb) ends in *-ing* and is used with forms of *to be (am, is, are—was, were—been): were seeing, will be seeing, has been seeing.* By learning the principal parts of verbs and their uses, you can avoid serious mistakes with verb forms (such as ''I seen'' or ''I have saw'').

LESSON 86

Regular and Irregular Verbs

Regular Verbs. Most verbs form their past and past participle forms by adding *-d* or *-ed* to the present form. Such verbs are called *regular verbs.*

PRESENT	PAST	PAST PARTICIPLE
believe	believed	(have) believed
risk	risked	(have) risked

Because the *-d* or *-ed* is sometimes difficult to hear and pronounce, you may carelessly omit this important verb ending in your writing. Avoid the error by remembering that the *-d* or *-ed* is used for every tense except the present and future.

NONSTANDARD	Last week Fran *ask* me to her party.
STANDARD	Last week Fran **asked** me to her party.
NONSTANDARD	Grandmother was *use* to hard work.
STANDARD	Grandmother was **used** to hard work.

HBJ material copyrighted under notice appearing earlier in this work.

Irregular Verbs. Many verbs that you often use are not regular. Because they do not form their past and past participle forms by adding *-d* or *-ed* to the present, they are called *irregular verbs.* To use them correctly, you must know their principal parts.

Memorize the principal parts of the following common irregular verbs. In repeating the principal parts to yourself, always say *have* with the past participle.

PRESENT	PAST	PAST PARTICIPLE
begin	began	(have) begun
come	came	(have) come
do	did	(have) done
drink	drank	(have) drunk
give	gave	(have) given
go	went	(have) gone
ride	rode	(have) ridden

EXERCISE. Fill the blank in each of the following sentences with the correct past form of the verb given before the sentence. (Add 5 points for each correct answer.)

ride   1. The rodeo champion had safely . . . . a bull.

suppose   2. We were . . . . to read the next chapter.

come   3. Alicia had finally . . . . home.

go   4. Has Gwen already . . . . to the laboratory?

ask   5. The dentist . . . . me to return Monday.

see   6. Last night we . . . . both pictures twice.

give   7. Flo . . . . me the book last night.

do   8. Benita . . . . all she could to help.

ride   9. She has . . . . every horse in the corral.

drink   10. Roger asked if I had . . . . the last soda.

begin   11. I . . . . to think you weren't here.

give   12. Have they . . . . anything to the rummage sale?

come   13. Perry and Alice . . . . to see you yesterday.

see   14. Has anyone ever . . . . a dodo?

go   15. Aunt Ev and Uncle Leo have never . . . . there.

drink   16. Aunt Pearl . . . . her coffee in great haste.

begin   17. We had . . . . to wonder what was wrong.

do   18. Gary has . . . . more than his share.

see   19. I had already . . . . the principal.

come   20. At last the lawyer . . . . to the point.

170

HBJ material copyrighted under notice appearing earlier in this work.

More Irregular Verbs

Memorize the principal parts of the following irregular verbs. In repeating them to yourself, always say *have* with the past participle.

PRESENT	PAST	PAST PARTICIPLE
break	broke	(have) broken
ring	rang	(have) rung
run	ran	(have) run
speak	spoke	(have) spoken
swim	swam	(have) taken
take	took	(have) taken
throw	threw	(have) thrown
write	wrote	(have) written

EXERCISE A. Fill the blank in each of the following sentences with a correct form of the verb given before the sentence. (Add 5 points for each correct answer.)

write   1. Had Jane .... any poetry before she studied medicine?

speak   2. "I have ....!" Melissa shouted, ending the argument.

throw   3. The bowler had .... a strike.

take   4. Had they .... her prisoner?

write   5. Before 1450, books were .... by hand in Europe.

break   6. Was your watch .... in the scuffle?

run   7. Suzie and Crystal .... all the way to the bus.

swim   8. I wish I'd .... out to the raft after you did.

throw   9. We had .... away the garbage.

run   10. Stan had just .... eighty yards for a touchdown.

take   11. Althea Gibson must have .... pride in her tennis skills.

ring   12. The clerk .... up fifty cents on the cash register.

swim   13. Yesterday Bret .... twenty lengths of the pool.

ring   14. I didn't know the bell had ....

break   15. Dad has never .... 90 on the golf course.

speak   16. Silence reigned; not one word was ....

HBJ material copyrighted under notice appearing earlier in this work.

swim   17. Helen had never .... in salt water.

take   18. Melodie .... the initiative and apologized.

write   19. Dale .... up the laboratory experiment last night.

speak   20. Miriam Colon .... to an interviewer about the Puerto Rican Traveling Theatre before the program was televised.

EXERCISE B. This exercise covers verbs in this lesson and in Lesson 86. There are ten incorrect verbs. Cross out the incorrect verb and write the correct verb form above it. (Add 10 points for each correct answer.)

MODERN DRAGONS

1   Yesterday afternoon our English teacher told us about the occurrence of

2   dragons in literature. I was taken aback when she said that dragons

3   actually do exist today. Before the bell rung, she gave us our assignment.

4   By Friday we were to turn in compositions we had wrote on the Komodo

5   dragon.

6   I went to the library immediately after school and begun work on my

7   report. Komodo dragons have existed since prehistoric times. No one

8   knows how they come to the Indonesian island of Komodo long ago.

9   Some scientists think the giant lizards might have swam to the island from

10   Asia, island-hopping along the way. This might have gave rise to the

11   legends about sea monsters. These creatures grow up to ten feet long and

12   weigh up to 300 pounds. Animals unlucky enough to have ran into

13   Komodo dragons have served as food. One hit with these creatures'

14   massive tails has throwed many an animal several yards. One bite from

15   their powerful jaws has broke many a creature, including humans, in two.

16   Komodos are, however, their own worst enemies. Hungry Komodos,

17   hemmed in by civilization, have took to eating members of their own

18   species.

HBJ material copyrighted under notice appearing earlier in this work.

The Irregular Verbs LIE and LAY

In order to use *lie* and *lay* correctly, you must understand the difference in meaning between them and memorize their principal parts.

The verb lie means to recline, to rest, or to be in place.

EXAMPLES   On Sundays I lie around reading the papers.
The key lies under the doormat.

The verb lay means to put or to place something.

EXAMPLE   Please lay the newspaper on the table in the hall.

Be able to write the principal parts of the two verbs from memory.

PRESENT	PRESENT PARTICIPLE	PAST	PAST PARTICIPLE
lie (to recline or rest)	(is) lying	lay	(have) lain
lay (to put something)	(is) laying	laid	(have) laid

If you are not sure whether to use *lie* or *lay,* ask yourself whether your intended meaning is "to recline (to be in place)" or "to put something." If it is "to recline," use a form of the verb *lie.* If it is "to put something," use a form of the verb *lay.* As a double check, notice whether the verb has a direct object. *Lie* never has an object. *Lay* usually does.

Next, ask yourself the *time* of the verb and select the principal part of the verb to express this: present, present participle, past, or past participle.

PROBLEM: We (lay, laid) our papers on your desk yesterday.
Meaning: place or put. The verb is *lay.*
Principal part: past. The past form of *lay* is *laid.*
Correct: We laid our papers on your desk.

PROBLEM: The dog is (lying, laying) on the porch.
Meaning: recline. The verb is *lie.*
Principal part: present participle. The present participle of *lie* is *lying.*
Correct: The dog is lying on the porch.

EXERCISE. Solve each of the following *lie-lay* problems by filling in the blanks. (Add 4 points for each correct answer.)

EX.   *Problem:* I must have (lain, laid) there an hour.

Meaning? .... *recline* .... Which verb? .... *lie* ....

Principal part? .. *past participle* .. Verb form ...... *lain* ...

Correct: I must have ...... *lain* ...... there an hour.

HBJ material copyrighted under notice appearing earlier in this work.

EX. *Problem:* She (lay, laid) the ice cubes on the hot stove.

Meaning? *to put something* Which verb? *lay*

Principal part? *past* Verb form? *laid*

Correct: She *laid* the ice cubes on the hot stove.

1. *Problem:* The cattle were (lying, laying) in the shade.

Meaning? .... Which verb? ....

Principal part? .... Verb form? ....

Correct: The cattle were .... in the shade.

2. *Problem:* These boulders have (lain, laid) here for centuries.

Meaning? .... Which verb? ....

Principal part? .... Verb form? ....

Correct: These boulders have .... here for centuries.

3. *Problem:* I could not (lie, lay) still any longer.

Meaning? .... Which verb? ....

Principal part? .... Verb form? ....

Correct: I could not .... still any longer.

4. *Problem:* Which rug (lies, lays) here?

Meaning? .... Which verb? ....

Principal part? .... Verb form? ....

Correct: Which rug .... here?

5. *Problem:* (Lying, Laying) her fork down, she looked up.

Meaning? .... Which verb? ....

Principal part? .... Verb form? ....

Correct: .... her fork down, she looked up.

HBJ material copyrighted under notice appearing earlier in this work.

More Practice with LIE and LAY

EXERCISE A. The forms of *lie* and *lay* are printed below. Refer to them as you do the following exercise. In the blanks below each problem sentence, write the information asked for. (Add 10 points for each correct line.)

PRESENT	PRESENT PARTICIPLE	PAST	PAST PARTICIPLE
lie (to *recline* or *rest*)	(is) lying	lay	(have) lain
lay (to *put* something)	(is) laying	laid	(have) laid

EX. When we came in, we (lay, laid) our coats on a chair.

meaning..*put*.... prin. part .*past*.... correct form..*laid*...

1. A heavy mist (lay, laid) in the valley.

meaning.......... prin. part .... correct form..........

2. Before Mother went to work, she (lay, laid) my carfare on the table.

meaning.......... prin. part .... correct form..........

3. The saucepan (lies, lays) under the stove.

meaning.......... prin. part .... correct form..........

4. You have (lain, laid) here long enough.

meaning.......... prin. part .... correct form..........

5. Someone had (lain, laid) the dishes on the chair.

meaning.......... prin. part .... correct form..........

6. Just (lying, laying) around the house is boring.

meaning.......... prin. part .... correct form..........

7. His work has (lain, laid) untouched for days.

meaning.......... prin. part .... correct form..........

8. Would the baby rather (lie, lay) on her back?

meaning.......... prin. part .... correct form..........

9. The old tractor is (lying, laying) behind the barn.

meaning.......... prin. part .... correct form..........

10. The movers (lay, laid) the new rug on the stairs.

meaning.......... prin. part .... correct form..........

HBJ material copyrighted under notice appearing earlier in this work.

EXERCISE B. Underline the correct one of the two verbs in parentheses. Although you are not asked to write the meaning or the time or tense of each verb, you should determine it carefully before deciding which form is correct. (Add 4 points for each correct answer.)

1. I couldn't (lie, lay) down the biography of Harriet Tubman until I'd read the last page.

2. Has the dog been (lying, laying) in the mud?

3. Ella (lay, laid) her books on the floor.

4. Hundreds of dollars were (lying, laying) on the counter.

5. They had (lain, laid) a board under each wheel.

6. The ambulance attendants (lay, laid) him gently on a stretcher.

7. Devon Harbor (lies, lays) three miles east of here.

8. Your pencil case is (lying, laying) over there.

9. Our chicken (lay, laid) two eggs this morning.

10. Kareem had (lain, laid) his books on my lunch bag.

Write the correct form of *lie* or *lay* in each blank.

11. I told my dog to . . . . down. He obeyed and . . . . down near the stove. He has been . . . . there for an hour.

12. When I entered, I noticed the tackle box . . . . on the floor. Olivia must have . . . . the box there yesterday.

13. You will find those clothes . . . . in the hamper, where I . . . . them last week. They have . . . . there for days.

14. A few moments ago I . . . . the exhausted cat on the porch. She has been . . . . very quietly. With your permission, I will . . . . her in a corner of the warm kitchen.

15. I will . . . . down on that sofa and read the magazine that is . . . . on the table. After I have read it, I will . . . . it down where I found it. The magazine will be . . . . there when you are ready to read it.

HBJ material copyrighted under notice appearing earlier in this work.

The Irregular Verbs SIT and SET

The verb <u>sit</u> means <u>to be in</u> or <u>to take a sitting position</u>.

EXAMPLES   Let's **sit** down here on the front steps.
How long has the lamp been **sitting** there?

The verb <u>set</u> means <u>to put</u> or <u>to place something</u>.

EXAMPLES   Let's **set** the flowerpot on the bottom step.
After **setting** the lamp on the table, the man went out.

Notice that *sit,* rarely has an object while *set* usually does.

PRESENT	PRESENT PARTICIPLE	PAST	PAST PARTICIPLE
sit (in a sitting position)	(is) sitting	sat	(have) sat
set (to put something)	(is) setting	set	(have) set

EXERCISE. In the first space at the right, tell whether the intended meaning of the verb is *to sit or stay in a sitting position* or *to place or put something*. In the second space, write the correct one of the two verbs in parentheses. (Add 4 points for each correctly marked sentence.)

	Meaning	*Verb*
EX. I was (sitting, setting) the flowers on the window ledge.	*put*	*setting*
EX. (Sitting, Setting) in the den, Mother called that it was Mrs. Martin.	*sit*	*sitting*
1. "Won't you (sit, set) here?" I said to Mrs. Martin.	. . . .	. . . .
2. She (sat, set) down and began talking about Newton's laws of motion.	. . . .	. . . .
3. "(Sit, Set) in this chair, Jo," she told me.	. . . .	. . . .
4. "Now (sit, set) that chair out of the way," she went on.	. . . .	. . . .
5. I (sat, set) down as instructed.	. . . .	. . . .
6. She showed me how to (sit, set) an object in motion by propulsion.	. . . .	. . . .

HBJ material copyrighted under notice appearing earlier in this work.

7. "As you (sit, set) here," she said, "lift both feet and kick them out quickly." . . . .

8. I did so, and the chair I was (sitting, setting) in moved backward. . . . .

9. (Sit, Set) the lamp there. . . . .

10. Why are you (sitting, setting) here? . . . .

11. Was he (sitting, setting) by her? . . . .

12. Please (sit, set) the box here. . . . .

13. Lucy has (sat, set) the groceries there. . . . .

14. Aunt Beth has (sat, set) in that chair every day for years. . . . .

15. I was (sitting, setting) perfectly still. . . . .

16. She asked the pupils to (sit, set) down. . . . .

17. While we waited for her, we (sat, set) near the window. . . . .

18. Who (sat, set) this cup here? . . . .

19. Just (sit, set) still, please. . . . .

20. I was (sitting, setting) up late. . . . .

21. Who (sat, set) at my desk while I was gone? . . . .

22. Her house (sits, sets) by the side of the road. . . . .

23. She always (sits, sets) her pocketbook on the table. . . . .

24. (Sitting, Setting) next to her, I enjoyed her conversation. . . . .

25. Did you notice where I (sat, set) my books? . . . .

HBJ material copyrighted under notice appearing earlier in this work.

The Verbs RISE and RAISE

The verb <u>rise</u> means <u>to go up</u>, <u>to get up</u>, or <u>to come up</u>.

EXAMPLE   When the fog rises, the sun will shine.

The verb <u>raise</u> means <u>to lift something</u>.

EXAMPLE   It's time to raise the curtain.

Notice that *rise* never has an object while *raise* often does.

PRESENT	PRESENT PARTICIPLE	PAST	PAST PARTICIPLE
rise (to go up)	(is) rising	rose	(have) risen
raise (to lift)	(is) raising	raised	(have) raised

Of the two verbs, only *rise* is irregular. *Raise* is perfectly regular, since it forms its past and past participle by adding *-d* to the present.

EXERCISE. In the first space at the right, tell whether the intended meaning of the verb is *to go up* or *to lift*. In the second space, write the correct one of the two verbs in parentheses. (Add 10 points for each correctly marked sentence.)

	Meaning	Verb
EX. The smoke is (rising, raising).	*go up*	*rising*
EX. The workers will have to (rise, raise) the house six inches.	*lift*	*raise*
1. The river has been (rising, raising) all night.		
2. The movers (rose, raised) the piano with ropes and a pulley.		
3. Before reaching the mountains, our plane (rose, raised) to 20,000 feet.		
4. The crowd (rose, raised) their hero to their shoulders.		
5. When the speaker sat down, Mr. Segal (rose, raised) to his feet.		
6. She was (rising, raising) to answer as the bell rang.		
7. The model plane (rose, raised) a short distance and then dropped.		

HBJ material copyrighted under notice appearing earlier in this work.

8. I (rose, raised) the car with a jack. . . . .

9. Her income has gradually (risen, raised). . . . .

10. She has (risen, raised) as high in her profession as a person can go. . . . .

REVIEW EXERCISE. Underline the correct one of the two verbs in parentheses. (Add 5 points for each correct answer.)

1. I was daydreaming as I (sat, set) in English class, waiting for the teacher to arrive.

2. I (began, begun) to imagine my rosy future.

3. I saw myself (sitting, setting) at a desk in the White House.

4. Papers (laying, lying) on the desk awaited my signature.

5. Reporters were (sitting, setting) around asking me questions.

6. "Now that I've (drank, drunk) my coffee, I'll speak," I said.

7. "I'll just (lay, lie) all my cards on the table," I continued.

8. I told them that I had (wrote, written) a speech for Congress.

9. Then I leaned back and (give, gave) them a summary of my speech.

10. "When I (came, come) here last January," I announced, "I had some new ideas about what government can do for education."

11. The reporters (began, begun) to show more interest.

12. (Rising, Raising) to my feet, I continued the news conference.

13. "Now, I (saw, seen) long ago the need for new laws," I said.

14. I (use, used) my powers of persuasion when I presented my program.

15. "All courses should be (taken, took) by choice, not by requirement."

16. "School officials have not (ask, asked) students for ideas for courses often enough," I stated.

17. "They have not (saw, seen) the need for students to take an active part in planning their education," I added.

18. "Students who have been (gave, given) responsibility can act with maturity," I continued.

19. "I have only (began, begun) to fight for educational reform," I shouted.

20. Suddenly a loud bell (rang, rung), the teacher arrived, and my daydream ended.

HBJ material copyrighted under notice appearing earlier in this work.

Consistency of Tense

Do not change needlessly from one tense to another.

When you are writing a composition, especially a story, you must be careful to keep your verbs consistent in tense. If your story is told in the past tense, you should, as much as possible, keep your verbs in the past tense. It may, of course, be necessary to shift the tense, but do not do so unless you have a good reason.

NONSTANDARD	After Nick *assembled* all the clues, he *solves* the clever crime. (mixed tenses—past with present)
STANDARD	After Nick assembled all the clues, he solved the clever crime. (consistent tenses—all past)
NONSTANDARD	My cousin *auditions* for six television roles and finally *got* a part in a series. (mixed tenses—present with past)
STANDARD	My cousin auditioned for six television roles and finally got a part. (consistent tenses—all past)
STANDARD	My cousin auditions for six television roles and finally gets a part. (consistent tenses—all present)

EXERCISE A. The following story contains examples of mixed tenses. Read the selection through and decide whether it should be in present or past time. Then make the tenses consistent by crossing out each incorrect verb and writing the correct form above it. (Add 10 points for each correct answer.)

SNAKES, ANYONE?

1   Last Saturday, Jack invites Sue to view his live snake collection.

2   Although she did not like snakes, she decides to accept his invitation, just

3   to satisfy her curiosity. So off she went! The snakes were housed in glass

4   cages in the empty half of Jack's garage. When Sue sees Jack handling the

5   snakes, she admires his skill and quickly recovered from her initial

6   dislike. In fact, she even decides to join him on a snake hunt.

7   After an hour of hunting in the wooded city park, Jack had captured a

8   half-dozen harmless snakes and turns them loose in the car. Since Sue was

9   now an enthusiast, she enjoys riding with them. On the way back, at

10   stoplights, it was great fun to watch the expressions of people in other cars

11   when they saw the live snakes curled around Sue's arm and crawling

HBJ material copyrighted under notice appearing earlier in this work.

12 across her shoulders. Some persons scream; others pointed; most stare

13 with open mouths. Jack and Sue smiled and waved and then drive on to

14 the snake farm.

EXERCISE B. Decide whether the following story should be in present or past time. Then make the tenses consistent by crossing out each incorrect verb and writing the correct form above it. (Add 10 points for each correct answer.)

BUSMAN'S HOLIDAY

1   Mr. William Clarke, a bus driver, was tired of following the same

2 crosstown route every day to the 205th Street subway station. Besides, it

3 is spring, and Mr. Clarke is thinking about getting away. As he swung the

4 huge bus out of its garage at 6:45 one Friday morning, the lure of the open

5 road was too much for him. He changes the sign on the front of his bus

6 from SUBWAY to SPECIAL and heads toward New Jersey.

7   Soon the crowded city streets were behind him. He is no longer

8 weaving through traffic, slamming on brakes, making change. After

9 fourteen hours, he stopped somewhere in Virginia, stretches out on the

10 broad rear seat, and falls asleep. The next night he was in Jacksonville,

11 Florida. Then the police received word from New York about the missing

12 bus and its driver. Clarke had advertised his position by telegraphing his

13 employers for money. The police find their man when he returned to the

14 telegraph office to get his money.

15   His employers did not look with favor upon the disappearance of an

16 $18,000 bus, nor do they send its driver the money he requested. They

17 sent the police, instead. Clarke returns by train with a detective. It seemed

18 best not to have him drive the bus on its return journey. There are too

19 many interesting routes to California!

HBJ material copyrighted under notice appearing earlier in this work.

Chapter Review

EXERCISE A. Select the correct one of the verbs in parentheses and write it in the blank at the right. (Add 5 points for each correct answer.)

1. The Wrights had (rode, ridden) in the plane twelve seconds.

1. . . . .

2. Yesterday he (came, come) in wearing purple socks.

2. . . . .

3. They have all (went, gone) to see the play.

3. . . . .

4. She often (sat, set) up all night working.

4. . . . .

5. Had he (wrote, written) two symphonies by 1853?

5. . . . .

6. The team (did, done) its best to win.

6. . . . .

7. We (saw, seen) many watermelon stands along the road.

7. . . . .

8. The architect (laid, lay) her plans on the table.

8. . . . .

9. Flo had (laid, lain) down to take a quick nap.

9. . . . .

10. The fireworks (began, begun) shortly after dark.

10. . . . .

11. I was (laying, lying) down when you phoned.

11. . . . .

12. Please go into the living room and (sit, set) down.

12. . . . .

13. Where have the girls (went, gone)?

13. . . . .

14. She's (rode, ridden) her bike to school regularly.

14. . . . .

15. The bell hasn't (rang, rung).

15. . . . .

16. I just (lay, laid) a new floor in the kitchen.

16. . . . .

17. By four o'clock the sun had (risen, raised).

17. . . . .

18. When the rain started, we (ran, run) for cover.

18. . . . .

19. We (saw, seen) Gina at the game.

19. . . . .

20. All day the temperature (rose, raised) steadily.

20. . . . .

EXERCISE B. If a sentence below contains no error in verb usage, write *C*, for *correct*, in the blank at the right. If a sentence contains an incorrect verb form, cross it out and write the correct form in the blank. (Add 10 points for each correctly marked sentence.)

1. Have you drank all the lemonade?

1. . . . .

2. The teacher give me a second chance.

2. . . . .

HBJ material copyrighted under notice appearing earlier in this work.

3. Algebra class has not yet begun.   3. ....

4. Has Mrs. Katakura spoke to you about the tour?   4. ....

5. Has Lori or Don threw curve balls?   5. ....

6. My watch was laying on the diving board.   6. ....

7. Perhaps they saw us when we did it.   7. ....

8. Yesterday Livvie swum acoss the lake.   8. ....

9. You could have took the girls with you.   9. ....

10. I was suppose to mow the lawn.   10. ....

EXERCISE C. The following story contains needless changes in tense. Read it through and decide whether it should be in present or past time. Then make the tenses consistent by crossing out each incorrect verb and writing the correct form above it. (Add 10 points for each correct answer.

1   The topic of sports programs was brought up at the school meeting last

2   Thursday. As expected, tempers flare as the topic is discussed. Neither

3   side wanted to listen to the other side. Both were sure the opposing side

4   had nothing to say and is merely acting out of ignorance.

5   Friday, students at Longfellow High School talk about what happens at

6   the meeting. Sylvia Polombo proposes an idea for calming tempers. It

7   would show how people could work together for the benefit of all.

8   Longfellow High School had tennis courts but no swimming pool.

9   Pershing High School had a swimming pool but no tennis courts. Sylvia

10   suggests that the two schools combine their after-school gym programs so

11   that both groups of students could have the benefit of both facilities.

12   The students adopt the proposal and presented it to the principal. Mr.

13   Byrd confer with the principal of Pershing High School. At the next

14   school meeting, he told those present about the students' idea. Influenced

15   by the spirit of cooperation that was shown by the students, the group

16   settles down to work out a peaceful solution to the sports issue.

HBJ material copyrighted under notice appearing earlier in this work.

Cumulative Review

A. In each of the following sentences, a complement is italicized. In the space at the right, name the complement, using these abbreviations: *s.c.* for subject complement; *d.o.*, direct object; *i.o.*, indirect object. (Add 10 points for each correct answer.)

EX. I put the baby *bird* back in its nest.   A. *d.o.*

1. Woodpeckers make their *nests* in hollow trees.   1. ....

2. That dangling bag of twigs must be an oriole's *nest*.   2. ....

3. The lazy cowbird uses the *homes* of other birds.   3. ....

4. Have you ever seen a three-story bird's *nest?*   4. ....

5. Lend *me* your camera for a moment.   5. ....

6. A snapshot of the parrot should be *colorful*.   6. ....

7. Jo's parrot speaks both *Spanish and English*.   7. ....

8. Crows and parrots seem unusually *intelligent*.   8. ....

9. A Chinese delicacy is *bird's-nest soup*.   9. ....

10. Give *Jo* a book about birds for her birthday.   10. ....

B. If a sentence contains an error in agreement of subject and verb or of pronoun and antecedent, cross out the incorrect word and write the correct word in the blank at the left. If a sentence is correct, write *C* (for *correct*) in the blank. (Add 5 points for each correctly marked sentence.)

.... 1. Was Sally or Fran the first to give a party?

.... 2. Nitrogen and phosphorus in the soil is necessary for a healthy lawn.

.... 3. Every one of the rats was either killed or captured.

.... 4. Neither of the kittens have green eyes.

.... 5. The cries of a lemur sounds like the howling of a wolf.

.... 6. Neither of these medicines are habit-forming.

.... 7. One of the lanterns on the jetty has gone out.

.... 8. Is *oodles* and *jiffy* considered colloquial?

.... 9. Before any person is hired, they must pass a test.

.... 10. Where's your brother and sister?

.... 11. Do either of these candidates appeal to you?

.... 12. When a person is criticized, they should not be angry.

HBJ material copyrighted under notice appearing earlier in this work.

185

.... 13. Everybody wanted to express their opinion.

.... 14. Both parts of the test were easy.

.... 15. If anyone is late, they must have a good excuse.

.... 16. I wrote to one of my friends, but they did not reply.

.... 17. Each of them cooked their own supper.

.... 18. Has Sue or Karen telephoned you?

.... 19. Both Elliot and Alice buy their books at Larsen's.

.... 20. One of the drivers lost control of their car.

C. Insert capital letters and punctuation where needed. Correct all sentence fragments and run-on sentences. (Add 2 points for each correct answer.)

A CURE FOR HALLOWEEN

1   At the Ritz theater last friday, I told Jim the following true story. While
2   waiting for the feature *monsters at large* to begin.
3   Late halloween night nobody disturbed the peace at the home of the
4   Cliftons, who live at 2224 Houston place. Earlier, children had rung the
5   doorbell every few minutes. And yelled Trick or treat! Finally Frank and
6   Ernest the two sons of dr. and mrs. Clifton decided to discourage the
7   would-be pranksters. By playing a trick on them with a six-foot metal
8   monster. One that could walk and talk about eight o'clock, when a group
9   of students from delwood elementary school arrived. The monster
10 clanked its way to the door. An eerie record that Ernest had bought at the
11 hudson novelty company began to play, its noise seemed to come from the
12 monsters moving lips. Help cried the groups leader Lets get out of here
13 After that, only a few curious children dared to ring the Cliftons doorbell,
14 eventually fear conquered curiosity and by nine o'clock the doorbell was
15 silent.

HBJ material copyrighted under notice appearing earlier in this work.

Spelling: How to Spell the /k/ Sound

The sound /k/ at the beginning of a word can be spelled with either the letter *k* or the letter *c*. How can you decide which letter to use? Look at the two lists below, and see if you can determine any patterns regarding the choice of *k* or *c*. What letters follow the *k* or *c*?

1	*2*
kit	cart
king	cabin
kidnap	comb
kindergarten	confess
killing	cube
keep	current
kernel	club
keyhole	climate
kerosene	crest
kerchief	cranberry

In list *1*, the second letter in each word is either an *i* or an *e*. The beginning *c* in the words in list *2* is followed by *a, o, u, l,* or *r.*

The sound /k/ is nearly always (see exceptions below) spelled *k* at the beginning of a word if the second letter in the word is *i* or *e*. Otherwise the /k/ sound is spelled with *c*.

EXCEPTIONS   The exceptions to the rule are almost all words borrowed from foreign languages. Although you may use many of these words infrequently, it is interesting to know how to spell them correctly and from what languages they come.

kale	(Scottish)	kola	(West African)
kangaroo	(Native Australian)	kosher	(Hebrew)
kapok	(Malay)	kowtow	(Chinese)
kayak	(Eskimo)	kudu	(Hottentot)
koala	(Native Australian)	kumquat	(Chinese)

EXERCISE A. Complete each word by writing *k* or *c* in the blank. Follow the rule you have learned. (Add 5 points for each correct answer.)

1. . . . .idney

2. . . . .ommerce

3. . . . .left

4. . . . .eel

5. . . . .obweb

6. . . . .eyboard

7. . . . .ufflink

8. . . . .itchen

HBJ material copyrighted under notice appearing earlier in this work.

9. ....andle

10. ....larinet

11. ....ettle

12. ....indliness

13. ....een

14. ....ushion

15. ....imono

16. ....obra

17. ....riminal

18. ....ennel

19. ....adet

20. ....rest

EXERCISE B. Use your dictionary to find five words (not taught in this lesson) that illustrate the use of the letter *k* for the beginning /k/ sound, and five that use the letter *c* for the /k/ sound. Write them in the columns below.

1. k ....

2. k ....

3. k ....

4. k ....

5. k ....

1. c ....

2. c ....

3. c ....

4. c ....

5. c ....

EXERCISE C. Give a brief definition for any five of the "exception" words given in this lesson. First write the word, and then, next to it, the definition. (Use a dictionary where necessary.)

1. ....

2. ....

3. ....

4. ....

5. ....

EXERCISE D. Be prepared to write from dictation the words taught in this lesson. (Add 2 points for each correctly spelled word.)

REVIEW EXERCISE. Use your knowledge of assimilation to correctly combine each prefix and word part to make a new word. Write the new word in the blank. (Add 10 points for each correctly spelled word.)

1. sub + cess = ...

2. ad + proach = ...

3. ad + ford = ...

4. sub + press = ...

5. ad + liance = ...

6. ad + gressive = ...

7. sub + focate = ...

8. ad + nounce = ...

9. sub + ceeding = ...

10. ad + cident = ...

188

HBJ material copyrighted under notice appearing earlier in this work.

Building Vocabulary: The Total Context

You can often form a good idea of a word's meaning from a very brief context—a sentence or two showing how the word is used. With many important words, however, you must consider a larger context.

To understand the word *democracy,* for example, you need some knowledge of political ideas and their history in America and Europe. To understand the word *utopian,* you should know that it comes from the title of a famous book, *Utopia,* by Thomas More—a description of a perfect (but perhaps impractical) government. Here are some ways in which you can get at the total context of important words like *democracy,* so that you can understand such words fully and use them accurately.

1. In a dictionary, find the meaning of any root words from which the word is formed. Many English words are formed from Latin or Greek roots that carry over their basic meanings into English.

2. Use an encyclopedia to check on matters of history that may have contributed to the meaning of the word.

3. Check references to literature in an encyclopedia or a reference book like the *Oxford Companion to English Literature.*

Notice how the suggestions above are applied in explaining the meanings of the following useful words.

august /au gúst/ *adj.* Majestic, noble, and awe-inspiring: *The people were silent in the august presence of the monarch.* The Latin word *augustus,* from which *august* comes, was used as a title by the Roman emperors, the most powerful and the most honored rulers of the ancient world.

bountiful /bóun tə fəl/ *adj.* Extremely generous; abundant: *Thanksgiving Day dinner is the most bountiful meal of the year.* The word comes from the noun *bounty,* which means both "great generosity and the kind of gift which would express generosity." *Bounty* might be used of the gifts monarchs or wealthy nobles would give or of the generous spirit in which they would be expected to give them.

discriminate /dis krím ə nāt/ *v.* To notice accurately the differences between two things; also, to make an unfair difference, to treat someone unfairly *(discriminate against).* The word's meaning depends on the preposition. With *between* or *among* it suggests a desirable quality, as when professional tasters *discriminate* among the dozens of different kinds of coffee from which they must choose. More commonly, with *against, discriminate* suggests a bad quality, as *to discriminate against someone because of that person's race or religion.*

eccentric /ek sén trik/ *adj.* Out of the ordinary, odd, peculiar in behavior, ideas, etc. The word comes from the Greek words *ek* (out of) and *kentron* (center) and means literally "*off center.*" Hence, in geometry, *eccentric* circles are circles that overlap but have different centers. An *eccentric* gear or wheel is mounted *off center* so that it does not go around with a circular movement.

gesture /jés chər/ *n.* A movement of the hands that carries meaning of some kind: *With a sweeping gesture, the umpire sent the player from the game. Gesture* can also mean any large action done more for effect than for the sake of achieving some goal: *When Jane competed for a scholarship, she hoped the gesture would please her parents, even if she didn't obtain one.*

imperious /im pír ē əs/ *adj.* Haughty, commanding. The word is connected with the Latin *imperator,* which at first meant a commanding general, later the all-powerful

HBJ material copyrighted under notice appearing earlier in this work.

Roman *emperor;* hence, the word literally means *"like an emperor":* With an imperious nod, the general silenced his soldiers.

indignation /ín dig nấ shən/ *n.* Anger aroused by a mean or unworthy action. The word is made up of the prefix *in- (not)* and a form of the word *dignity:* we feel *indignation* for something that is beneath the *dignity,* or sense of worth, of the person who does it.—indignant, *adj.*

mediocre /mế dē ố kər/ *adj.* Ordinary. *Mediocre* goes back to the same Latin word as *middle;* a *mediocre* book or movie is one that is "right in the middle," neither good nor bad, not outstanding in any way.

perspective /pər spék tiv/ *n.* The true relationship of objects, events, ideas, etc., or the ability to view them in this way: *By studying history, one gains perspective on the meaning of current events.* In painting, *perspective* is the art of depicting objects on a flat surface so that they look as they would in reality, seen in depth.

radiant /rấ dē ənt/ *adj.* Coming in straight lines, or rays, as light and heat do, from a central source; hence, often, very happy, because we think of happiness as lighting up a person in the same way: *After winning the tennis tournament, Joan was simply radiant.* The word comes from the Latin *radius,* the spoke of a wheel, an accurate picture of the way light travels outward from the sun or any other source.—radiate, *v.*

EXERCISE. In the light of the definitions above, study the context in which each italicized word is used. Circle *C (correct)* for any word that is used correctly and appropriately. Circle *I (incorrect)* for any word that is used incorrectly or inappropriately. (Add 10 points for each correct answer.)

C I 1. Some colleges actually *discriminate* against athletes.

C I 2. An *eccentric* person is just like everyone else.

C I 3. Skillful public speakers emphasize their ideas with *gestures.*

C I 4. Stand back so that you can see the painting in *perspective.*

C I 5. A potbellied stove is a good example of *radiant* heating.

C I 6. A *mediocre* performance on a test usually earns a good mark.

C I 7. The queen's *august* bearing impressed all who met her.

C I 8. Public *indignation* drove the governor back to private life.

C I 9. The *bountiful* river irrigates the entire valley.

C I 10. Napoleon was perhaps the most *imperious* ruler of all time.

HBJ material copyrighted under notice appearing earlier in this work.

CHAPTER 10

Using Pronouns Correctly

Notice in the following examples that a few pronouns change form according to the way they are used in a sentence. *I, he, she, we,* and *they* (used as subjects) change to *me, him, her, us,* and *them* (when used as objects).

SUBJECT OF VERB	VERB	OBJECT OF VERB
I		me
he		him
she	like (s)	her
we		us
they		them

The grammatical term used to name the relation of a pronoun to other words in the sentence is *case*. The pronouns used as subjects are said to be in the *nominative* case; the pronouns used as objects are said to be in the *objective* case. In order to use pronouns correctly, you must know the forms of the pronouns in these two cases. Say the lists to yourself this way:

NOMINATIVE CASE I, he, she, we, they
OBJECTIVE CASE me, him, her, us, them

When you have memorized the case forms, you should learn when to use the nominative forms and when to use the objective forms.

LESSON 97

Uses of the Nominative Case: Subject

The subject of a verb is in the nominative case.

The following pronouns are used as subjects of a verb: *I, he, she, we, they.* (The pronouns *you* and *it*, whether used as subjects or objects, keep the same form).

	Subject	*Verb*
EXAMPLES	1. Janet and I	have been traveling.
	2. Janet and he (she)	have been traveling.
	3. Janet and we	have been traveling.
	4. Janet and they	have been traveling.
	5. We girls	have been traveling.

HBJ material copyrighted under notice appearing earlier in this work.

Note: In sentences like number 5 that contain common expressions such as *we girls, we boys, us girls, us boys,* do not be misled by the words following the pronoun. Drop these words (*girls, boys*) from the sentences, and determine the correct pronoun in the usual way. Never use an objective pronoun as the subject of a verb.

NONSTANDARD   *Us* girls have been traveling.
STANDARD   **We** girls have been traveling.

EXERCISE. In the spaces provided, write the subject and the verb in each of the following sentences. Notice that the pronouns used as subjects are nominative pronouns. Most of the subjects are compound. (Add 5 points for each correct numbered item.)

	Subject	*Verb*
EX. Mary and he often quarrel.	*Mary, he*	*quarrel*
1. Jo and she save dimes and pennies.	....	....
2. We girls caught a few dogfish.	....	....
3. Can Ed or she operate this edger?	....	....
4. We girls swam in the deep water.	....	....
5. He and I then built a raft.	....	....
6. Are she and I partners?	....	....
7. We and they met in the finals.	....	....
8. Did you and she have soup?	....	....
9. Karen and I had dessert.	....	....
10. Do you and she speak Spanish?	....	....
11. My parents and they are friends.	....	....
12. Have you and he been absent?	....	....
13. You and we will work together.	....	....
14. The coach and she disagreed.	....	....
15. Maybe you and I will be chosen.	....	....
16. Have Arturo and they already gone?	....	....
17. Can Sue and I have the softball?	....	....
18. Stan and he look like brothers.	....	....
19. Did you and she have mumps?	....	....
20. We boys ate fried grasshoppers!	....	....

HBJ material copyrighted under notice appearing earlier in this work.

Uses of the Nominative Case: Subject Complement

A subject complement is in the nominative case.

A complement is a word that completes the meaning of a verb. It is the third part of a three-part sentence base. (The first two parts of a sentence base are, of course, the subject and the verb.)

	Subject	*Verb*	*Complement*
EXAMPLES	This	is	she.
	The leader	was	he.
	These people	could be	they.

A pronoun used as a subject complement almost always follows a form of the verb *to be: am, are, is, was, were,* and verbs ending in *be* or *been (may be, could be, have been,* etc.). When a pronoun is used as a subject complement, it refers to the same person as the subject.

EXAMPLES   This is **she**.   (*She* and *this* mean the same person.)
The leader was **he**.   (*He* and *leader* mean the same person.)

EXERCISE. In the space provided, write the subject complement in each of the following sentences. Notice that the pronouns used as subject complements are nominative pronouns. Some of the complements are compound. (Add 10 points for each correct sentence.)

Subj. Comp.

EX. The guests of honor are Ted and she.   *Ted, she*

1. It was probably they.   . . . .

2. That is she.   . . . .

3. I thought you were he.   . . . .

4. That may be she.   . . . .

5. It could not have been she.   . . . .

6. The winner will be either Bill or he.   . . . .

7. What would you have done if you had been they?   . . . .

8. My best friends are Langston and she.   . . . .

9. It would have been either Phyllis or she.   . . . .

10. It was we girls.   . . . .

HBJ material copyrighted under notice appearing earlier in this work.

Uses of the Objective Case: Object of the Verb

The object of a verb is in the objective case.

The following pronouns are used as objects of verbs: *me, him, her, us, them.* (*You* and *it*, as you know, have the same form whether they are used as subjects or objects.)

		Objects
EXAMPLES	He challenged	Cliff and me.
	I have seen	Walter and him.
	Did you invite	Frances or her?
	Will he include	you and them?
	They sent	us girls the prize.

Note: Indirect objects, as well as direct objects, are in the objective case. In the last sentence, *prize* is the direct object; *us* is the indirect object. (The noun *girls* is an appositive.)

EXERCISE. In the first space at the right of each sentence, write the verb. In the second space, write the correct pronoun from the pair in parentheses. (Add 10 points for each correctly marked sentence.)

	Verb	*Pronoun*
EX. Larry surprised Leroi and (me, I).	*surprised*	*me*
1. I will ask my mother and (she, her).		
2. You can believe Anne and (I, me).		
3. Did anyone tell Dorothy and (she, her)?		
4. I met Sue and (he, him) in Chicago.		
5. Will you take (we, us) girls with you?		
6. Do you remember Ella and (they, them)?		
7. I was expecting Harold and (she, her).		
8. You could help (we, us) boys.		
9. I recognized you and (them, they).		
10. Did she mean Nan or (me, I)?		

HBJ material copyrighted under notice appearing earlier in this work.

Uses of the Objective Case: Object of a Preposition

The object of a preposition is in the objective case.

A prepositional phrase begins with a preposition. The final word in a prepositional phrase is the object of the preposition that begins the phrase.

	Object	*Object*	*Object*
EXAMPLES	at him	in them	from us

The objective forms of the personal pronouns are used as objects of prepositions: *me, him, her, us, them.*

EXAMPLE   The rider was coming <u>toward Jim and me</u> (him, her, us, them).

WORDS COMMONLY USED AS PREPOSITIONS

about	before	by	like	to
above	behind	concerning	near	toward
across	below	down	of	under
after	beneath	during	off	up
against	beside	except	on	upon
among	between	for	over	with
around	beyond	from	past	within
at	but (meaning *except*)	in	through	without

Note: When any of these words are used as adverbs, they do not have an object.

EXERCISE.   Write the preposition in each of the following sentences in the first space at the right. In the second space, write the correct pronoun from the pair in parentheses. (Add 10 points for each correctly marked sentence.)

	Prep.	*Pronoun*
1. Bill sat behind Nadine and (I, me).	. . . .	. . . .
2. Will you go with Dad and (me, I)?	. . . .	. . . .
3. The dog was between Al and (her, she).	. . . .	. . . .
4. There were letters for Lucy and (he, him).	. . . .	. . . .
5. No one but you and (her, she) saw the play.	. . . .	. . . .
6. I played against Alicia and (they, them).	. . . .	. . . .
7. The work falls to you and (we, us).	. . . .	. . . .

HBJ material copyrighted under notice appearing earlier in this work.

8. Who was talking to you and (they, them)? . . . .

9. Come with Gretchen and (I, me). . . . .

10. It was about Beth and (she, her). . . . .

Now that you have learned some uses of both nominative and objective pronouns, you are ready for more practice in selecting the correct pronoun in a sentence. First, determine how the pronoun is used. If it is used as the subject of a verb or as a subject complement, select a pronoun in the nominative case. If it is used as the object of a verb or preposition, select a pronoun in the objective case.

Most errors in pronoun usage occur when the pronoun is part of a compound subject or object. An easy way to select the correct form is to say the sentence aloud, omitting the first two words in the compound construction. In most sentences, your ear will tell you the correct pronoun.

EXAMPLES   Bob and (he, him) called.   (*He* called. Bob and *he* called.)
Ask Betty and (she, her).   (Ask *her*. Ask Betty and *her*.)

REVIEW EXERCISE. Four uses of the nominative and objective pronouns are listed below with abbreviations opposite them. In the first space at the right of each of the following sentences, write the proper abbreviation to indicate in which of these four ways the pronoun is used in the sentence. In the second space, write the correct one of the two pronouns in parentheses. (Add 10 points for each correctly marked sentence.)

NOMINATIVE USES	OBJECTIVE USES
subj. = subject of verb	*o.v.* = object (direct or indirect) of verb
s.c. = subject complement	*o.p.* = object of preposition

	Use	*Pronoun*
EX. Jan and (I, me) borrowed a lantern.	*subj.*	*I*
1. (We, Us) adventurers explored the cave.	. . . .	. . . .
2. Marvin gave Joe and (I, me) some advice.	. . . .	. . . .
3. Her brother and (she, her) sang ballads.	. . . .	. . . .
4. That must be (they, them) now.	. . . .	. . . .
5. Between you and (I, me), we were a hit.	. . . .	. . . .
6. The principal saw Diane and (we, us).	. . . .	. . . .
7. You and (she, her) make a good team.	. . . .	. . . .
8. Have Jane and (he, him) gone shopping?	. . . .	. . . .
9. It was certainly (they, them).	. . . .	. . . .
10. It's up to Sue and (she, her).	. . . .	. . . .

HBJ material copyrighted under notice appearing earlier in this work.

Pronoun Practice

EXERCISE A. The four uses of pronouns are listed below with abbreviations opposite them. In the first space at the right of each of the following sentences, write the proper abbreviation to indicate in which of these four ways the italicized pronoun is used in the sentence. In the second space, put a *C* if the pronoun is correct. If the pronoun is incorrect, cross it out and write the correct form in the space. (Add 10 points for each correctly marked sentence.)

NOMINATIVE USES	OBJECTIVE USES
subj. = subject of verb	*o.v.* = object (direct or indirect) of verb
s.c. = subject complement	*o.p.* = object of preposition

	Use	*Pronoun*
EX. Have you or *her* ever heard of Hob Creek?	*subj.*	*she*
EX. Someone mentioned the creek to *us* girls.	*o.p.*	*C*
1. It must have been *him* and Paul.	....	....
2. A few of *us* girls decided to fish there.	....	....
3. Jo and *me* could see the fish.	....	....
4. I quickly called Myra and *she*.	....	....
5. "You and *she* drop your hooks here!" I yelled.	....	....
6. *Us* girls saw two fish approach our hooks.	....	....
7. They really surprised Jo and *I*.	....	....
8. Instead of biting, they stared at *we* girls.	....	....
9. To Jo and *I* they seemed to say, "Suckers!"	....	....
10. Then they swished their tails and haughtily swam away from *us*.	....	....

EXERCISE B. Write the correct pronoun in the blank before each sentence. (Add 5 points for each correct answer.)

.... 1. Did you hear Sally and (I, me)?

.... 2. We need you and (her, she) for our softball team.

.... 3. Don and (he, him) are always working in the laboratory.

.... 4. Have you and (they, them) ordered yet?

.... 5. The test seemed hard to Lou and (he, him).

.... 6. What marks did you and (her, she) get in English?

HBJ material copyrighted under notice appearing earlier in this work.

. . . . 7. Valerie and (I, me) thought it was easy.

. . . . 8. Liz and (she, her) are going to take Spanish next year.

. . . . 9. Larry and (I, me) would rather take Latin.

. . . . 10. Every law affects you and (I, me).

. . . . 11. The senator and (him, he) have arrived.

. . . . 12. The camp bus left Mary and (them, they) behind.

. . . . 13. This should be an easy course for you and (she, her).

. . . . 14. You and (me, I) are not old enough to drive.

. . . . 15. Did you see Nancy and (he, him) at the karate meet?

. . . . 16. At least, I thought it was (they, them).

. . . . 17. Janet and (her, she) were repairing their bicycles.

. . . . 18. You and (I, me) will play against Mimi and (she, her).

. . . . 19. She thought that (we, us) girls had been absent.

. . . . 20. I'll call for you and (they, them).

EXERCISE C. Write sentences using the words below as instructed. (Add 10 points for each correct sentence.)

subj. = subject of verb	*o.v.* = object of verb
s.c. = subject complement	*o.p.* = object of preposition

EX. Carol and he (s.c.): *That must be Carol and he now.*

1. we students (subj.): . . . .

2. us students (o.p.): . . . .

3. Sasheen and they (subj.): . . . .

4. Sasheen and they (s.c.): . . . .

5. you and I (subj.): . . . .

6. you and me (o.v.): . . . .

7. you and me (o.p.): . . . .

8. Willis or he (subj.): . . . .

9. Willis or him (o.v.): . . . .

10. Willis or him (o.p.): . . . .

HBJ material copyrighted under notice appearing earlier in this work.

Pronouns After THAN and AS

After than and as introducing an incomplete construction, use the form of the pronoun you would use if the construction were complete.

Study the following examples of pronouns used after *than* and *as:*

EXAMPLES   The boys were as scared <u>as we</u>.   (= as we were)

He helped John more <u>than I</u>.   (= than I helped John)

He helped John more <u>than me</u>.   (= than he helped me)

You can see that the words *than* and *as* introduce incomplete constructions. In order to tell what pronoun to use after *than* and *as,* you must complete the sentence in your mind. The words in parentheses show how the sentences may be completed. Notice that in the second and third sentences either *I* or *me* may be correct, depending on your intended meaning.

EXERCISE. In the space after each sentence, write the words you would use to complete the incomplete construction. Begin with *than* or *as*. Select the correct pronoun from those given. Which pronoun you choose will sometimes depend on how you complete the construction. (Add 10 points for each correct sentence.)

EX. Sarah likes her more than (I, me) = ...*than she likes me.*....

EX. Is he as popular as (she, her) = ...*as she is?*.........

1. I can't swim as well as (she, her) = ...

2. Ms. Weldelkin said Carl did better than (he, him) = ...

3. These pants fit you better than (I, me) = ...

4. Mr. Clark praised us more than (they, them) = ...

5. He paid Ben more than (I, me) = ...

6. You are not so heavy as (he, him) = ...

7. I expect more of Loretta than (she, her) = ...

8. They play tennis better than (we, us) = ...

9. I wish you would work as hard as (she, her) = ...

10. I can carve turkey better than (she, her) = ...

HBJ material copyrighted under notice appearing earlier in this work.

REVIEW EXERCISE. In the space before each sentence, write *C* if the italicized pronoun is correct. If it is incorrect, write *I*, cross out the incorrect pronoun, and write the correct form above it. (Add 4 points for each correctly marked sentence.)

C. EX She writes better reports than *I*.

I. EX. Are you telling Bob and ~~I~~ *me* the truth?

.... 1. She fries eggs better than *me*.

.... 2. Should Mark and *I* display our paintings?

.... 3. He discussed the solution with Pete and *she*.

.... 4. Mike's a better Ping-Pong player than *him*.

.... 5. Does your cousin remember Polly and *me*?

.... 6. You can count on *us* boys.

.... 7. The fastest runners were *us* freshmen.

.... 8. She was even more stubborn than *I*.

.... 9. Did you get a letter from Marian and *her*?

.... 10. I phoned Helen and *she* last night.

.... 11. They went out with Jimmy and *him*.

.... 12. Are the tickets for both you and *I*?

.... 13. You and *I* had better go to the library this afternoon.

.... 14. Those desks are getting too small for you and *him*.

.... 15. No, *him* and *me* are getting too big for the desks.

.... 16. Are you going to the game with Agnes or *she*?

.... 17. Mrs. Leibowitz invited Noreen and *me*.

.... 18. You and *me* had better get that lawn mowed.

.... 19. In science Beth sits in front of Pete and *I*.

.... 20. Was it *them*?

.... 21. We helped Fred and *he* with the lesson.

.... 22. Mr. Lawrence thought that *we* three were guilty.

.... 23. Annette taught Ann and *I* a French folk song.

.... 24. After Ginny and *I* came the other guests.

.... 25. I can decorate the tree better than *him*.

HBJ material copyrighted under notice appearing earlier in this work.

Chapter Review

In the proper columns below, list the forms of the pronouns that change according to how they are used.

NOMINATIVE	OBJECTIVE
. . . .	. . . .
. . . .	. . . .
. . . .	. . . .
. . . .	. . . .
. . . .	. . . .

EXERCISE A. In the first space at the right of each sentence, tell whether the pronoun in parentheses is used as (1) subject of verb; (2) subject complement; (3) object of verb; (4) object of preposition. Use the abbreviations *subj.*, *s.c.*, *o.v.*, and *o.p.* In the second space, write the case of the pronoun required by its use: *nom.* or *obj.* In the third space, write the correct pronoun. (Add 10 points for each correctly marked sentence.)

	Use	Case	Pronoun
EX. Sue and (her, she) built a trailer.	*subj.*	*nom.*	*she*
1. (They, Them) and Max saw June yesterday.	. . . .	. . . .	. . . .
2. It couldn't have been (her, she).	. . . .	. . . .	. . . .
3. Who was nominated by Leslie and (him, he)?	. . . .	. . . .	. . . .
4. Julio and (she, her) went to Syracuse.	. . . .	. . . .	. . . .
5. They elected Peg and (I, me).	. . . .	. . . .	. . . .
6. Are Phil and (he, him) ready?	. . . .	. . . .	. . . .
7. Did Nina and (she, her) get home?	. . . .	. . . .	. . . .
8. Mother drove Esther and (they, them).	. . . .	. . . .	. . . .
9. Were you talking to Alex and (we, us)?	. . . .	. . . .	. . . .
10. Was that (she, her)?	. . . .	. . . .	. . . .

HBJ material copyrighted under notice appearing earlier in this work.

EXERCISE B. If a sentence below is correct, write *C* in the space provided. If it is incorrect, write *I*, cross out the incorrect pronoun, and write the correct form above it. (Add 4 points for each correctly marked sentence.)

C. EX. She and her sister volunteered.

I. EX. Sarah can play tennis better than ~~me~~. *I*

.... 1. Have you or he ever seen a flying saucer?

.... 2. Tell Richard and I what *reciprocal* means.

.... 3. Us boys were in the middle of the lake when the storm hit.

.... 4. Can you or they think of a better way to raise money?

.... 5. Miss Savalas kept Rick and me in her office.

.... 6. Has she invited he and Laura?

.... 7. The girls have to ride with him and Mrs. Holmes.

.... 8. Who packed this lunch for her and Sarah?

.... 9. Are you sure it wasn't them and Thelma?

.... 10. No, her and Vic were at the movies.

.... 11. That picture didn't appeal to Vera or me.

.... 12. Her and Carol will be at camp for two months.

.... 13. No, she and Bill went alone.

.... 14. She can skate faster than either you or he.

.... 15. Who's going sailing with Paula and I?

.... 16. He told Toni and I the whole story.

.... 17. No one spoke except him and Bob.

.... 18. It was the best movie that Yvonne or we had ever seen.

.... 19. It was them, all right.

.... 20. The play was written by Mr. Goldman and her.

.... 21. Mr. Edelman wanted Ned and I.

.... 22. My sister looks like my father and I.

.... 23. He and Mother went shopping.

.... 24. The teacher told Nancy and I about the term paper.

.... 25. Karen arrived later than him.

HBJ material copyrighted under notice appearing earlier in this work.

Cumulative Review

A. Choose the correct word in parentheses and write it in the space provided. (Add 5 points for each correct answer.)

.... 1. Each of us (has, have) various ways of analyzing character.

.... 2. According to Joe, if you want to analyze someone's character, ask (them, him) for a sample of handwriting.

.... 3. Yesterday Helene (give, gave) Joe a long note.

.... 4. Of course, Joe immediately (lay, laid) her note on his desk and examined her handwriting.

.... 5. "One of your *o*'s (are, is) looped," he mumbled.

.... 6. "A few of your *t*'s (are, is) crossed high," he added.

.... 7. Helene was (setting, sitting) on the edge of her chair.

.... 8. She grew curious and (asks, asked) Joe for his analysis.

.... 9. Joe said, "I (saw, seen) aggressiveness and secretiveness in your handwriting."

.... 10. "I shouldn't have (wrote, written) that note," she sighed.

.... 11. "We have only (began, begun) to analyze," Fran said.

.... 12. Helene stared at us and then quickly (departs, departed).

.... 13. Fran (rose, raised) from her chair.

.... 14. "Have I ever (spoke, spoken) to you about dreams?"

.... 15. Then Fran sat down again, (lay, laid) her hands on her desk, and proceeded to lecture us.

.... 16. "Dreams explore thoughts that (lie, lay) hidden in our minds."

.... 17. "Dreamers can discover (his, their) subconscious desires."

.... 18. "Neither handwriting nor a dream (reveal, reveals) the true character of a person," I bluntly interrupted.

.... 19. "(Sit, Set) still," Fran said, "and listen while I enlighten you further."

.... 20. "A person's countenance, attire, gait, and laughter can also (shows, show) what that person is."

HBJ material copyrighted under notice appearing earlier in this work.

B. Add capital letters and punctuation. Remove fragments and run-on sentences. (Add 1 point for each correct answer.)

1 My older brother jerry got married. Last june after he graduated from
2 college. Mom dad and I had all hoped that he and Judy. Who is now my
3 sister in law would decide to have the wedding near here but they chose
4 niagara falls instead. Most of Judys family and several of my aunts and
5 uncles live within a hundred miles of there. at first, my father thought
6 about driving the car up to the wedding, but he decided. That driving
7 would take too long, so we flew up on a jet.

8 My brother met us in Buffalo new york, and drove us to our hotel near
9 niagara falls. Mom Dad, and I spent most of the first day sightseeing.
10 Which we all enjoyed. We visited american Fall and horseshoe, or
11 canadian Fall and we went on a boat ride on the niagara river that evening
12 we met most of Judys family and heard about all the wedding plans.

13 The next day jerry took me to the groom's groom a clothing shop. To
14 get my final fitting for my tuxedo. I hadnt known it. But Jerry had
15 planned on my being an usher. As soon as I saw the fancy tuxedo and
16 heard that I was going to be in the ceremony. I got nervous. When I told
17 Jerry, he said What do you have to be nervous about Im the one whos
18 getting married.

19 I answered well at least i dont have to do that.

20 He laughed and told me. That some day I would and that then It would
21 be his turn to be my usher I just shook my head.

22 That afternoon we went to a rehearsal for the wedding. When I saw
23 what i had to do. I felt less nervous.

24 Everything went according to plan. Except the best man got Judys ring
25 stuck inside of Jerrys and he and Jerry had some trouble getting them
26 apart. I had stopped feeling nervous when the ceremony began and I
27 didn't have any trouble being usher.

28 Everybody said that it was a good omen for Jerrys and Judys marriage
29 that the rings got stuck together I don't know. Whether thats true or not. I
30 just hope nothing like that goes wrong if i ever have my own wedding.

HBJ material copyrighted under notice appearing earlier in this work.

Usage: Unnecessary Words and Letters

The words *of, here,* and *there* sometimes slip into our speech and writing where they do not belong.

had of, off of

NONSTANDARD	If I *had of thought* about it, I would have told you.
STANDARD	If I **had thought** about it, I would have told you.
NONSTANDARD	He took the jacket *off of* the hanger.
STANDARD	He took the jacket **off** the hanger.

off of for from

NONSTANDARD	I got this pen *off of* Jane.
STANDARD	I got this pen **from** Jane.

this here, that there

NONSTANDARD	*This here* question has me stumped.
STANDARD	**This** question has me stumped.
NONSTANDARD	*That there* notebook is mine.
STANDARD	**That** notebook is mine.

EXERCISE A. If a sentence is correct, mark it *C*; if it is incorrect, mark it *I*. Cross out the incorrect word, and write the correct word above it. If the word is unnecessary, simply cross it out. (Add 10 points for each correctly marked sentence.)

.... 1. It is forbidden to dive off of the dock.

.... 2. Does this here wallet belong to you?

.... 3. The motor has been running well.

.... 4. That there remark was very annoying.

.... 5. Reuben fell off of the bridge.

.... 6. I wish you had of warned me.

.... 7. We bought our tickets off of the seller at the gate.

.... 8. That girl over there is my cousin.

.... 9. This here book is exciting.

.... 10. You can get dance tickets off of any sophomore.

Do not add s to words ending in <u>where</u>.

NONSTANDARD	Some*wheres* around here is a melon patch.
STANDARD	Some**where** around here is a melon patch.

HBJ material copyrighted under notice appearing earlier in this work.

Do not add an <u>s</u> to <u>way</u> unless it is plural.

NONSTANDARD Oak Ridge is a long *ways* from here.
STANDARD Oak Ridge is a long **way** from here.
STANDARD There are two **ways** to go.

EXERCISE B. Cross out each error below and write your correction in the blank at the right. If a sentence has no usage error, write *C* (for *correct*) in the blank. (Add 5 points for each correct answer.)

1. That fire must be somewhere near here! . . . .

2. "I can't find *gnat* anywheres in my dictionary." . . . .

3. You hadn't ought to put salt in the sugar bowl. . . . .

4. Kate always walks a short ways with me. . . . .

5. He makes friends everywheres he goes. . . . .

6. Paul seldom behaves as good as he should. . . . .

7. We hadn't ought to eat so much. . . . .

8. It's quite a ways to Portland. . . . .

9. I'll bring my record player to Katje's when I go. . . . .

10. She'll go anywheres the crowd goes. . . . .

Write in the blank the letter of the correct form (*a* or *b*).

11. a. This here animal is a hare. b. This animal is a hare. . . . .

12. a. It fell off of the bed. b. It fell off the bed. . . . .

13. a. We looked everywhere. b. We looked everywheres. . . . .

14. a. Had he ought to go? b. Ought he to go? . . . .

15. a. You sing well. b. You sing good. . . . .

16. a. He wishes you had told him. b. He wishes you had of told him. . . . .

17. a. That there lunch is for you. b. That lunch is for you. . . . .

18. a. It must be somewheres. b. It must be somewhere. . . . .

19. a. I made this here sweater for you. b. I made this sweater for you. . . . .

20. a. An Olympic champion lives somewhere around here. b. An Olympic champion lives somewheres around here. . . . .

HBJ material copyrighted under notice appearing earlier in this work.

Spelling: Always Write *u* after *q*

When you hear the sound /kw/ in a word, you can be sure that it is spelled *qu*. In the English language, the letter *q* is *always* followed by a *u*. Here are some common words containing the sound /kw/:

*qu*iet   fre*qu*ent

*qu*ote   ade*qu*ate

In a few words, all of which are borrowed from French, the letter *qu* have the sound /k/. You must simply memorize such words. Here are some you should know how to spell. Look at them, say them to yourself, and write them.

bou*qu*et   uni*qu*e

cro*qu*et   physi*qu*e

con*qu*er   mysti*qu*e

REMEMBER   Always spell /kw/ with *qu*.

EXERCISE A. In the blank next to each word below, indicate whether the letters *qu* represent the sound /kw/ or the sound /k/. (Add 10 points for each correct answer.)

EXAMPLE acquaint ...*kw*....

1. quality   ..../..../....
2. picturesque   ..../..../....
3. quota   ..../..../....
4. acquire   ..../..../....
5. etiquette   ..../..../....

6. equipped   ..../..../....
7. liquor   ..../..../....
8. quite   ..../..../....
9. equal   ..../..../....
10. conqueror   ..../..../....

EXERCISE B. Write *qu* plus a vowel to complete each word correctly. Listen for the vowel sound that comes after the *qu*. Use the chart "Vowel Sounds and Their Common Spellings" on page 26, if you wish. If you need to do so, consult a dictionary. The definitions in parentheses will help you think of the words. (Add 10 points for each correctly spelled word.)

1. .....z   (a brief test)

2. conse.....nce   (result)

3. anti.....   (very old)

4. .....et   (silent)

5. obli.....   (slanting)

6. .....rantine   (isolation because of contagious disease)

7. delin.....nt   (in violation of the law)

HBJ material copyrighted under notice appearing earlier in this work.

8. co.....tte   (a flirt)
9. .....tation   (someone else's words)
10. con.....red   (defeated)

EXERCISE C. Study all the words taught in this lesson, and be ready to write them from dictation. (Add 4 points for each correctly spelled word.)

REVIEW EXERCISE. Complete each word by writing *k* or *c*, whichever is correct, in the blank. (Add 4 points for each correct answer.)

1. ....idney   14. ....imono
2. ....ube   15. ....adet
3. ....onfess   16. ....ernel
4. ....ettle   17. ....ranberry
5. ....andle   18. ....erosene
6. ....een   19. ....larinet
7. ....ommerce   20. ....lub
8. ....ennel   21. ....ale
9. ....obra   22. ....attle
10. ....angaroo   23. ....iss
11. ....eyboard   24. ....ocoa
12. ....riminal   25. ....ream
13. ....limate

HBJ material copyrighted under notice appearing earlier in this work.

Building Vocabulary: Words to Learn

abject /áb jekt/ *adj*. Brought low in spirit, general condition; contemptible: *The abject poverty of the London slums in the nineteenth century was almost beyond belief.*

allude /ə lúd/ *v*. To refer to something indirectly; to mention without describing fully: *When the man asked if I had been brought up in a barn, he was alluding to my failure to shut the door.*—**allusion**, *n*.

anticipate /an tís ə pāt/ *v*. To look forward to or expect; to do ahead of time: *Priscilla anticipated the outing with pleasure. The waitress had anticipated our order.*—**anticipation**, *n*.

compulsory /kəm púl sər ē/ *adj*. Necessary or required. *School attendance is usually compulsory until the age of sixteen.*

cringe /krinj/ *v*. To crouch or draw back in fear: *The prisoner cringed when he saw the jailer approaching.*

definitive /di fín ə tiv/ *adj*. Final and not likely to be replaced: *The President has not yet made a definitive statement on taxes.*

phenomenal /fi nóm ə nəl/ *adj*. Highly unusual: *Hank Aaron broke Babe Ruth's phenomenal home run record.*

recur /ri kúr/ *v*. To happen, or occur, again; to come to mind again: *The same objections recur every time this question comes up. As Jeff waited for the race to begin, all his old uneasiness recurred.*

seditious /si dísh əs/ *adj*. Inciting public disorder or rebellion against the government: *The British considered the writing of Thomas Paine to be seditious.*

stamina /stám ə nə/ *n*. The strength and vigor needed in any long-continuing activity; endurance: *Long-distance running requires greater stamina than tennis.*

EXERCISE. Fill each blank with the word from this lesson that makes the best sense in the context. (Add 10 points for each correct answer.)

1. After a(n) . . . . run of bad luck and injuries, the team has at last won its first game of the season.

2. If extracurricular activities were made . . . . , we probably would not enjoy them as much.

3. The protesters were charged with . . . . activities, but were soon freed because of insufficient evidence.

4. Ms. Potemkin explained that in the poem the poet . . . . to Artemis, the goddess of the moon in Greek mythology, when he speaks of the Queen of the Night.

5. Mountain climbing probably requires greater . . . . than any other sport, but Annie Peck climbed until the age of eighty-two.

6. Dorothea Dix was horrified by the . . . . conditions mental patients were forced to live under.

7. Before the contest Thelma insisted that she did not . . . . any difficulty in breaking the school athletic record.

8. The pleasant things of the day . . . . to me as I try to go to sleep at night.

HBJ material copyrighted under notice appearing earlier in this work.

9. If you insist on a(n) .... answer immediately, then the answer is "no."

10. The thief .... pitifully when the detective seized him by the shoulder and told him he was under arrest.

REVIEW EXERCISE.   In the space to the left, write the letter of the best meaning for the italicized word. (Add 4 points for each correct answer.)

.... 1. *compassion* for those suffering

.... 2. a *glamorous* profession

.... 3. children often *sulk*

.... 4. an *inflexible* will

.... 5. *atrocious* behavior

.... 6. *subsist* on bread and water

.... 7. *bicker* over money

.... 8. *arduous* duties

.... 9. *isolate* from reality

.... 10. *eccentric* behavior

a. to quarrel in a petty way

b. barely live

c. firm, unyielding

d. odd, peculiar

e. to cut off from contact

f. pity with desire to help

g. requiring hard work

h. savage, wicked

i. act cross

j. attractive, fascinating

Circle *T* for a true statement or *F* for a false one. Your answer will depend on the meaning of the italicized word.

T F 11. You would probably still be hungry after a *bountiful* meal.

T F 12. A *mediocre* player would not be likely to make the school team.

T F 13. A person falsely accused of cheating would feel *indignation*.

T F 14. A *slovenly* appearance makes a good impression on an employer.

T F 15. An *intercepted* message would probably be delivered promptly.

T F 16. A person with good *elocution* is easy to understand.

T F 17. The San Francisco earthquake and fire were a terrible *cataclysm*.

T F 18. We do not expect great *rectitude* in a rabbi or minister.

T F 19. A *discreet* person might be trusted with a secret.

T F 20. Most businesses prefer *incompetent* employees.

T F 21. A large city offers a wide choice of *cultural* activities.

T F 22. To *allege* a fact is to offer proof that it is true.

T F 23. We *condescend* to people we treat as equal.

T F 24. A football team that often loses would be called *invincible*.

T F 25. A person who has *succumbed* to a disease will soon recover.

HBJ material copyrighted under notice appearing earlier in this work.

CHAPTER 11

Sentence Combining

This chapter of ENGLISH WORKSHOP will help you combine short, choppy sentences into longer, smoother sentences. By combining sentences in a variety of ways, you will gain experience in joining closely related ideas, in showing logical relationships, and in adding interest to your writing style.

LESSON **108**

Combining Sentences with Adjectives, Adverbs, and Prepositional Phrases

Combine two or more short, choppy sentences by taking adjectives, adverbs, and prepositional phrases from one sentence and placing them into another.

EXAMPLES   The golfer missed the ball.
The golfer was nervous.

The <u>nervous</u> golfer missed the ball.   (The adjective *nervous* combines with the first sentence.)

The actor spoke the lines.
The actor spoke clearly.

The actor spoke the lines <u>clearly</u>.   (The adverb *clearly* combines with the first sentence.)

The artist drew a sketch.
The artist drew with a pencil.

The artist drew a sketch <u>with a pencil</u>.   (The prepositional phrase *with a pencil* combines with the first sentence.)

You can often combine sentences in different ways.

EXAMPLES   The sun shone on the runners.
The sun was bright and hot.
The sun shone during the race.

During the race the bright, hot sun shone on the runners.
or
The sun, bright and hot, shone on the runners during the race. (Notice how the positions of the adjectives *bright* and *hot* and the prepositional phrase *during the race* can change.)

211

HBJ material copyrighted under notice appearing earlier in this work.

As you combine sentences, notice that the placement of adjectives, adverbs, and prepositional phrases can affect the meaning of what you write.

EXAMPLE   On the way <u>to the bank</u> we saw an armored car.

We saw an armored car on the way <u>to the bank</u>. (The meanings of the two sentences are different.)

Before you complete the following exercise, you may want to review the use of commas with adjectives and introductory words and phrases.

EXERCISE. On the lines provided, combine each of the following sets of sentences into one sentence by using adjectives, adverbs, or prepositional phrases. You may leave out any unnecessary words. (Correct answers may vary. Add 20 points for each correct sentence.)

1. Hopi villages contain many buildings called pueblos.

   The buildings are square. ....

   ....

   ....

2. Hopi tribes have lived in pueblos.

   They have lived in them for more than eight hundred years. ....

   ....

   ....

3. The Hopi tend farms.

   They are skilled and resourceful.

   They tend farms in an extremely harsh climate. ....

   ....

   ....

4. The Hopi grow, spin, and weave cotton into cloth.

   The cotton is from their farms.

   The cloth is beautiful. ....

   ....

   ....

5. A woman rules a Hopi clan.

   She is elderly.

   She rules by tradition. ....

   ....

   ....

HBJ material copyrighted under notice appearing earlier in this work.

Combining Sentences Through Coordination

Combine related elements of two or more sentences by using the conjunction
and, but, or *or.*

EXAMPLES   Mom entered the contest.
Dad entered the contest.

Mom <u>and</u> Dad entered the contest. (*And* joins the two subjects.)

Our team played hard.
Our team still lost the game.

Our team played hard <u>but</u> still lost the game. (*But* joins the two verbs.)

You must keep up your grades.
You will lose the scholarship.

You must keep up your grades, <u>or</u> you will lose the scholarship. (*Or*
joins the two sentences.)

While sentences can often be combined through the use of conjunctions, a
careful writer will never string together ideas that belong in separate sentences.
Joining unequal or unrelated ideas in a single sentence results in *weak
coordination*.

STRONG COORDINATION   The principal told a joke and the students laughed. (*And* joins
two related ideas.)

WEAK COORDINATION   The band plays well and needs new uniforms. (*And* joins two
unrelated ideas.)

Before you begin this exercise, you may want to review agreement of
compound subjects and verbs and the use of commas in compound sentences.

EXERCISE. On the lines provided, combine each of the following pairs of
sentences into one sentence by using conjunctions. Be sure that subject and verb agree
in number in the combined sentence. Add commas where necessary. (Correct answers
may vary. Add 10 points for each correct answer.)

1. Good diet is important for physical fitness.

   Regular exercise is important for physical fitness. ....

   ....

   ....

2. You must exercise your muscles.

   They will begin to weaken. ....

   ....

   ....

3. Food is essential for your body.
   Oxygen is essential for your body. ....
   ....
   ....

4. Your body can store food.
   It cannot store oxygen. ....
   ....
   ....

5. Exercise makes the lungs more efficient.
   It strengthens the heart. ....
   ....
   ....

6. Swimming is an excellent form of exercise.
   Jogging is an excellent form of exercise. ....
   ....
   ....

7. Cycling every day conditions the body.
   Walking every day conditions the body. ....
   ....
   ....

8. Moderate exercise does not cause fatigue.
   Moderate exercise does not damage the heart. ....
   ....
   ....

9. Exercise helps you do more.
   Exercise helps you feel less tired. ....
   ....
   ....

10. Begin an exercise program slowly.
    You could hurt yourself. ....
    ....
    ....

HBJ material copyrighted under notice appearing earlier in this work.

Combining with Appositive Phrases and Participial Phrases

APPOSITIVE PHRASES

An **appositive phrase** is a group of words that explains or identifies a noun or pronoun. It is set off from the rest of a sentence by commas.

EXAMPLE   We talked with Mrs. Peters, <u>the editor in chief</u>.

You can combine short, related sentences by using an appositive phrase.

EXAMPLE   Mary won the school tournament.
She is an excellent tennis player.

Mary, <u>an excellent tennis player</u>, won the school tournament.
(appositive phrase: *an excellent tennis player*)

EXERCISE A. Combine each of the following pairs of sentences into one sentence by using an appositive phrase. Add commas where necessary. (Correct answers may vary. Add 20 points for each correct sentence.)

EX. Blues music is usually sad in tone.
The music is a popular art form. *Blues music, a popular art form, is usually sad in tone.*

1. W. C. Handy published "The Memphis Blues" in 1913.
He was one of the first blues musicians. ....

....

2. Handy also wrote "The St. Louis Blues."
It is perhaps the most famous blues song. ....

....

3. Louis Armstrong was an innovative trumpeter.
He was a famous blues instrumentalist. ....

....

4. Bessie Smith's blues compositions made her famous during the 1920's.
They were simple songs full of power and beauty. ....

....

5. B. B. King continues the blues tradition.
He is a contemporary singer and composer. ....

....

HBJ material copyrighted under notice appearing earlier in this work.

PARTICIPIAL PHRASES

A **participial phrase** is a group of words that begins with a participle* and is used as an adjective to modify a noun or pronoun.

EXAMPLE Edgar wrote a poem *describing a beautiful sunset*.

You can combine short, related sentences by using a participial phrase.

EXAMPLE Frank eluded the tacklers.
He crossed the goal line.

Eluding the tacklers, Frank crossed the goal line. (participial phrase: *eluding the tacklers*)

When it comes at the beginning of a sentence, a participial phrase is followed by a comma.

EXERCISE B. Combine each of the following pairs of sentences into one sentence by using a participial phrase. Add commas where necessary. (Correct answers may vary. Add 20 points for each correct sentence.)

EX. Many blues songs describe disappointments in love.

They are popular. *Many blues songs describing disappointments in love are popular.*

1. Blues music includes odd notes.

   The notes are deliberately played out of tune. ....

   ....

2. Traditional blues lyrics consist of stanzas.

   The stanzas contain three lines each. ....

   ....

3. "The Memphis Blues" was written for a political campaign.

   This song made blues music popular. ....

   ....

4. Blues music has strongly influenced many American composers.

   These composers include George Gershwin. ....

   ....

5. Today there are many rock songs.

   These songs reflect the influence of the blues. ....

   ....

*A *present participle* is a verb form ending in *-ing*. A *past participle* is most often formed by adding *-ed* to the verb.

216

HBJ material copyrighted under notice appearing earlier in this work.

Combining Sentences with Adjective Clauses

An **adjective clause** is a subordinate clause used as an adjective to modify a noun or pronoun. An adjective clause usually begins with a relative pronoun: *who, whom, whose, which,* or *that.*

EXAMPLE   The referee pointed to the player <u>who had committed the foul</u>.

You can often combine two related sentences by changing one of the sentences into an adjective clause and by adding a relative pronoun.

EXAMPLES   Ask the clerk.
The clerk is behind the counter.

Ask the clerk <u>who is behind the counter</u>.

We saw the meteor shower.
The newspaper had predicted the shower.

We saw the meteor shower, <u>which the newspaper had predicted</u>.

Use commas to set off adjective clauses unless the clause specifies "Which one?" and is therefore essential to the meaning of the sentence.

NONESSENTIAL   My bike, which is a ten-speed, has a light frame.   (commas needed)
ESSENTIAL   The driver who ran the stop sign received a ticket.   (no commas)

EXERCISE A.   On the lines provided, combine the following pairs of sentences by changing one sentence into an adjective clause. Add commas where necessary. (Correct answers may vary. Add 10 points for each correct sentence.)

EX.   The sinking of the *Empress of Ireland* was a disaster.

This disaster caused the deaths of more than one thousand people. *The sinking of the Empress of Ireland was a disaster that caused the deaths of more than one thousand people.*

1. The ship was bound for London.

The ship set sail from Quebec on May 28, 1914. . . . .

. . . .

. . . .

2. The ship was traveling downstream.

The ship suddenly encountered a wispy fog near the mouth of the St.

Lawrence River. . . . .

. . . .

. . . .

HBJ material copyrighted under notice appearing earlier in this work.

3. The captain of the *Empress* spotted the lights of another ship.
   The ship was passing nearby. ....

   ....

   ....

4. The captain decided to change direction.
   He had miscalculated the position of the other ship. ....

   ....

   ....

5. Tragically, the other ship changed its direction also.
   This ship was called the *Storstad*. ....

   ....

   ....

6. The freighter *Storstad* knifed into the *Empress of Ireland*.
   The *Storstad* could not stop its momentum. ....

   ....

   ....

7. The collision almost split the *Empress*.
   The ship sank within fifteen minutes. ....

   ....

   ....

8. On board the *Empress of Ireland* were many people.
   They acted with great heroism. ....

   ....

   ....

9. A passenger rescued a young girl by carrying her on his back.
   She could not swim. ....

   ....

   ....

10. One man had also survived the sinking of the ocean liner *Titanic*.
    He was pulled from the water. ....

    ....

    ....

HBJ material copyrighted under notice appearing earlier in this work.

Combining Sentences with Adverb Clauses

An **adverb clause** is a subordinate clause used as an adverb.

EXAMPLE   We cheered <u>when the team won</u>.   (tells *when* we cheered)

You can often combine sentences by changing one of the sentences into an adverb clause and by adding one of the following subordinating conjunctions:

after	as if	before	than	when	wherever
although	as though	if	unless	whenever	while
as	because	since	until	where	

EXAMPLES   We were sleeping.
The storm arrived.

<u>While we were sleeping</u>, the storm arrived.   (The sentence *We were sleeping* has been rewritten as an adverb clause, *while we were sleeping*.)

They will continue trying.
They succeed.

They will continue trying <u>until they succeed</u>.   The sentence *They succeed* has been rewritten as an adverb clause, *until they succeed*.)

Often you may vary the style of your sentences by placing an adverb clause either *in front of* or *after* the main clause.

EXAMPLES   We all went swimming because the day was so hot.
Because the day was so hot, we all went swimming.
(Note the use of the comma after an introductory adverb clause.)

EXERCISE. On the lines provided, combine each of the following pairs of sentences by changing one sentence into an adverb clause. Choose appropriate subordinating conjunctions from the list on this page. Add commas where necessary. (Correct answers may vary. Add 10 points for each correct sentence.)

1. The comedian entertained the audience.

   The stagehands changed the sets. ....

   ....

   ....

2. The assignment was difficult.

   Jules was able to finish in time. ....

   ....

   ....

HBJ material copyrighted under notice appearing earlier in this work.

219

3. Rosa does well in her audition.

   She may receive a part in the play. ....

   ....

4. The athletes began to practice the plays.

   The coach assigned the various positions. ....

   ....

5. Paul learned his routine well.

   He coached the other members of the team. ....

   ....

6. A hush fell upon the study hall.

   The teacher walked into the room. ....

   ....

7. Carla's group will not play at the dance.

   The student government votes money to pay them. ....

   ....

8. Lucy did her homework in the afternoon.

   She wanted to go to the fair in the evening. ....

   ....

9. Francisco was the best artist.

   We asked him to draw the mural. ....

   ....

10. We could not leave on the field trip.

    The buses came. ....

    ....

HBJ material copyrighted under notice appearing earlier in this work.

Combining Sentences with Noun Clauses

A **noun clause** is a subordinate clause used as a noun.

EXAMPLE   This gift is <u>what I wanted</u>.

You can often combine sentences by changing one of the sentences into a noun clause and by using one of these connecting words: *that, what, whatever, where, who, whoever, whom, whomever, why.*

EXAMPLES   You pick someone.

This person will win the nomination.

<u>Whomever you pick</u> will win the nomination.   (The word *someone* in the first sentence has been dropped, and the connecting word has been added to form the noun clause *Whomever you pick*.)

EXERCISE. On the lines provided, combine each of the following pairs of sentences into one sentence. If necessary, choose appropriate introductory words from the list given above. (Correct answers may vary. Add 10 points for each correct sentence.)

EX. We now realize something about the Beatles.

The Beatles changed the course of popular music. *We now realize that the Beatles changed the course of popular music.*

EX. Many teen-agers prefer rock music to all other music.

This preference disturbs some adults. *That many teenagers prefer rock music to all other music disturbs some adults.*

1. The singer told us something about the auditorium.

The auditorium was filled to capacity. . . . .
. . . .
. . . .

2. Someone will win the trophy.

He will have the best batting average in the league. . . . .
. . . .
. . . .

HBJ material copyrighted under notice appearing earlier in this work.

3. Why had the referee made that call?
   The coach wanted to know. ....

   ....

   ....

4. We had put the car keys somewhere.
   We could not remember. ....

   ....

   ....

5. The golfer's ball had gone somewhere.
   The golfer could not discover where. ....

   ....

   ....

6. The actor told us something.
   It was something we wanted to hear. ....

   ....

   ....

7. A person will buy this car.
   That person will have to fix it. ....

   ....

   ....

8. Give the record to someone.
   You decide upon the person. ....

   ....

   ....

9. Solar cells work somehow.
   How they work is baffling to me. ....

   ....

   ....

10. The scene should include a car chase.
    The director insisted. ....

    ....

    ....

HBJ material copyrighted under notice appearing earlier in this work.

Review of Sentence Combining

EXERCISE. Rewrite each of the following groups of sentences by combining choppy sentences into longer, smoother sentences. Use the lines provided. (Correct answers may vary.)

A. Stonehenge is in southern England.

Stonehenge is the ruins of a monument.

The monument is from the Stone Age.

People used this monument.

They used it for performing religious rites.

They used it for observing the stars.

The monument contains a great circle of stone columns.

The columns weigh more than 40 metric tons.

The columns rise 7 meters above the ground.

....

....

....

....

....

....

....

....

....

....

B. Maxine Hong Kingston is an award-winning writer.

She is the daughter of Chinese immigrants.

She grew up in California.

She was influenced by two cultures.

The cultures were American and Chinese.

Some of Kingston's stories feature Fa Mu Lan.

Fa Mu Lan is a woman warrior.

Her deeds depart from Chinese traditions.

HBJ material copyrighted under notice appearing earlier in this work.

....
....
....
....
....
....
....
....
....
....

C. Franck Klusky was a Polish medium.

He claimed a special ability.

He said that he could make people and animals appear out of the air.

One of his apparitions left handprints in a bowl of wax.

The apparition then disappeared.

The handprints were smaller than the hands of any of the witnesses.

These witnesses were present during this strange event.

....
....
....
....
....
....
....
....
....
....

HBJ material copyrighted under notice appearing earlier in this work.

Review of Sentence Combining, Continued

EXERCISE. Rewrite each of the following paragraphs by combining choppy sentences into longer, smoother sentences. Use the lines provided. (Correct answers may vary.)

A. Americans owe much to a Spanish governor of Louisiana. He was Bernardo de Galvez. He gave the patriots guns and supplies. He seized British warships. He did these things during the Revolutionary War. He had French volunteers. He had Indian volunteers. He captured five forts. He tried to drive the British out of Louisiana. He died after the war. He was ministering to the victims of an epidemic. Americans were grateful. They named the city of Galveston in his honor.

....

....

....

....

....

....

....

....

....

....

....

....

B. Nicholas Cugnot was a French artillery captain. He invented the automobile in 1770. It was the first successful automobile. The contraption was ugly. It had three wheels. The wheels were wooden. It resembled a large tricycle. A boiler produced steam. The boiler was coal-fired. The boiler was in front. The steam pushed two pistons. The pistons were on either side of the front wheel. The automobile moved at the speed of four kilometers per hour. This speed included time for stopping. The machine stopped every few hundred meters and regained steam pressure. The

HBJ material copyrighted under notice appearing earlier in this work.

machine slipped on wet roads. The machine had steering problems. Cugnot's success inspired other daring inventors.

. . . .
. . . .
. . . .
. . . .
. . . .
. . . .
. . . .
. . . .
. . . .
. . . .
. . . .

HBJ material copyrighted under notice appearing earlier in this work.

CHAPTER 12

Composition

Effective writing requires careful planning and organization. An organized plan is often called a *process*. The *writing process* consists of prewriting, writing, revising, proofreading, and preparing the final version.

Prewriting is all the thinking you do when you are not actually expressing your ideas. Most prewriting will occur before you begin your first draft; however, you will use prewriting skills throughout the writing process. These skills include: determining your purpose, identifying your audience, gathering information, choosing a limited subject, and ordering facts and ideas.

Writing the first draft will require your using punctuation, grammar, and usage to create sentences and paragraphs that express your ideas clearly. During this stage you will write your thesis statement and develop it through the introduction, body, and conclusion of your composition.

Revising means looking back over your composition to make sure that your sentences and your words best express your ideas. At this stage you will also want to check your facts to be certain that they are correct and are organized to support your ideas clearly.

Proofreading is the stage in which you search through your composition for mistakes in grammar, usage, and mechanics (spelling, punctuation, and capitalization) and make corrections.

Preparing the final version completes the writing process. In this step you will prepare a clean copy of your composition according to correct manuscript form and your teacher's directions.

Although the writing process has five separate stages, you will move back and forth among these stages whenever you are writing. By carefully applying the skills you learn in the writing process, you will be able to organize and present your ideas effectively in a written composition.

LESSON **116**

What Is a Paragraph?

A paragraph is a group of closely related sentences developing one topic.

In this chapter the word *subject* refers to a broad area of knowledge, while the word *topic* refers to a limited subject.

A paragraph may be short or long but it must always stick to just one topic. Writers usually state this topic in the first sentence of a paragraph and then

HBJ material copyrighted under notice appearing earlier in this work.

227

develop it in the remaining sentences. If a sentence is not closely related to the topic, it should be eliminated from the paragraph.

The following paragraph begins by stating the author's delight and excitement at an Indian bazaar. The paragraph then gives details that explain her delight.

AN INDIAN BAZAAR

To me an Indian bazaar is a source of endless delight and excitement. It is usually a series of plain wooden stalls on which are piled, with unconscious artistry, brightly colored fruits, vegetables, spices, gleaming silver jewelry, brilliant silks and cottons or charming, grotesque painted wooden toys. The vendors who can't afford a stall sit on the sidewalk outside the market, their baskets stacked behind them, their wives in vivid cotton saris crouching in the shade, and in front of them are spread carpets of scarlet chillies drying in the sun, small hills of saffron, turmeric, coriander, ginger, cinnamon—all the magical names from the old days of the spice trade with the Indies. With a worn stone mortar and pestle the vendor or his wife will grind your spices for you, blending them according to your particular taste, and weigh them in tiny brass scales strung on twine and balanced delicately in one hand. In all transactions you receive a pleasantly individual attention—nothing is standardized.[1]

All of the sentences in this paragraph are closely related to the topic, the excitement of an Indian bazaar. If the author had decided to end the paragraph with a sentence like "Shopping in a supermarket is easier," the paragraph would have gone off in an entirely different direction, introducing a new topic that has nothing to do with the other sentences.

EXERCISE. In the space provided, write *P* for any sentence group that is a paragraph and *X* for any sentence group that does not contain a series of sentences developing one topic.

1. .... Because people do not pick up after themselves, Jim and I must do it for them. The cart, however, can hold only so much litter. Jim likes sweeping the sidewalk more than picking up bottles. I wish more companies would sell soft drinks in returnable glass bottles. Actually, I do not complain as much as I could.

2. .... Trying to leave school a few minutes early for a game is not simple. You must be very careful not to do anything wrong, or else your teacher will ask you to clean the blackboards. Also, you must be sure that you have not made a date to meet someone right after school. Finally, you must secure your principal's permission to leave before class is officially dismissed.

3. .... Rita told the rest of us girls that her bike runs smoother and faster since she started following a short monthly maintenance routine. First she tightens all loose bolts and nuts and checks to make sure

[1] "Return to India" by Santha Rama Rau. Copyright © 1960 by Santha Rama Rau. Reprinted by permission of William Morris Agency, Inc., on behalf of Santha Rama Rau.

HBJ material copyrighted under notice appearing earlier in this work.

that no parts are bent, broken, or missing. Then she turns her bike upside down, balances it on its seat and handlebars, and lightly oils the chain as she turns the pedals. While she has the wheels sticking up where they are handy, she taps the spokes and tightens any that wiggle. Finally, she puts a few drops of oil on the wheel hubs, brake levers, pedals, and other points that need lubrication. After setting her bike back on its wheels, she finishes her routine by going for a short ride to work the oil into where it will do the most good.

4. .... Most people enjoy a good adventure film. *The Three Musketeers* is an example of a good adventure film. Why, however, do people enjoy science-fiction films? Perhaps they are fascinated by outer space. Some people would probably travel into space if they were given the chance. Is there a recent movie about outer space that has not attracted millions of viewers?

Note: Following most of the lessons in this chapter, you will find directions and hints about using the writing process. Many of these directions and hints will apply to all writing assignments. So, before you begin this lesson's assignment, look through the rest of the chapter to pick up helpful tips that you can begin using right away.

LESSON **117**

Writing the Paragraph: The Topic Sentence

The sentence that states the topic of the paragraph is called the topic sentence. The other sentences in the paragraph develop the idea expressed by the topic sentence.

Read the following paragraph. The topic sentence is italicized. Note how it is developed by the other sentences, each of which adds information concerning the idea expressed in the topic sentence.

AN ASTRONAUT'S TRAINING

The boys' training at the Cape was not so much arduous as tedious. It was sedentary, even. It involved no flying. Some days they would be briefed on launch procedures. Or they would drive out to the launching base and go inside an old converted ratshack hangar, Hangar S, and sit all day in a simulator known as the "procedures trainer," which on the inside was a replica of the capsule they would ride in during flight. Or technically they sat in there all day; in fact, they were lying down. It was as if you took a chair and pushed it over backward so that its back was on the floor and then sat in it.[1]

―――――――――

[1] From *The Right Stuff* by Tom Wolfe. Copyright © 1979 by Tom Wolfe. Reprinted by permission of Farrar, Straus & Giroux, Inc., and International Creative Management.

HBJ material copyrighted under notice appearing earlier in this work.

Paragraph Outline　The simple organization of the preceding paragraph can be shown by a brief outline.

TOPIC　The boredom of an astronaut's training
1. No flying
2. Briefing on procedures
3. Spending day in hangar
4. Sitting all day in training capsule

Before you write a paragraph, jot down a simple outline like this. Following such an outline as you write will make your paragraph clear, and your readers will find it easy to follow your ideas.

EXERCISE.　Underline the topic sentence in each of the following paragraphs. Then in the space provided make an outline of the subtopics of the paragraph, using the outline form shown above.

1. I never call a stupid fellow a "birdbrain" because I know that birds are intelligent. In my backyard I have seen a sparrow pick up a stale crust of bread, fly to the birdbath, and dip the crust into the water in order to soften the food for her young. Across the street is a blue jay that has as much sense as the sparrow. The jay watches a squirrel find nuts, patiently waits until he cracks and starts eating them, and then dives down and snatches a good meal. I remember reading about a sea gull that used similar tactics. Wanting to eat a clam but unable to break its shell, the gull placed the clam behind a parked convertible and dived menacingly at the driver. Finally the annoyed driver backed up, obligingly smashed the clam, and thus provided a tasty meal for the wise bird.

TOPIC: . . . .

1. . . . .

2. . . . .

3. . . . .

2. The changes worked in fine-looking, cleareyed youngsters who adopt the ring as a profession are sometimes shocking to observe. You see them at the start fresh and unmarked, and you live through their gradual disintegration. The knotted ears and the smashed noses are the least of their injuries. Their lips begin to thicken, and their eyes seem to sink deeper and deeper into the cavernous ridges above them, ridges that are thickened and scarred from battle. Many of them acquire little nervous tics. Their voices change to husky, half-intelligible whispers. Some of them go blind. Their walk is affected. Worst of all, sometimes they cannot remember, or they say queer things. The industry laughs and says, "Don't pay attention to him. He's punchy!"[1]

[1] From *Farewell to Sport* by Paul Gallico. Copyright © 1938, renewed 1966 by Paul Gallico. Reprinted by permission of Alfred A. Knopf, Inc.

HBJ material copyrighted under notice appearing earlier in this work.

TOPIC: . . . .

1. . . . .   6. . . . .

2. . . . .   7. . . . .

3. . . . .   8. . . . .

4. . . . .   9. . . . .

5. . . . . 10. . . . .

WRITING ASSIGNMENT. Write a well-organized paragraph of about 100 words explaining a topic. Before writing, make a paragraph outline like the ones you have been making in this lesson. Hand in your outline with your paragraph. Develop a topic of your own choice or select one of the following:

SUGGESTED TOPIC SENTENCES

1. It is great fun to fish (hike, ski) at sunrise.
2. Each of my friends has at least one characteristic that amuses me.
3. Every pet has a distinctive personality.
4. The changes in a teen-ager growing up are sometimes surprising.
5. I have learned how to live on an allowance.
6. A good sport knows how to lose and how to win.
7. History is my favorite subject for three reasons.

Prewriting. As in any composition assignment, write about a subject with which you are familiar. Be certain to limit your subject to a specific topic that you can develop from an organized outline of facts and ideas.

Writing. State your topic sentence in your paragraph, usually at the beginning. Be sure you use complete sentences that are linked by clear transitions.

Revising. Reread your paragraph several times. Examine each sentence to make sure that it presents necessary information and sticks to your topic.

Proofreading. If you can, put your paragraph away for a day or so before you proofread it. Doing that will give you a chance to see it more objectively so that you will be better able to spot mistakes.

Preparing the final version. Here are several manuscript guidelines that are widely used and accepted: (A *manuscript* is any word processed, typewritten, or handwritten paper as distinguished from a document printed on a printing press.)

1. Use lined composition paper or, if you type, white 8½ × 11-inch paper.
2. Write on only one side of a sheet of paper.
3. Write in blue, black, or blue-black ink, or typewrite.
4. Leave a margin of about two inches at the top of a page and margins of about one inch at the sides and the bottom. The left-hand margin must be straight; the right-hand margin should be as straight as possible.
5. Always follow your teacher's instructions for any particular guidelines, such as where to place your name, the class, the date, and the title of your manuscript.

HBJ material copyrighted under notice appearing earlier in this work.

Strong Topic Sentences: A Practice Lesson

A strong topic sentence has a carefully stated and limited topic.

A strong topic sentence prepares the reader for what will follow in the paragraph. It gives the reader clear direction.

Weak topic sentences do not focus on a single limited topic; they do not tell the reader what to expect in a paragraph. Strong topic sentences do the opposite; they focus the reader's attention on a single, clearly limited topic, which can be developed in a paragraph. For example, compare weak and strong topic sentences for the following paragraph outline:

SUBJECT   The delights of acquiring new friends
    1. Talking to new people
    2. Learning how other people live
    3. Introducing new friends to old friends
    4. Helping new friends adjust
    5. Being someone new friends can rely upon

WEAK TOPIC SENTENCES   1. It's fun to acquire new friends.
    2. Acquiring friends is delightful.

STRONG TOPIC SENTENCES   1. Acquiring new friends is an opportunity for personal growth.
    2. New friends can often become a greater source of joy than old friends.

Notice that the strong topic sentences make statements that are more specific than those made in the weak topic sentences. Avoid making generalized statements in your topic sentences. Instead, specify your topic sentence by using precise nouns and verbs, along with adjectives and adverbs that focus on a limited topic you can develop with particular facts and details.

EXERCISE. After each of the following paragraph outlines, write a strong topic sentence for a paragraph based on the outline.

A. SUBJECT: Caring for tropical fish

    1. Outfitting the tank

    2. Keeping the tank clean

    3. Choosing different species of fish

    4. Studying the habits of the fish

Topic sentence: ....
....

HBJ material copyrighted under notice appearing earlier in this work.

B. SUBJECT: Building a tree house

    1. Choosing the right tree

    2. Finding the right place for the house

    3. Locating scrap wood

    4. Gathering additional materials

Topic sentence: ....

....

C. SUBJECT: My first-grade classroom

    1. Participating in activities

    2. Acquiring friends

    3. Paying attention to the teacher

    4. Obeying rules

Topic sentence: ....

....

D. SUBJECT: Swimming in a pool

    1. Obeying the lifeguard

    2. Diving

    3. Using inner tubes and rafts

    4. Swimming long distances

    5. Playing games

Topic sentence: ....

....

E. SUBJECT: The benefits of a sports program

    1. Keeping in good physical shape

    2. Uplifting the emotions

    3. Improving coordination skills

    4. Learning teamwork

    5. Learning from victory or defeat

Topic sentence: ....

....

HBJ material copyrighted under notice appearing earlier in this work.

Writing the Paragraph: Sticking to the Topic

Every sentence in a paragraph should be closely related to the topic.

As you read the following paragraph, observe that the topic is stated in the first sentence and that each of the following sentences is closely related in meaning to the topic.

Unlike any other sport, football is played solely for the benefit of the spectator. If you take the spectator away from any other game, the game could still survive on its own. Thus tennis players love tennis, whether or not anyone is watching. Golfers are almost churlish in their dedication to their game. Ping-Pong players never look around. Basketball players can dribble and shoot for hours without hearing a single cheer. Even baseball might survive the deprivation, despite the lack of parks. Softball surely would. But if you took away the spectators, if you demolished grandstands and boarded up the stadium, it is inconceivable to think that any football would be played in the eerie privacy of the field itself. No football team ever plays another team just for the fun of playing football. Army plays Navy, Michigan plays Purdue, and P.S. 123 plays P.S. 124, only with the prospect of a loud crowd on hand.[1]

Any idea that does not support the topic or that is only vaguely related to it—such as the idea that some wrestlers fight only to please the spectators or that some professional football players earn more money than senators —would, if included, disrupt the unity of the paragraph above. You can write unified paragraphs if you will (1) begin with the topic, (2) stick to it, and (3) eliminate any unrelated idea.

EXERCISE A. Four paragraph outlines are given below. Each outline contains unrelated ideas that should not be included in the paragraph. In the space after each outline, write a topic sentence. Then draw a line through any unrelated ideas, leaving a good paragraph outline, but with the topic sentence below the list of ideas.

EX. Developing a good news story

Interview people involved	~~Friends at the news office~~
Organize material	Research background information
~~Wear the right clothes~~	Check sources

Topic sentence: *The careful reporter follows several steps to develop a story.*

1. Benefits of exercise

Better muscle tone	Improved coordination
Limber body	Inexpensive activity
Difficult exercises	Increased rate of concentration

[1] From "My Crusade Against Football" by Wade Thompson in *The Nation Magazine*, April 11, 1959. Copyright 1959 by The Nation Associates, Inc. Reprinted by permission of the Nations Associates, Inc.

HBJ material copyrighted under notice appearing earlier in this work.

Topic sentence: ....

....

2. Values of a course in public speaking

Increased self-confidence	A hard course .
The teacher of the course	Improved ability to plan a talk
	Course liked by Jack
Improved pronunciation	Easy homework assignments

Topic sentence: ....

....

3. Ways to earn money

Delivering newspapers	Saving money
Mowing lawns	Baby-sitting
Asking parents for more allowance	Washing cars
	Doing volunteer work

Topic sentence: ....

....

EXERCISE B: Each of the following paragraphs contains at least one sentence that is not closely related to the topic of the paragraph, which is expressed in the first sentence. Draw a line through these unrelated sentences. (Some paragraphs contain two or more unrelated sentences.)

1. *It was opening night and I was scared.* I peeked out from behind the curtains and saw the full auditorium. The curtains were a deep purple color and in need of repair. So vividly did my fright heighten my ability to see that I was able to pick out faces I knew from the back row. My aunt and uncle told me last week they would come to the show. My left leg started spasming and my hands became clammy. I knew that at the moment the houselights dimmed and the orchestra started playing I would be all right. Until then I would go through this opening night ritual of sheer fear.

2. *One of the things I like about fishing is the surprises you get when you pull in your line.* I particularly remember one experience in Florida. I sat dozing with my back braced against a gently swaying palm and occasionally catching a redfish. Dad and Mother had gone shopping. In the midst of my daydreaming, I finally noticed that my line, bit by bit, was running out into the blue water of the tropical Atlantic. There were several fishing boats in the distance. Calmly I started to reel in. The line felt exactly as if I had a five-pound rock tied to the hook. When at last I managed to pull in my catch, I found a baby octopus clinging to the end of my line!

3. *It is more fun to go swimming in the ocean surf than in a lake.* The water in a lake is usually still and offers no opposition to you as you swim. The water

HBJ material copyrighted under notice appearing earlier in this work.

in the ocean, however, is always tumbling over in great breakers which try to knock you down and swirl you around. Swimming in a river is likely to be hard because of the current. Otherwise it is very much like swimming in a lake. In the ocean you must be constantly on guard, ready to dive under the waves or fight through them. In a lake you have only to keep afloat. If the fun of constant excitement is what you want, the ocean is the place for you.

WRITING ASSIGNMENT. Write a paragraph giving advice. The advice may be on any subject with which you believe you have had enough experience to set yourself up as an adviser. The list below may be helpful.

SUGGESTED PARAGRAPH SUBJECTS

1. To a younger brother (sister)
2. To a new ninth-grader
3. To a teacher
4. To a new student in junior high
5. To a beginner in tennis (any sport)
6. On playing first base (any position, any sport)
7. To parents
8. On makeup
9. On eating between meals
10. On sunbathing
11. On learning to play the violin (any instrument)
12. On selecting an outfit
13. On buying a camera
14. On appropriate school clothes
15. On dating
16. On going steady
17. On getting a job
18. On buying a bike

Prewriting. To make sure that no unrelated ideas get into your paragraph, make an outline before you begin writing.

Writing. Begin your paragraph with a topic sentence. Be certain that every other sentence is closely related to the topic sentence. (Following a well-organized outline will ensure that all your sentences relate to your topic.)

Revising. With your teacher's permission, try exchanging papers with classmates to find out whether they can spot any unrelated ideas in your paragraph and whether you can spot any in theirs.

Proofreading. As in revising, it is often useful to have someone else look over your paper to help spot mistakes you miss.

Preparing the final version. Write legibly and neatly. If you are using unlined paper, try to keep your sentences straight. Form your letters carefully, so that n's do not look like u's, a's like o's, and so on. Dot the i's and cross the t's. If you are typing, do not strike over letters or cross out words. If you have to erase, do it neatly.

HBJ material copyrighted under notice appearing earlier in this work.

Writing the Paragraph: Developing the Topic Sentence

Experienced writers sometimes put the topic sentence in the middle or at the end of the paragraph. Sometimes they omit it entirely. But you will do well always to put your topic sentence first. Writing it first will help you to keep the other sentences closely related to it. Furthermore, you will naturally proceed to *develop* in your paragraph the idea in the topic sentence.

Developing an idea is different from merely restating it. In a good paragraph the sentences *add* specific information that makes the topic sentence more meaningful.

A paragraph may be developed by specific details, examples, reasons, or incidents that support the topic sentence.

1. Use details to develop a paragraph. Specific details make a paragraph interesting and full of meaning. Generalizations, however, usually make the topic dull and unconvincing. Compare the two paragraphs below.

THE PRAIRIE DOG AND THE RATTLESNAKE

GENERAL *The prairie dog and the rattlesnake are terribly frightened of each other*. The prairie dog is afraid because it knows that the rattlesnake is dangerous. The rattlesnake fears the prairie dog because it attacks in groups. There is evidence that the rattlesnake is more afraid of the prairie dog than of any other burrowing animal.

SPECIFIC *The prairie dog and the rattlesnake are terribly frightened of each other*. The prairie dog fears for its own life if it is a small dog, and if an adult it fears for that of its young, considered a delicacy by the rattlesnake. On the other hand, the rattlesnake will enter the prairie-dog hole for only two reasons: protection from sudden danger, or a meal. The snake has come to know that if he is observed entering a prairie-dog burrow, the dog rallies his neighbors quickly and they furiously set about to block up the entrance of the burrow, thus entombing and killing the rattlesnake. It is interesting to note that if a person throws a bit of dirt down a burrow which a rattler has just entered, the rattler will scurry to the surface in panic. But if the same trick is tried while he is in the hole of any burrowing animal other than the prairie dog, the snake will ignore the trick and will stay calmly underground.[1]

The second paragraph is the better of the two because it is developed in more specific detail.

2. Use examples to develop a paragraph. An example is a definite reference to a specific thing. If you were writing a criticism of the equipment in your school, you might refer to such things as broken window shades,

[1] From "The Prairie Dog" by Lanvil Gilbert, in Texas Folklore Society Publication XXVIII, *Madstones and Twisters*. Reprinted by permission of Southern Methodist University Press.

HBJ material copyrighted under notice appearing earlier in this work.

carved-up desks, and worn-out blackboards. The writer of the following paragraph is commenting on a kind of television comedy that, he suggests, has been overworked. He develops his point humorously with slightly exaggerated *examples* of scenes that recur on many family comedy programs.

FATHER IN TV COMEDIES

A never-failing source of fun is Father's efforts to do minor repairs in the home. He cannot change a fuse without blowing out the lights in the entire neighborhood. If he puts a washer in the kitchen faucet, the shower in the bathroom explodes, flooding the house. There are endless hours of glee in his attempts with a paintbrush, which usually end on a hilarious note as Father falls headfirst into a can of paint. Junior usually comes to the rescue here with an ingenious invention of his own for paint removal, thus proving that his experiments with the chemistry set have not been in vain. The fact that the remover also removes Father's hair and skin is only incidental.[1]

3. Use reasons to develop a paragraph. Whenever you are presenting an opinion or one side of an argument, you give reasons to support or explain your point. Notice that the writer of the following paragraph gives several reasons for his opinion.

ADVANTAGES OF THE RAILROAD

There are several good reasons why the railroads should tackle the short-haul job. Even today they can carry traffic between many of our cities, during peak hours, faster than most of us can drive the same runs in our private cars. The explanation is that the railroads already possess the physical characteristics of any sensible rapid ground-transport system—the rights of way directly connecting our metropolitan centers. Their terminals are far better located than any airport can be. Moreover, excellent studies have shown that a railroad right of way can accommodate twenty times more people than an express highway lane and that it costs only one fifth as much to transport people by rail as by road.[2]

4. Use incidents from your experience to develop a paragraph.
Sometimes a topic sentence can be most effectively developed by telling a brief story, an incident, or an anecdote. As you read the following paragraph, notice that the writer uses a story not merely as an interesting incident but as convincing evidence to support the topic stated in the first sentence.

CHIMPANZEE COMMUNICATION

Since both chimpanzees and baboons are well known for their intelligence, it is not really surprising that to some extent individuals of the two species are able to communicate with each other. One day, for example, a female baboon passed very

---

[1] From "Out on a Limb with Father" by Michael Pine in *Literary Cavalcade*. Copyright © 1965 by Scholastic Inc. Magazine; copyright © renewed 1984. Reprinted by permission of Scolastic Inc.
[2] From "Unsnarling Traffic" by John I. Snyder in *Harper's* Magazine. © 1958 by *Harper's* Magazine. Reprinted by permission of *Harper's* Magazine.

HBJ material copyrighted under notice appearing earlier in this work.

close to Mr. Worzle (a chimpanzee) and seemed to startle him slightly. He raised his arm and gave a soft threat bark, at which she instantly crouched and presented submissively. Mr. Worzle then reached his hand toward her rump and almost certainly touched her in reassurance. At any rate her posture became relaxed and she sat quite close to him. We have seen many other incidents of this sort.[1]

EXERCISE A. First, underline the topic sentence of each paragraph below. Then give the method used to develop the topic: *details, examples, reasons,* or an *incident.*

1. New York is a city of things unnoticed. It is a city with cats sleeping under parked cars, two stone armadillos crawling up St. Patrick's Cathedral, and thousands of ants creeping on top of the Empire State Building. The ants probably were carried up there by the wind or birds, but nobody is sure; nobody in New York knows any more about the ants than they do about the panhandler who takes taxis to the Bowery; or the dapper man who picks trash out of Sixth Avenue trash cans; or the medium in the West Seventies who claims, "I am clairvoyant, clairaudient and clairsensuous."[2]

Developed by . . . .

2. Believe it or else: aerosol sprays are the deadly product X. The propellant gases they release may be a time bomb. Harmless in the air we breathe, these gases slowly rise miles above the earth where years later they apparently attack the ozone, the layer of the upper atmosphere that protects us from the sun's most lethal ultraviolet rays. Without that ozone shield, man could not survive.[3]

Developed by . . . .

3. Yet the French legacy to all of North America is incalculable and far-ranging. You have only to glance at the map, westward from Quebec twelve hundred miles to Duluth (named for Sieur Du Lhut), and then follow the names of the river towns down to Baton Rouge and New Orleans, to see how many places that we take for granted as Yankee establishments were founded by the French. There are many other places whose origin is not so obvious because of the gift of later settlers for fracturing the French names. Marietta, Ohio, was named after Marie Antoinette, and Narbonne turned into Jawbone. And an Irish railroad gang, coming on a lake in Arkansas that the French had named L'eau Froid, struggled a while and left it on the map as Low Freight.[4]

Developed by . . . .

[1] From *In the Shadow of Man* by Jane van Lawick-Goodall. Copyright © 1971 by Hugo and Jane van Lawick-Goodall. Published in Great Britain by William Collins Sons & Co., Ltd. Reprinted by permission of William Collins Sons & Co., Ltd. Houghton Mifflin Company and Collins Publishers.

[2] From *Fame and Obscurity* by Gay Talese. © 1970 by Gay Talese. Published by Harper & Row, Publishers, Inc. Reprinted by permission of Harper & Row, Publishers, Inc.

[3] From "Not With a Bang, But With a Psssssst!" in *New Times* Magazine, March 7, 1975. Reprinted by permission of *New Times* Magazine.

[4] From *Alistair Cooke's America* by Alistair Cooke. Copyright © 1973 by Alistair Cooke. Reprinted by permission of Alfred A. Knopf, Inc.

HBJ material copyrighted under notice appearing earlier in this work.

4. In spite of the exercise of every caution in avoiding inferences and reporting only what is seen and experienced, we all remain prone to error, since the making of inferences is a quick, almost automatic process. We may watch a car weaving as it goes down the road and say, "Look at that *drunken driver*," although what we *see* is only *the irregular motion of the car*. The writer once saw a man leave a one-dollar tip at a lunch counter and hurry out. Just as the writer was wondering why anyone would leave so generous a tip in so modest an establishment, the waitress came, picked up the dollar, put it in the cash register as she punched up ninety cents, and put a dime in her pocket. In other words, the writer's description to himself of the event, "a one-dollar tip," turned out to be not a report but an inference.[1]

Developed by ....

EXERCISE B. Each of the following topic sentences may be developed by at least one of the methods described in this lesson. Decide which method you would use to develop the topic, and write it on the *final* line. Then, on the lines below each sentence, list the details, examples, or reasons, or write a note summarizing a story which you would use to develop the topic.

1. I have several ambitions in life, not just one. ....

....

....

....

Developed by ....

2. Sometimes ....is very annoying...................

....

....

....

Developed by ....

3. Homework should not be assigned over a vacation. ....

....

....

....

....

Developed by ....

[1] Adapted excerpt from "Reports, Inferences, Judgments" in *Language in Thought and Action,* Fourth Edition, by S. I. Hayakawa. Copyright © 1978 by Harcourt Brace Jovanovich, Inc. Published by Harcourt Brace, Jovanovich, Inc. Reprinted by permission of Harcourt Brace Jovanovich, Inc.

HBJ material copyrighted under notice appearing earlier in this work.

4. I prefer life in the country (city) to life in the city (country). . . . .

. . . .

. . . .

. . . .

. . . .

Developed by . . . .

WRITING ASSIGNMENT. From the four paragraphs outlined above, choose the one you think you could develop best. Write the topic sentence first. Then develop the topic, using the material from your outline. Write 100-150 words.

WRITING ASSIGNMENT. Select one of the following as a topic sentence and develop it, using at least 100 words. In parentheses are suggested methods and prewriting questions for developing ideas about each topic. If you wish, you may change the wording of the sentence you choose.

1. Observing the faces of people while walking down the street can be an interesting experience. (*Details:* What can you tell about the people you see? What do you imagine each person does? Have you ever been proven wrong in your judgment?)
2. At times I act as though I am superstitious. (*Examples:* When do you act superstitious? Exactly what do you do? Can you present three particularly interesting actions?)
3. Everyone should have a hobby. (*Reasons:* Why is a hobby desirable? In what ways does it contribute to a person's happiness?)
4. I have difficulty making friends with other people's pets. (*Incident:* Which one of your experiences can best illustrate this statement? What did you do to make friends? How did the pet respond?)
5. If people keep calm during a severe storm (tornado, hurricane, blizzard), they can avoid getting hurt. (*Incident:* What is an incident that can prove the topic? How did a calm person avoid injuries in a particular storm? What exactly happened?)
6. I don't (do) like diving. (*Reasons:* What thoughts flash across your mind as you stand on the end of a diving board? What do you dislike (like) about diving: the height of the board, the apparent solidity of the water, hitting the cold water?)
7. A television set is an idiot box. (*Reasons:* Why exactly is a television set an idiot box? Why would only an idiot watch certain programs? Why do you think some television characters behave like idiots?)
8. A television set is a wonderful teaching machine. (*Reasons:* Why is television a better teacher than a lecturer or a textbook? Why do television fans learn more in front of television sets than they do in classrooms? Why do they remember what they learn?)
9. Homesickness can be a miserable illness. (*Story:* What do you remember about one of your most severe attacks of homesickness? How was it a miserable experience? What happened? What did you think, feel, do?)
10. Almost anything can be a miracle. (*Examples:* What are a half-dozen things that could be considered miracles? Could such things as a sunrise or a flower be looked upon as a miracle? Do any other "ordinary" occurrences at times appear especially wonderful?)

HBJ material copyrighted under notice appearing earlier in this work.

WRITING ASSIGNMENT. Choose one of the following topic sentences, make an outline, and then write a unified, interesting, well-developed paragraph of at least 100 words.

1. Doubting your own ability can be a serious handicap.
2. I prefer swimming in a lake to swimming in the ocean.
3. Although you may not know it, I am really a wonderful person.
4. In the near future a solution will have to be found to the problem of feeding all the hungry people in the world.
5. I think it is very important (not very important) for the United States to maintain its military superiority.
6. Many people have recurring dreams that trouble them.
7. If I ever write books, they will be tales of science fiction (adventure, romance, etc.).
8. A cartoon can often make a point quicker than an essay.
9. I never have trouble writing, but once the writing becomes an assignment, my mind becomes blocked.
10. One day I would like (not like) to throw my hat into the political arena.

Prewriting. To generate facts and ideas about your topic, try asking the 5 W-How? questions: Who? What? When? Where? Why? How? Who is affected by my topic? Who uses my topic? What makes up my topic? What does my topic mean? When is my topic useful? When did my topic begin? Where is my topic popular? Where is my topic used? Why is my topic important? Why does my topic look or act as it does? How does my topic work? How is my topic used?

Writing. Some writers find it useful to say their ideas out loud and then copy down what they have said. Write complete sentences and try to make them as correct as possible, but remember: this is only your first draft. The important thing at this stage is to get your ideas clearly stated in writing. You will be going back over your paragraph during the next two stages of the writing process to make corrections and improvements.

Revising. When you read your paragraph, be critical. Ask yourself: Do these ideas make sense? Could someone who is not as familiar as I am with these ideas understand what I have written? Could I choose any better words to make my paragraph clearer? Have I left out any information?

Proofreading. Check your capital letters to make sure that they cannot be mistaken for lower case letters.

Preparing the final version. Be sure you have written your paragraph's title, your name, and any other information required by your teacher on your paper.

HBJ material copyrighted under notice appearing earlier in this work.

Arranging Ideas in a Paragraph

Achieve coherence in a paragraph by arranging details in chronological order, spatial order, or order of importance.

Paragraphs in which sentences flow smoothly and naturally from one to another are said to have *coherence*. One of the best ways to achieve coherence is through a clear arrangement of ideas.

When you are writing about how to make or do something, such as how to build a campfire or how to somersault, organize the steps of the process in the order in which they must be carried out. This is called *chronological,* or *time, order*. Chronological order is also useful in story writing. The following example of chronological order is a brief story about an after-dinner walk. Words that help indicate chronological order are underlined.

A SUNSET IN ETHIOPIA

After our meal we went for a stroll across the plateau. The day was already drawing to a close as we sat down upon a ledge of rock near the lip of the western precipice. From where we sat, as though perched high upon a cloud, we looked out into a gigantic void. As we sat, the sun sank fast, and the heavens in the western sky began to glow. It was a coppery fire at first, the orange streaked with aquamarine; but rapidly the firmament expanded into an explosion of red and orange that burst across the sky sending tongues of flame through the feathery clouds to the very limits of the heavens. When the flames had reached their zenith, a great quantity of storks came flying from the south. Then, gathering together, they flew off into the setting sun, leaving us alone in peace to contemplate. The sun died beyond the hills; and the fire withdrew.[1]

It is sometimes useful to describe something or to tell a story by organizing details according to their position in space: left to right, back to front, etc. The following paragraph uses *spatial order* to help achieve coherence.

THE STUDY

I worked at a commodious green-topped table placed directly in front of the west window which looked out over the prairie. In the corner at my right were all my books, in shelves I had made and painted myself. On the blank wall at my left the dark, old-fashioned wallpaper was covered by a large map of ancient Rome, the work of some German scholar. Cleric had ordered it for me when he was sending for books from abroad. Over the bookcase hung a photograph of the Tragic Theater at Pompeii, which he had given me from his collection. When I sat at work I half-faced a deep, upholstered chair which stood at the end of my table, its high back against the wall.[2]

[1] From *Sanamu: Adventures in Search of African Art* by Robert Dick-Read. Copyright © 1964 by Robert Dick-Read. Reprinted by permission of A. P. Watt Ltd.

[2] From *My Antonia* by Willa Cather. Copyright 1918, 1926, 1946 by Willa Sibert Cather; copyright 1954 by Edith Lewis; renewed 1977 by Walter Havighurst. Reprinted by permission of Houghton Mifflin Company.

HBJ material copyrighted under notice appearing earlier in this work.

243

When a paragraph states reasons, they may be arranged in logical order: from the least to the most important reason or from the most to the least important reason. Reasons arranged in their order of importance are easier for the reader to follow.

In the following paragraph, the author lists the destructive effects of acid rain, from the least important effect (holes in nylon stockings) to the most important effect (the death of freshwater fish).

ACID RAIN

Acid rain is very destructive. It eats holes in nylon stockings and corrodes stone and metal buildings. The marble Lincoln Memorial in Washington D.C. has been severely damaged by the fallout of acid pollutants. Acid rain also threatens many types of living things, particularly fish in freshwater lakes. In many lakes in the Northeast, salmon and trout have vanished. Restocking the lakes with new fish has been largely useless.

Occasionally a writer may arrange details by more than one method. For example, a paragraph about tornadoes may focus on the creation of tornadoes (chronological) and the shape of tornadoes (spatial).

EXERCISE. In the space provided, write C (for chronological), S (for spatial), and I (for order of importance) to show which method is best for developing each subject. Choose only one method for each subject.

1. . . . . Steps in baking a cake

2. . . . . A baseball stadium

3. . . . . Redecorating a room

4. . . . . The qualities of a friend

5. . . . . Cleaning out the garage

6. . . . . How to prepare for a test

7. . . . . A school activity

8. . . . . How to fix a desk lamp

9. . . . . Plans for the future

10. . . . . How to play basketball

WRITING ASSIGNMENT. Write one paragraph using one of the topics in the preceding exercise or a topic of your own choice. Arrange the details, examples, or reasons in your paragraph chronologically, spatially, or in order of importance.

Prewriting. Take the time to set down your pen, sit back, and think about your topic for a few minutes before you write anything.

Writing. In addition to choosing the right word, choose the right punctuation to present your facts and details clearly.

Revising. Eliminate all repetitive statements. Do not use the same word repeatedly; instead, find synonyms and alternate phrasings.

Proofreading. Be sure that all letters and marks of punctuation are clearly written and cannot be mistaken for other marks and letters.

Preparing the final version. Be sure you have clearly marked any changes you have made.

HBJ material copyrighted under notice appearing earlier in this work.

Using Transitional Devices

Transitional devices are connecting words or phrases that show the relationships between details, examples, or reasons in a paragraph.

Transitional devices help to connect sentences and to show the arrangement of a paragraph. The following list contains some of the most common transitional devices.

ADDITION: and, then, likewise, further, also, too, besides, in addition, next, another, furthermore

COMPARISON: similarly, likewise, in the same way, as if, in comparison, more (most) important, just as, equally as

CONTRAST OR ALTERNATIVE: but, yet, however, nor, even though, nevertheless, despite, on the contrary, although, instead, rather, except, on the other hand

POSITION: here, beside, there, opposite to, where, under, around, above, below, first (second, third, . . .)

ORDER OR TIME: as, meanwhile, at the same time, soon, now, later, afterward, in the past, before, as soon as, then, last

CAUSATION: for, for this reason, since, because, so that, if, unless, until, through, whether, whenever

RESULT: hence, therefore, accordingly, so, consequently, due to, thus, then, as a result, owing to, because of

SUMMARY: in conclusion, altogether, in brief, in short, in other words, finally

EXAMPLE: such as, specifically, to illustrate, in fact, for example, for instance, in this case, namely

Note: Some transitions fall under more than one category; for example, last could be used to show position or order or to introduce a summary. When you consult the above list, look through several categories before deciding upon a transitional word or phrase.

In the following paragraph transitional devices are underlined. The author uses them to arrange the details of his paragraph chronologically.

A KITTEN AT PLAY

A kitten is playing with its classical plaything, a ball of wool. Invariably it begins by pawing at the object, first gently and inquiringly with outstretched forearm and inwardly flexed paw. Then, with extended claws, it draws the ball toward itself, pushes it away again, or jumps a few steps backward, crouching. It lies low, raises its head with tense expression, glaring at the plaything. Then its head drops so suddenly that you expect its chin to bump the floor. The hind feet perform peculiar, alternately treading and clawing movements as though the kitten were seeking a firm hold from which to spring. Suddenly it bounds in a great semicircle and lands on its toy with stiff forepaws, pressed closely together. It will even bite it, if the game has reached a pitch of some intensity. Again it pushes the ball, and this time it rolls under a cupboard which stands too close to the floor for the kitten to get underneath. With an elegant "practiced" movement, it reaches with one arm into the space and fishes its play-

HBJ material copyrighted under notice appearing earlier in this work.

thing out again. It is <u>at once</u> clear to anyone who has ever watched a cat catching a mouse, that our kitten, which we have reared apart from its mother, is performing all those highly specialized movements which aid the cat in the hunting of its most important prey—the mouse. In the wild state, this constitutes its "daily bread."[1]

WRITING ASSIGNMENT. Use the following paragraph outline or one of your own to write a paragraph in which transitional devices help connect the sentences. Underline the transitional devices in the paragraph you write.

TOPIC Preparing for a long-distance run
  1. Selecting proper equipment
  2. Eating the right foods
  3. Choosing a course
  4. Stretching muscles

Prewriting. As you organize your facts and ideas, pay close attention to how they are related. Do facts contradict each other? If so, plan a transition to show contrast. Are facts and ideas linked together by cause and effect? If so, plan for transitions that show causation and result. Does an idea summarize facts and information? If so, plan a transition to indicate where the summary begins or where the facts are placed as examples.

Writing. Most transitions require careful placement in the sentence. Be sure that your transitions clearly show the relationship(s) you are trying to express.

Revising. As you look over your paragraph, be sure you have included all the information needed to establish similarities, differences, and other relationships among your facts and ideas.

Proofreading. In addition to careful placement, transitions also require careful punctuation. Consult the sections in your text dealing with parenthetical expressions, introductory clauses and phrases, connectives, and other lessons on comma usage.

Preparing the final version. Whenever you have more than one page, number all pages after the first one. Page numbers are usually placed in the center of the top line or in the upper right-hand corner. Number your pages according to your teacher's instructions.

[1] From "On Feline Play" in *Man Meets Dog* by Konrad Lorenz. Copyright 1953 by Konrad Lorenz; copyright renewed 1983 by Konrad Lorenz, Marjorie Kerr Wilson and Annie Eisenmenger. Reprinted by permission of Houghton Mifflin Company, and Konrad Lorenz.

HBJ material copyrighted under notice appearing earlier in this work.

Writing an Expository Paragraph That Gives Information

An expository paragraph may give information about something by presenting facts, examples, or reasons.

You have already learned the principles of organizing an expository paragraph. It should state its topic clearly, it should be arranged in logical order, and it should contain transitional devices to join sentences and to make the arrangement clear.

The following expository paragraph gives information about tsunamis (tsōō-nä′mē), or tidal waves. Notice that the writer develops the paragraph by means of examples.

TSUNAMIS

Topic
Sentence

Examples
(1–3)

Tsunamis have an extraordinary range.[1] In 1833, for example, when volcanic explosions destroyed Krakatoa, an island between Java and Sumatra, seismic waves traveled all around the world.[2] A 1946 earthquake in the Aleutian trench caused a wave that did great damage when it hit the Hawaiian Islands some 2,200 miles away.[3] The wave that followed the 1964 Good Friday Alaska quake wrought considerable destruction on the Oregon and northern California coasts, including the death of a family camping overnight on an Oregon beach.*

The following topic outline could serve for the model paragraph.

SUBJECT   The range of tsunamis
1. Waves from 1833 Krakatoa explosion
2. Wave from Aleutian trench to Hawaiian Islands
3. Wave after 1964 Alaska quake

WRITING ASSIGNMENT. Use the following list of information to write an expository paragraph. Begin your paragraph with a topic sentence. Arrange the information in logical order. (Be sure to use complete sentences.)

Five planets visible to the naked eye: Mars, Venus, Mercury, Saturn, Jupiter
The order of these planets, by distance from the Sun: Mercury (closest), Venus, Mars, Jupiter, Saturn
The brightest of these planets: Venus
The smallest of these planets: Mercury
The largest of these planets: Jupiter
The least bright of these planets: Saturn
The planet most often thought to support life: Mars

*From p. 227 in *More Misinformation* by Tom Burnam. Copyright © 1980 by Tom Burnam. Published by Lippincott/Crowell. Reprinted by permission of Harper & Row, Publishers, Inc.

HBJ material copyrighted under notice appearing earlier in this work.

WRITING ASSIGNMENT. Using one of the lists provided, write an expository paragraph that conveys information. If you wish, you may prepare your own list to work with.

A. Basic Basketball Maneuvers
1. dribbling
2. the tip-off
3. passing
4. shooting
5. the lay-up
6. the dunk

B. Television Favorites
1. movies
2. personalities
3. different kinds of shows
4. commercials
5. reruns
6. music videos

Prewriting. When developing a paragraph from categories like those above, be sure that you limit your topic sufficiently so that you can cover it in the space you have. Remember that you will want to use specific facts and details to illustrate and support your topic, which should be stated in a single sentence.

Writing. As you develop the notes in your outline, be sure that you use conjunctions and other transitions to create varied sentences that are informative and interesting. Compound and compound-complex sentences usually require careful punctuation. Pay special attention to the proper use of commas, semicolons, and other marks used to connect phrases and clauses.

Revising. Here is a sample revised paragraph with the revisions marked to help you recognize how and why to revise your own paper.

THE TWO HAMMERS THAT EVERY FRAMING CARPENTER NEEDS

Every framing carpenter needs at least two hammers. A curved-claw hammer and a straight-calw hammer are both necessary. Curved-claw hammers weigh sixteen ounces and are used for most nailing chores and for pulling bent nails. Straight-claw hammers weigh 20 ounces, which are used for other kinds of nailing jobs such as driving cement nails and roofing and for breaking up hard substances like concrete and other stuff. Sometimes carpenters need additional special hammers, too. Like tack hammers, ballpeen hammers, sledge hammers, or different kinds of mallets. However, Even these jobs requiring special hammers can be done with curved-claw and straight-claw hammers, although using an unsuitable But the wrong hammer can make it more difficult — careful, precise work harder to do a good job.

Proofreading. One good way to proofread is to cover your paragraph with a sheet of paper, then move the paper down line by line and read each sentence backward and forward. Doing this will help you catch misspellings, missing words, and other common mistakes.

Preparing the final version. Before handing in your final version, always read it over one last time to make sure that you have not made any errors while recopying.

HBJ material copyrighted under notice appearing earlier in this work.

Writing an Expository Paragraph That Explains

An expository paragraph may explain a process, or how something works.

When you tell someone how to sharpen a knife or how to prepare a recipe, you are explaining a process. To write an effective explanation of a process, you must be sure to include all the essential steps in their correct order. Transitional expressions, such as *first, next,* and *finally,* help to make this order clear.

The following paragraph explains the process of baking cornbread in a Dutch oven. Its steps are arranged chronologically, which is the order most often used to explain a process.

BAKING CORNBREAD

Steps Arranged In Chronological Order (1–7)
　　　Dutch ovens were usually used for baking bread and biscuits, but they could also be used for baking cakes and potatoes, roasting meats, and heating soup and stew. Here's how to bake cornbread in one. ¹Preheat the oven and the lid on the coals. ²Then carefully grease the whole inside of the oven with a piece of pork rind. ³Mix up the batter by combining two cups of cornmeal, one cup of flour, one cup of buttermilk, and a spoonful of salt and soda. ⁴Sprinkle a handful of cornmeal on the sides and bottom inside the oven so the bread won't stick, and then pour the batter in, making sure the oven is level so the bread will be the same thickness all around. ⁵Using some tongs, place the lid on the oven and cover it with hot coals. ⁶The bread will be ready in fifteen to twenty minutes depending on how hot the coals are. ⁷It can be slid out by removing the lid and tipping the oven, or it can be cut right in the oven and taken out with a fork or large spoon.*

WRITING ASSIGNMENT. Rearrange the following list of information into a logical order. Then, write an expository paragraph that explains the process that it outlined.

Honey is made from nectar, which bees gather from different plants and flowers.
Honey is taken from the hive by beekeepers.
Bees store honey in wax cells in the hive.
Nectar changes into honey through enzyme action in the bodies of bees.
The honey ripens in the hive and thickens because of evaporation.

*Excerpt from *The Foxfire Book* edited by Eliot Wigginton. Copyright © 1968, 1969, 1970, 1971, 1972 by The Foxfire Fund, Inc. Reprinted by permission of Doubleday & Company, Inc.

HBJ material copyrighted under notice appearing earlier in this work.

WRITING ASSIGNMENT. Using one of the subjects below or one of your own, write an expository paragraph that explains a process.

How to fix a flat tire

How to keep score in tennis

How to fly a kite

How to repot plants

How to carve a pumpkin for Halloween

How to apply for a job

Prewriting. Begin by limiting your topic to a process that you can fully describe in one paragraph. Create your topic outline by noting down each step in the process, including any necessary materials or special instructions. Be sure to define any tems your audience might not know.

Writing. Use transitional words and phrases to link together the steps of the process in any easy-to-follow sequence. Make sure that your wording is precise so that your audience will not have any difficulty completing the process successfully.

Revising. Here is a process explanation with its parts and transitions marked to help you recognize how they are interrelated.

GET THE BEST DEAL

Introduction   Whether you are buying a radio, a shirt, or a new car, you can get the

Transition signalling first step   best deal by following these simple steps. First, know what you want and how much you want to spend. If you don't know these two things, you may likely spend more than you wish or you should for something you don't

Transition signalling second step   want. Next, shop around and compare prices. You can save time doing this by using the telephone. If you can wait, watch the newspaper aand other sources for sales and specials, which usually change daily and weekly.

Transition signalling third step   Last, try not to buy something without thinking it over first. Sometimes, you may have to act quickly to get a good deal, but in most cases you can take at least a few hours to talk to others and to reconsider the purchase.

Conclusion   Making wise purchases will pay off: You will save money, giving you more money to buy other things, and you will not waste your money on things you do not want or need.

Proofreading and *Preparing the final version.* Look at each individual word and mark of punctuation as you proofread. If you have any doubt about the correctness of what you have written, check your textbook or some other authority. Take your time to recopy your paper as neatly as possible.

HBJ material copyrighted under notice appearing earlier in this work.

Writing a Persuasive Paragraph

A persuasive paragraph presents an argument that leads its audience to change a position or to take some course of action.

The argument in a persuasive paragraph begins with a topic sentence that states a debatable opinion. Self-evident or generally accepted opinions (such as, a good diet is healthful) and personal preferences (such as, I like ice cream better than pie) are not debatable and, therefore, are not suitable for development in a persuasive paragraph.

The body of a persuasive paragraph contains a series of several logically related reasons that support the stated opinion with convincing facts and information. The persuasive paragraph ends with a clincher sentence that summarizes the stated opinion and often suggests a course of action.

The following persuasive paragraph argues that conditions in contemporary life have caused an increase in the use of clichés. The first sentence introduces the author's opinion, which is supported by several sentences of evidence. The last sentence clinches the argument by tying together the supporting evidence and the stated opinion.

> Topic Sentence — Our speech is probably more crammed with clichés today than ever before. The torrent of printed and recorded matter that is dumped on us every hour in the newspapers and from radio and television is bound to be repetitious and stereotyped. The brightest, gabbiest day in the world's history never produced one millionth, in fresh, original, and honest expression, of the bulk of what cascades over us every day. All of this stuff is of necessity
> Clincher Conclusion — prepared in furious haste. There is neither time nor energy for care or thought and the inevitable result is a huge heap of clichés.*

WRITING ASSIGNMENT. Choose one of the following subjects or a subject of your own and limit it by stating your opinion about it. Then, write a persuasive paragraph that develops an argument supporting your opinion.

1. The 55-mile-an-hour speed limit
2. State lotteries
3. Movie ratings
4. Being paid for good grades
5. Curfews
6. Non-cigarette-smoker's rights
7. Mandatory physical education
8. Leash laws for pets

Prewriting. When you are noting information to support your argument, keep in mind opposing views that you may want to refute. Generally, you will want to organize your supporting information with your strongest reason given either last, so that it will linger in your audience's mind, or first, so

---

*From "The Road to Vulgarity," by Bergen Evans in *Harper's Bazaar*, September 1957. Reprinted by permission of Jean W. Evans.

HBJ material copyrighted under notice appearing earlier in this work.

that it will catch your audience's attention. Make sure that your reasons for your argument do not simply restate your opinion. Instead, give facts and details that differ from the topic sentence and from each other.

Writing. Be careful that you do not word your opinions as facts or your factual evidence as opinions. The verbs *should, ought to*, and *can* are used to express opinions. Adjectives that state judgments, like *good, bad, ridiculous, excellent, wonderful, worthless*, and *disgusting*, also express opinions. Factual support generally comes from objective information, which does not express personal feelings. If additional supporting information occurs to you while you are writing, pause a moment to determine if it will provide stronger evidence for your argument. If it does, insert it wherever it will logically fit.

Revising. Read your paper over, criticizing as you go. Ask yourself: Is this argument complete? Does it make sense? Will it convince my audience that my position is correct? If you have any doubts about your argument, try rearranging the order of your ideas and information. Eliminate wordy constructions and unnecessary information. Streamline your argument so that your audience can follow it with little difficulty. A serious, logical, objective tone is generally the most convincing way to present your argument. Therefore, avoid using slang, emotional appeals, and other informalities.

Proofreading and *Preparing the final version.* As you reread your paragraph several times, focus each reading on a different aspect, such as spelling, punctuation, or usage. Your final version should be clean, without smudges or stray marks on the page, as well as correct and interesting.

HBJ material copyrighted under notice appearing earlier in this work.

Choosing Effective Nouns and Verbs

Your assignment in this lesson will be to write a story. In stories your choice of nouns and verbs is especially important. Writers of uninteresting stories often use many vague nouns and weak (usually linking) verbs to talk *about* settings, characters, and actions. Writers of good stories use vivid nouns and strong action verbs to make the readers *see* the settings and the characters' actions.

As you read and compare the following groups of sentences, notice especially the difference that vivid nouns and action verbs make in presenting (1) a setting, (2) characters, and (3) an action.

1

DULL   He stopped his horse at the stream and looked across. He observed the trees. Then he looked at the fields beside the stream, where vegetables grew.

VIVID   He stopped his horse at the stream and sat looking across the narrow ribbon of water to the bare-branched peach trees. He was seeing them each springtime with their age-gnarled limbs transfigured beneath veils of blossom pink; he was seeing them in autumn laden with their yellow fruit, small and sweet. Then his eyes searched out the indistinct furrows of the fields beside the stream, where each year the corn and beans and squash drank thirstily of the overflow from summer rains.[1]

2

DULL   People who had been pleasant became sad. Douglas tried but could not eat the food, nor could Tom and Dad. People just did not like the food.

VIVID   Smiling people stopped smiling. Douglas chewed one bite of food for three minutes. He saw Tom and Dad do the same. People swashed the food together, making roads and patterns, drawing pictures in the gravy, forming castles of the potatoes, secretly passing meat chunks to the dog.[2]

3

DULL   The signal from the pitcher was clear. I was ready to catch a ball at least two feet outside the plate, but when he threw the ball, I was surprised.

VIVID   He called that he was going to throw a fast-breaking curve and warned me to expect the ball at least two feet outside the plate. Then he wound up and let it go, and that ball came whistling right down the groove for the center of the plate.[3]

[1] From ''Chee's Daughter'' in *Wood to Burn* by John W. White.
[2] From *Dandelion Wine* by Ray Bradbury. Published by Curtis Publishing Co.
[3] From *Farewell to Sport* by Paul Gallico. Copyright 1938, renewed 1966 by Paul Gallico. Reprinted by permission of Alfred A. Knopf, Inc.

HBJ material copyrighted under notice appearing earlier in this work.

Vivid, specific nouns and verbs are better than vague ones.

Notice the specific words (in italics) that can be substituted for the following very general nouns and verbs.

1. say—*whisper, mumble, shriek, bark, grunt, bluster*
2. move—*flit, drift, rush, shuffle, slide, jog, sway*
3. music—*jazz, waltz, lullaby, psalm, polka, ditty*

A vivid, specific verb is usually better than an ordinary verb modified by an adverb.

In the following pairs, notice that the single verb at the right is more effective than the verb-adverb combination at the left. It describes the action more forcefully.

VERB-ADVERB	VERB
1. looked steadily	stared
2. walked slowly, carelessly	strolled
3. cried loudly	howled
4. cooked noisily	sizzled

A vivid, specific noun is usually better than an ordinary noun modified by an adjective.

Again, notice that the single noun at the right is more effective than the adjective-noun pair. It calls up a single, precise picture.

NOUN-ADJECTIVE	NOUN
1. flat-bottomed, clumsy rowboat	scow
2. large, unruly crowd	mob
3. rapid, rushing river	torrent
4. sharp, short answer	retort

EXERCISE A. List at least five specific words that could be substituted for each vague word below.

1. eat: . . . .

2. a message: . . . .

3. go: . . . .

4. a building: . . . .

5. take: . . . .

HBJ material copyrighted under notice appearing earlier in this work.

EXERCISE B. On a separate sheet of paper, rewrite each of the following sentences, replacing ineffective words with more vivid ones.

1. The young man raised the window, took a worn, brightly colored square of cloth from his pocket, and moved it vigorously back and forth.

2. She put up her hands, took the ball out of the hands of the intended receiver, and went across the goal line.

3. Cars were going rapidly past us and noisily going around the sharp turn beyond.

4. Jimmy swam noisily into midstream, and then he called frantically that a big fish was after him.

5. A group of jet planes passed rapidly and noisily overhead and went quickly out of sight.

WRITING ASSIGNMENT. Write a story of at least 150 words about an experience you have had that would be interesting to others.

The following list of topics may help you think of an experience that you would enjoy writing about.

1. The time I played the hero
2. A blabbermouth keeps a secret
3. Searching for a ghost
4. Just good luck?
5. A dog chooses me
6. My kid brother at the zoo
7. Nobody laughed
8. A false alarm
9. Was my face red!
10. The day I appeared on TV
11. Laws should be obeyed
12. I'll never be the same again
13. The funniest sight I ever saw
14. I had to take the blame
15. The time I took charge
16. Spending my first allowance
17. The longest hour of my life
18. My secret ambition
19. Overcoming a handicap
20. Someone who influenced me

Prewriting. Limit your story to a single incident. For example, you might choose to write about what you did at camp. Since you could not present in 150 words all of your experiences, you would need to limit your story to only one experience—such as taking an overnight canoe trip or winning a swimming meet. Decide upon the *purpose*, or one main effect (amusement,

HBJ material copyrighted under notice appearing earlier in this work.

fright, surprise), that you want your story to have on your readers. Then, select those facts and details that will help you achieve that purpose.

Writing. Begin with action and end before you risk losing your readers' interest. Avoid a dull, rambling introduction. Bring your story to a close as soon as you have presented its climax. Carefully choose vivid, specific nouns and verbs.

Revising. Strike out all unnecessary details from your story and be certain that you have presented the remaining details in an order that your reader can easily follow.

Proofreading and *Preparing the final version.* Check the spelling of any words that you often misspell or that are unfamiliar to you. Recopy your story to make a neat, clean paper to hand in.

HBJ material copyrighted under notice appearing earlier in this work.

Using Comparisons

Your writing can be made more interesting by the use of comparisons. For instance, when you are describing a thing or an action, you can often make it clearer and more arresting by comparing it to something else. Such a comparison is called a *figure of speech*. You may make comparisons in two ways, either by saying something is or acts *like* something else or by saying it *is* something else.

Read the following comparisons and notice how effective they are.

1. Like some prehistoric dragon belching smoke and fire, the rocket rises from the launching tower.
2. She is as inconsiderate as an alarm clock.
3. It is as vulnerable as a newborn turtle, searching for its way to the sea.
4. It all seemed blurred, unreal, like a picture in the newspaper.
5. A flock of pigeons that fly by have the look, in the dull light, of wastepaper blown by the wind.
6. The climber came quickly and heavily down the slope, swaying from side to side like a puppet dancing at the end of a string.
7. The child moved as quickly and excitedly as a kitten playing with a rubber ball.
8. The vendor's stand is an oasis during the dry summer months.
9. I would have about as much chance as an icicle in July.
10. The girl's eyes were like two small chips of blue tile.

EXERCISE A. Make effective comparisons by filling the blanks in the following sentences. Compare yours with those written by other students in your class.

1. She stared at me like . . . .

2. The clown had large feet, shaped like . . . .

3. He seemed as confused as . . . .

4. The cars climbing the distant hill looked smaller than . . . .

5. Falling water in the sunlight was like . . . .

6. The twins were as close as . . . .

HBJ material copyrighted under notice appearing earlier in this work.

7. To the frightened boy the moving shadows were ....

....

8. The heavy fog was ....

....

9. The sailboats skimmed the water more lightly than ....

....

10. To press his clammy hand was like ....

....

EXERCISE B. Comparisons of all kinds are made with words—sometimes a single word, sometimes a phrase, a clause, or an entire sentence. In the passages below, put parentheses around the part or parts of each sentence that express a comparison of any kind. Be ready to discuss the passages, showing what the comparisons mean.

The enormous, blood-red sun was setting behind Kenya's rolling Ngong Hills as the big cat crouched low in the tall, dry grass. Every muscle aquiver, he watched a Thomson's gazelle in the distance. Then, with movements as smooth and deliberate as pouring honey, he began slinking forward.

Slowly, cautiously, the big cat approached unnoticed until he was just 100 yards away. Suddenly, like a golden missile set loose on the darkening plain, he launched into open attack, streaking toward the startled Tommy, who at once began a desperate pattern of run, weave and dodge. But the gazelle had sensed its danger too late. Even with its 45-mile-per-hour speed—plenty to escape from a lion or leopard attacking from any distance—the gazelle was no match for the cheetah. The drama ended quickly, in an explosive cloud of red dust.

. . . . .

The cheetah seems almost painfully aware that he lacks the power, presence and savagery of the other king-sized tooth-and-clawers. Except on rare occasions, he goes only after the smaller antelopes, killing quickly and cleanly. It is in keeping with his character that when he tries to roar, the sound that comes out is more like a "meow." In moments of contentment he may even chirp like a bird.[1]

---

[1] Excerpt from "The Cheetah: Nature's Speed King," by Emily and Ola d'Aulaire in *International Wildlife* January-February '71. Copyright 1971 by The Reader's Digest Assn., Inc. Reprinted by permission of Reader's Digest Association, Inc.

HBJ material copyrighted under notice appearing earlier in this work.

WRITING ASSIGNMENT. Describe in about 150 words a scene or an event with which you are familiar. Here are some suggested topics for this assignment:

1. Watching a sunrise
2. Standing on a mountaintop
3. Riding across the desert
4. The high-school locker room
5. A visit to the zoo
6. A crowd at the beach
7. Watching a parade
8. A thrilling sight
9. An audience at the theater
10. Fans in the stadium
11. A supermarket on Saturday
12. A destructive storm
13. The corner drugstore
14. An automobile accident
15. Your room at midnight

WRITING ASSIGNMENT. You have learned two ways to make your writing interesting: (1) by selecting nouns and verbs carefully; (2) by using comparisons. In this assignment show how effectively you can do these two things.

Write another story or another description. Your story may be an experience of your own, one you learned about from someone else, or one you imagined. Here is a good chance to try your hand at mystery or science fiction, if you wish. If you prefer to write a description again, you may make it either full of action or mostly stationary like a word picture of a place you are fond of.

The following lists may suggest a topic for your composition.

STORIES

1. My invention changed the world.
2. A fight nobody won
3. My first trip into space
4. The night I stayed in Transylvania
5. Was it a person, a beast, or a ghost?
6. My talking horse (dog, cat)
7. The teacher read my mind
8. I dashed to the rescue.
9. I solve a mystery.
10. Who was to blame?
11. I always learn the hard way.
12. My first experience as a millionaire

DESCRIPTIONS

1. My school in the year 2000
2. Night sounds at camp
3. Cloud formations
4. A sight I'll never forget
5. An impressive painting
6. The beach in early fall
7. A lake after a shower
8. A table set for Thanksgiving
9. The crowd at a sports event
10. The smells from a bakery
11. The inside of a clock (radio)
12. The moods of the ocean.

Prewriting. Present interesting details. Use several comparisons and vivid verbs and nouns to make your readers *see* the color and the action of the scene. Begin by listing all the actions, colors, and sounds that you may use in your description. Then cross from the list any details that you decide not to include. Arrange your material in a clear, logical order—which detail did you notice first, second, third? Like a photographer setting up a camera, select a definite position from which to view the scene or event. If you wish to move and describe what you see as you go, do so, but let your readers know your movement.

HBJ material copyrighted under notice appearing earlier in this work.

Writing. Be sure that you use a variety of sentences to make your paragraph interesting and to help relate your details to one another.

Revising. Check to make sure that your comparisons make sense and are complete.

Proofreading and *Preparing the final version.* Reread your paper several times. Try to leave a little break between each reading so that you can have a fresh view each time you revise. When you prepare your final version, make sure that you recopy your paper accurately.

HBJ material copyrighted under notice appearing earlier in this work.

Writing a Narrative Paragraph

The narrative paragraph tells "what happened."

The narrative paragraph tells a brief story or anecdote. It focuses on a single event, such as a visit to the dentist or an interesting dream. Often a narrative paragraph can illustrate a topic such as a parent's kindness or a friend's absent-mindedness. Details in the paragraph are usually arranged in chronological order.

In the following example of a narrative paragraph, the author tells the story of a large meteor's fall to earth. Notice that the author includes specific details of place and time.

METEOR

Details of Place and Time

Transitional Device

Transitional Device

One of the most spectacular falls occurred in Norton County, Kansas, in 1948. It was a sunny February day with a blue sky overhead. At about five in the afternoon in the small town of Jennings, eleven-year-old Creta Carter was taking the family laundry down from a clothesline in her backyard. Suddenly a brilliant ball of fire blossomed out in the clear sky, flashing directly across her field of view. Several detonations of sound followed rapidly one upon another like a cannonade, and the fireball turned into a red streak followed by an angry boiling cloud. The air was filled with hissing sounds. Undismayed by frightening apparitions, Creta calmly watched the smoking mass fall and marked the place where it disappeared behind the town's largest building. Although the ball of fire was bright enough to be seen for hundreds of miles, Creta was one of the few people to have her face tipped up to the sky at exactly the instant when the object burst into flames.[1]

Before you write a narrative paragraph, make an outline of the events you wish to narrate. List each step in chronological order. The following outline could serve for the model paragraph.

SUBJECT The fall of a meteor
  1. Sunny February day, five in the afternoon
  2. Creta Carter in her backyard
  3. Ball of fire in the sky
  4. Cannonlike sounds
  5. A red streak
  6. Hissing sounds
  7. Disappearance of the meteor behind a building

[1] From *Earth's Aura* by Louise B. Young, Copyright © 1977 by Louise B. Young. Reprinted by permission of Alfred A. Knopf, Inc.

HBJ material copyrighted under notice appearing earlier in this work.

WRITING ASSIGNMENT. Using one of the following subjects or one of your own, write a narrative paragraph. Prepare an outline in chronological order before you begin to write.

A moment of good luck
Teamwork and the success it brings
My first experience with ___
A lesson I learned the hard way
People are not always what they seem.

Prewriting. To generate facts and ideas for a narrative paragraph, you need to ask *What happened?* When you have listed several specific items, stop and see how they are related. Will your narrative aim to entertain, to make a point, or both? When you answer this question, you will have the purpose of your paragraph. Make sure that all your facts and details help achieve your purpose. Also fill in any additional information needed to tie together what you already have. Organize your information in an outline.

Writing. Present your facts to unfold the event or incident in a logical, interesting series of actions. Generally, narratives are best told in chronological order, ending with the climax.

Revising. Be sure that the sequence of actions is linked together with the right transitions. Make certain that no actions are out of place or unrelated to other actions in your narrative.

Proofreading and *Preparing the final version.* As with all other assignments, carefully check your paper for spelling, usage, and punctuation errors. During the revision and proofreading stages, you probably made a number of changes on your paper. If so, neatly recopy your paragraph before handing it in.

HBJ material copyrighted under notice appearing earlier in this work.

Writing a Descriptive Paragraph

A descriptive paragraph tells what something looks, sounds, feels, tastes, or smells like.

A descriptive paragraph usually focuses on a single object or scene and depends upon a close observation of details. To convey impressions vividly, a descriptive paragraph uses words that appeal to the reader's senses. For example, on a hot day the sidewalk *glitters* (sight), the insects *hiss* (sound), the chrome on a car *scorches* the fingers (touch), and so on. Effective nouns and verbs are the most important elements of a descriptive paragraph.

The following paragraph describes a turtle as it moves along the ground. Notice the close observation of details, the vivid verbs and nouns, and the appeal to the senses. Notice, too, that the writer arranges details in spatial order, which is often the best organization for a descriptive paragraph.

THE TURTLE

Appeal to Senses

Close Observation of Details

Vivid Verbs

Concrete Nouns

The sun lay on the grass and warmed it, and in the shade under the grass the insects moved, ants and ant lions to set traps for them, grasshoppers to jump into the air and flick their yellow wings for a second, sow bugs like little armadillos, plodding restlessly on many tender feet. And over the grass at the roadside a land turtle crawled, turning aside for nothing, dragging his high-domed shell over the grass. His hard legs and yellow-nailed feet threshed slowly through the grass, not really walking, but boosting and dragging his shell along. The barley beards slid off his shell, and the clover burrs fell on him and rolled to the ground. His horny beak was partly open, and his fierce, humorous eyes stared straight ahead. He came over the grass leaving a beaten trail behind him, and the hill, which was the highway embankment, reared up ahead of him.[1]

Before you write a descriptive paragraph, make an outline of the spatial order of the scene or object you wish to describe. The following outline could serve for the model paragraph.

SUBJECT A turtle moving in the grass
1. The sun's warmth
2. Insects under the grass
3. Turtle moving over the grass
4. Trail behind, embankment ahead

[1] From *The Grapes of Wrath* by John Steinbeck. Copyright 1939 by John Steinbeck; © renewed 1967 by John Steinbeck. Reprinted by permission of Viking Penguin Inc.

HBJ material copyrighted under notice appearing earlier in this work.

WRITING ASSIGNMENT. Using one of the subjects below or a subject of your own, write a descriptive paragraph. Prepare an outline before you begin to write. Be sure to include vivid nouns and verbs that appeal to the senses. Organize the description spatially.

A favorite room at home   A local meeting spot
A sunset   The appearance of an unusual person
A scary place

Prewriting. Jot down a list of sensory details about your topic. How does it look? feel? smell? taste? sound? Look over your list and decide whether your description will be *objective* (giving a factual, accurate picture of what you are describing without revealing your opinions or feelings about it) or *subjective* (offering an impression of what you are describing showing your attitudes and personal feelings). To organize your descriptive details, order them according to their spatial relationships, for example, top to bottom, one side to the other, front to back, inside to outside.

Writing. Keep in mind that the purpose of the descriptive paragraph is to present a sensory picture of whatever you are describing. To do this, you must use vivid, exciting words that will make your reader share your view.

Revising. Check to be certain that you have been consistent throughout your paragraph. Do not mix objective and subjective words and comparisons. Notice in the following paragraph how the description changes from objective to subjective.

THE LOOK OF AN ALLIGATOR

The mud-brown water stretched maybe ten feet across. On the other side a gray-green alligator, nearly as long as the ditch was wide, lay flat on his ivory belly. His slitted eyes looked like glassy cat's-eye marbles, frozen in the two knobs protruding from the top of his leathery head. Some people buy alligator-skin belts, purses, and other things, but nobody would want to touch a live gator's slimy hide even if the gator would let you, which he wouldn't because a gator is so mean he'd bite your hand off. You can tell a gator would enjoy sinking his big white teeth into you by the smile gators always seem to have on their faces. I bet that most old-time stories about dragons were really about gators.

The paragraph above could be revised by changing either the first three sentences to make them more subjective or the last three sentences to make them more objective. Notice also that the last sentence in this paragraph does not offer descriptive information but, instead, introduces a new topic. Remember always to organize the content of your paragraphs so that it is appropriate to your topic, tone, and point of view.

Proofreading and *Preparing the final version.* Try going over your paper backward from the end to the beginning to help you catch misspellings and other errors you might miss while reading along normally. Whenever your teacher gives directions for manuscript format, be sure to write them down.

HBJ material copyrighted under notice appearing earlier in this work.

Paragraphing and Outlining a Composition

A paragraph is a series of sentences developing a main topic. A composition is a series of paragraphs developing a main thesis. For example, the paragraph on page 259 develops the topic that tsunamis, or tidal waves, travel great distances. If the writer wished to discuss how people can protect themselves from tsunamis or what current research shows about these killer waves, he would use these ideas as topics for other paragraphs.

Dividing a composition into paragraphs makes it much easier to read. Readers know that a new paragraph means some kind of change in the content. When a writer starts a new paragraph, the readers, in effect, are being told that a different phase of the thesis is about to be discussed. In general, begin a new paragraph when you introduce a new topic.

An outline is an important aid in writing any composition. The outline of a composition lists in order the main topics, which are usually the topics of the paragraphs. These are preceded by Roman numerals. Subtopics, preceded by capital letters, are the supporting details that you use in developing a paragraph.

EXAMPLE   *Thesis Statement:* Tornadoes have violent winds which trigger freak accidents and cause much destruction.

    I. Violent winds
        A. Break measuring instruments
        B. Probably whirl at speeds of over 450 miles an hour
        C. Create an area of low pressure, almost a vacuum
   II. Freakish accidents
        A. Straws pushed through wooden posts
        B. A baby carried three miles without serious harm
        C. Whole house lifted thirty feet
  III. Destructive force
        A. Property destroyed
        B. People killed

EXERCISE. As you read the following composition, decide what the thesis is and study the plan of its development. Then fill in the blanks below, giving the thesis, the main topics, and the subtopics of the outline.

WINDSHIELD WASHER

Handy windshield squirt-washers can be made easily from empty plastic bottles of the type used for spray deodorants. Use two of these sprayers—one containing water for muddy windshields and the other a window-cleaning solution—for cutting through oily film.

HBJ material copyrighted under notice appearing earlier in this work.

Remove the nozzles of the sprayers by giving them a slight twisting pull. Wash out the containers and the nozzles before refilling. Replace the nozzles securely, cap tightly with original stoppers, and label with waterproof tape.

When the windshield needs cleaning, squirt water or cleaner solution on the glass and let your windshield wipers do the rest. For best results, the plastic bottle should be made to give a squirting rather than a spraying action by tilting the nozzle slightly lower than the rest of the bottle.[1]

Central Idea: ....

   I. ....

      A. ....

      B. ....

  II. ....

      A. ....

      B. ....

      C. ....

      D. ....

 III. ....

      A. ....

      B. ....

WRITING ASSIGNMENT. Write a composition of 3 or 4 paragraphs, expressing your ideas on one of the subjects in the list below or, if you wish, on a subject of your own. First write what the thesis of your composition will be. Then make an outline by paragraphs like the one you made in the preceding exercise. The outline is to be handed in with your composition. Be sure you have a topic sentence in each paragraph and that each paragraph sticks to its topic.

Your purpose in this composition is to show how well you can organize ideas. In other words, do not tell a story. Instead, present factual information.

SUGGESTED COMPOSITION SUBJECTS

1. How to build birdhouses
2. How to have a healthy dog
3. Types of singers
4. Teen-age eating habits
5. Three ways to make friends

6. How to be different
7. How to get high grades
8. Planning a party
9. How to avoid boredom
10. Types of teen-age activities

[1]"Windshield Washer" by Alex H. Kizer, Jr., in *1001 How-to Ideas*. Reprinted by permission of Davis Publishing Company.

HBJ material copyrighted under notice appearing earlier in this work.

WOOD TO BURN

1. No chapter in railroad history can rival the popular appeal of the wood-burning era. Its great funnel-shaped smokestack, gallant red paint, and polished brass have endeared the wood burner to generations of Americans. Its appearance during a Western film raises an excitement second only to that caused by the nick-of-time arrival of the cavalry. Ah, but those imperial clouds of heavy black smoke pouring from Hollywood's iron horses are as phony as the wagon master's peril. No scrap of wood has touched their grates in a half century, and all that glorious plumage is generated by an oil burner. The wood burner's light, billowing gray smoke and its accompanying shower of sparks have never been shown in a modern film.

2. Railway locomotives burned an astonishing amount of wood. In the 1850's they were devouring four or five million cords yearly, according to one estimate. The little Rochester, Lockport and Niagara Falls Railroad (seventy-six miles) required nearly thirteen thousand cords annually, while the mighty New York Central cremated over two hundred ten thousand cords a year. If the quantities consumed seem staggering, think of the physical labor in cutting, hauling, splitting, and stacking this mountain of logs. Think also of the expense of storing and transporting it to wood depots along the line. Think of the thousands of small farmers and unskilled laborers this trade supported. In Massachusetts alone some fifty-three hundred men were engaged in woodcutting.

3. Wood burning had come to the American railway as naturally as the strap rail track. It was clearly the cheapest, most abundant fuel. There had been a brief flirtation with coal burning, but only anthracite was available, and it proved difficult to burn in the narrow fireboxes of the day. Wood was easily ignited and burned readily—indeed, it burned too readily. It was a bulky fuel of rather low calorific value. Great quantities had to be handled and carried, which meant frequent refuelling stops if tender size was to be held within reasonable limits. In addition, it proved a volatile agent under the forced draft of a rapidly running locomotive. The pyrotechnic display sent sparks into neighboring fields, wood lots, and barns. Dickens called it "a storm of fiery snow." The railroads were accused of burning more wood outside than inside the locomotive's firebox. A rash of claims and lawsuits seemed to follow every errant spark. One of the most distressing fire losses occurred on the Newcastle and Frenchtown line when sixty thousand dollars' worth of fresh bills burned up on one of its trains. Travellers sometimes complained of singed clothing and flesh; one asserted that some ladies "were almost denuded." The problem grew to such proportions that a legion of inventors tried to perfect an effective spark arrester. Over a thousand patents were granted, but few of the designs

HBJ material copyrighted under notice appearing earlier in this work.

can be said to have been more than half successful, and most fell far short of that. Sizzling embers continued to spew freely from the fiery chariot's chimney.[1]

In the space to the left, write the letter of the words that best complete each statement. (Add 10 points for each correct answer.)

.... 1. The primary purpose of the author is (a) to tell a story, (b) to set forth and explain an idea, (c) to write vivid description.

.... 2. The thesis of the composition is that (a) wood-burning engines were dangerous, (b) the history of the wood-burning engine excites the imagination, (c) the engine was inefficient.

.... 3. Paragraph 1 is developed by (a) reasons, (b) examples, (c) facts.

.... 4. Paragraph 1 (a) develops the thesis of the composition, (b) gives the author's personal reaction to the era, (c) explains why people like the wood-burning locomotive shown in movies.

.... 5. Paragraph 2 is developed by (a) facts, (b) examples, (c) incident.

.... 6. In paragraph 2 the topic is (a) stated in the first sentence, (b) given in the last sentence, (c) not stated but clearly implied.

.... 7. A good topic sentence covering paragraph 3 would be (a) Wood-burning locomotives were dangerous. (b) The advantages of wood as fuel were balanced by its disadvantages. (c) Attempts to invent an efficient spark arrester were not entirely successful.

.... 8. Paragraph 3 is developed by a combination of (a) examples and incidents, (b) facts and incidents, (c) facts and examples.

.... 9. In general this article is developed by (a) reasons, (b) facts, (c) examples, (d) incidents.

.... 10. Which of the following descriptions is made vivid by the use of comparison? (a) a bulky fuel of rather low calorific value, (b) the pyrotechnic display sent sparks into neighboring fields, (c) a storm of fiery snow.

WRITING ASSIGNMENT. Your assignment is to write a composition setting forth an opinion or idea. First state your opinion or idea; then strive to convince your readers of the truth of your opinion by vividly describing an event that illustrates or supports your idea.

HBJ material copyrighted under notice appearing earlier in this work.

[1] From "Wood to Burn" by John H. White in *American Heritage*, December 1974. © 1974, American Heritage Publishing Company, Inc. Reprinted by permission of American Heritage Publishing Co., Inc.

Choose one of the following sentences (or use a sentence of your own), and use it as the thesis for your composition. Write a short introductory paragraph stating the thesis and explaining its exact meaning. Then prove your point by giving a vivid account of an event that is interesting, specific, and pertinent. Finally, write a short concluding paragraph that restates in an emphatic way your thesis.

COMPOSITION THESES

1. Basketball (football, tennis) is full of surprises.
2. High school is full of disappointments.
3. I am a firm believer in children's liberation.
4. Common sense is as important as book learning.
5. Television is not really a wasteland.
6. A person in love is tolerant, not blind.
7. Sitting at a desk in school all day makes me feel roped in.
8. Lucky breaks are the keys to success.
9. In reality, luck is pluck.
10. Backseat drivers cause more accidents than they prevent.
11. At times all of us are players acting parts as though the world were a stage.
12. An apparent calamity can turn out to be a real blessing.
13. I know that experience is the best teacher.
14. Chivalry is not dead.
15. A childhood experience can explain an irrational fear.
16. It pays to listen after the bell rings!
17. Prejudice is ignorance.
18. Never do today what you can put off until tomorrow.
19. Some times it is better to run than to fight.
20. The punishment should fit the crime.

REVIEW EXERCISE B. Carefully read the following composition so that you can correctly fill in the blanks that follow. Observe especially the way that the author organizes and develops his ideas.

SPORTS RECORDS WILL ALWAYS BE BROKEN

1. In the last Olympic Games, records were smashed by the dozen. There are no mystery about why, and there seems little doubt that world records in sports will continue to drop. The reasons are (1) gimmicks, (2) new training methods, and (3) size.

2. The gimmick is the most important in giving athletes that extra half second or half inch. Swimmers shave all the hair off their bodies, and records drop. Great, beefy hammer throwers put ballet slippers on their feet and find that they can spin faster and thus sling the iron ball farther. High divers, who used to tuck their knees under their chins when somersaulting, now spread their knees slightly and tuck their heads between them. This provides a tighter tuck, a faster spin, more somersaults per dive. Pistol shooters file down the hammers of their weapons until they weigh only a few grams. Because these feathery

HBJ material copyrighted under notice appearing earlier in this work.

hammers do not jar the gun as much as the old ones did, pistol scores are now higher.

3.   Though gimmicks may explain the records, the explanation of the plethora of athletes today who would have been considered supermen or superwomen in the past is training, training, training. Gus Stager, a wonderful college swimmer at Michigan in 1948, used to practice once a day, "swimming a couple of miles, then kicking maybe 1000 yards, then doing a few wind sprints." He is coach at Michigan now, and all his swimmers work out twice daily, nearly all year long. He has even experimented with three workouts a day, one devoted to building strength, one to speed, one to conditioning. "Training used to be more casual," Stager says. "We're religious about it today."

4.   If gimmicks and training explain many broken records, another factor must not be overlooked: size. There is better nutrition in the world today and less sickness, and the human body is getting bigger all the time. The bigger people get, the higher they will jump and, presumably, the faster they will run. Until they have used up the entire day for training, stopped growing, and ceased inventing gimmicks, there can be no record set that will not be broken.[1]

In your own words, complete the following statements about the article you have just read. (Add 10 points for each statement supported by the article.)

1. The first paragraph is not a presentation of the first main point in the author's outline, but it does serve to ....

....

2. The first sentence is closely related to the title because of the repetition of

....

3. The thesis of the composition is ....

4. The author's main points are ....

....

5. The topic of paragraph 2 is stated in its .... sentence.

6. The method used to develop this topic is (examples, reasons, story).

....

7. The author makes a good transition (bridges the gaps between ideas) by referring to .... and .... at the start of paragraph 3.

8. The author develops this topic by using ....

[1] From "Sports Records Will Always Be Broken" by Robert Daley, in *The New York Times Magazine*, September 18, 1960. © 1960 by The New York Times Company. Reprinted by permission of The New York Times Company.

HBJ material copyrighted under notice appearing earlier in this work.

9. The words that link the main idea of paragraph 3 to the main idea of paragraph 4 are ....

10. The topic of paragraph 4 is ....

Now on a separate sheet of paper, write an outline of "Sports Records Will Always Be Broken." You should find three main topics and at least two subtopics for each main topic.

WRITING ASSIGNMENT. Your assignment is to write a composition (about 4 paragraphs long), using the technique of Robert Daley, the author of "Sports Records Will Always Be Broken." First decide upon your thesis. Then write an outline of the main points you will cover. In the first paragraph of your composition, state your thesis, repeat the key words or ideas of the title, and list the main topics of your outline. Then develop each main topic into a paragraph by using specific facts, reasons, or examples. Discuss your first main topic in the second paragraph, the second topic in the third paragraph, and so on. Bridge the gaps between paragraphs by referring to preceding key words or ideas. In your final paragraph write a strong last sentence that emphatically restates your thesis.

COMPOSITION SUBJECTS

1. Why people love science fiction
2. Why you are your dog's best friend
3. Why baseball is more popular than ever before
4. Why fads attract teen-agers
5. Why we keep making and breaking resolutions
6. Why television will never completely replace the movies
7. Why people study history
8. Why I shall always be an optimist (*or* a pessimist)
9. Why my friends like me
10. Why a sense of humor is often helpful

HBJ material copyrighted under notice appearing earlier in this work.

Letter Writing: The Form of the Friendly Letter

A friendly letter, like a conversation with a friend, is a two-way process. Unless you write letters yourself, you are not likely to have the enjoyment of receiving them from your friends. With this thought in mind, master the proper form for a friendly letter. Think, too, about the qualities that an effective friendly letter should have.

There are many acceptable forms for letters. There is, however, one form that is always correct. In the following lessons you will review this form.

The parts of a friendly letter are shown below.

1. The letter is centered on the page with margins at top and bottom and on both sides. Even if the letter continues on a second page, there should be a margin at the bottom of the first page.

2. The *heading* is in the upper right-hand corner, but it is not crowded far into the corner. Remember the margins. The first line of the heading is the writer's street address, or the number of the post office box or rural route (for example, *P.O. Box 785* or *R.F.D. 3*). The second line is the writer's city and state, separated by a comma. The ZIP code follows the state without

> 17 Montrose Avenue
> Portland, Maine 04103
> April 23, 1986
>
> Dear Joan,
> _____
> _____
> _____
> _____
> _____
> _____
>
>   Sincerely yours,
>   Helen

A Model Friendly Letter Form

HBJ material copyrighted under notice appearing earlier in this work.

punctuation between them. The third line is the date, with a comma after the number of the day.

3. The *salutation* is *Dear* . . . followed by a comma. It begins at the left margin.

4. The *closing* begins just to the right of the middle of the page and is followed by a comma. Only the first word is capitalized. The following closings are commonly used in friendly letters: *Sincerely yours, Love, As ever, Affectionately yours,* or just *Sincerely,* or *Affectionately.*

Place the address and the return address on the envelope as shown below. (See page 284 for information on ZIP codes and state codes.)

Helen Carter
17 Montrose Avenue
Portland, Maine 04103

Miss Joan Adams
18 Rosehill Terrace
Waterloo, Iowa 50701

A Model Envelope

EXERCISE. The parts of the following headings are mixed up and out of the proper order. On a sheet of paper, write the headings correctly and add omitted punctuation.

1. March 5 1985
   Honolulu Hawaii 96821
   14 Aulena Place

2. 250 Evergreen Avenue
   January 24 1985
   Madison Wisconsin 53704

3. Fort Dodge Iowa 50501
   P.O. Box 215
   December 10 1985

4. Little Rock Arkansas 72206
   January 24 1985
   R.F.D. 2

HBJ material copyrighted under notice appearing earlier in this work.

Letter Writing: The Contents of the Friendly Letter

A friendly letter is very personal. It is like a visit from its writer. What is said and the style in which it is said should sound like the person writing the letter. Above all else, when you write a letter, *be yourself, be natural.* This does not mean that if you are a poor speller, you may misspell several words, or that if you find it hard to be neat, you may send a messy letter. It does mean that you should write as you would talk if you were with the friend to whom you are writing.

Study the following bits of advice on writing a friendly letter.

1. Write what you think will interest your friend. A letter to a friend your age will, of course, differ from a letter to your grandmother.

2. Give a detailed account of one topic rather than a general account of many topics. Details are interesting; generalities are dull.

3. Don't begin with, "How are you? I am well," or "I haven't anything else to do, so I thought I'd write you a letter."

4. Express interest in what your friend has been doing.

Here is a good friendly letter written to a member of the "gang" who has moved away.

125 Greene Avenue
Pueblo, Colorado 81005
September 25, 1986

Dear Anita,

Say, do you have any idea how much the editors of our school paper are missing you this year? Now that you're not here to give us your "latest scoops," our paper is really suffering. Honest! In fact, the last issue was only four pages, not six.

Geraldo told me yesterday, when we took our driving lesson, that he had a postcard from you last week. He also told me to be sure to bring you up-to-date about our driving experience. Yesterday was an experience all right! After thirty hours of classroom work, we've started work on our six hours of actual driving. Have you ever tried to drive in harness? Well, I've got black and blue marks all over me because of those seat belts in the front seats. Boy, those sudden stops really catch a person off guard!

I hope that you can come over for a weekend soon. Dad and Mom say to insist that you do. What can I say to entice you? Well, the new bowling alley, just six blocks from our house, is finished now. After losing the challenge tennis match at camp last summer, I've decided to take up bowling seriously—and now I bet I can beat you. Want to show me I'm wrong?

Tomorrow night I'm going to a party at Hank's, and I'll tell you all about that in my next letter.

Sincerely,
Julie

HBJ material copyrighted under notice appearing earlier in this work.

WRITING ASSIGNMENT. Write a friendly letter that is interesting and in acceptable form. Use regular stationery. Fold and place the letter in a properly addressed envelope to hand in.

Here are some suggestions for this assignment.

1. Write a letter to a friend your own age. Make your letter interesting by giving specific details about the people, places, and activities that you know your friend will want to hear about.
2. Write a letter to an older person, such as a grandparent, an uncle, or a former teacher. Make the content of your letter fit the interests of the receiver. For instance, a grandparent would be especially interested in family news; a former teacher would probably be interested in your activities at school; an uncle might like to hear all about your recent camping trip.

ZIP CODES AND STATE CODES

The United States Postal Service recommends the use of two-letter codes for states, the District of Columbia, and Puerto Rico. The Service also recommends the use of nine-digit ZIP codes. When including these codes, the address should look like this:

EXAMPLE   Ms. Rita Bryant
4025 Salmon Ave.
Sausalito, CA 94965-2525

The following list contains two-letter codes for states, the District of Columbia, and Puerto Rico. Notice that the codes do not include periods.

Alabama AL	Louisiana LA	Ohio OH
Alaska AK	Maine ME	Oklahoma OK
Arizona AZ	Maryland MD	Oregon OR
Arkansas AR	Massachusetts MA	Pennsylvania PA
California CA	Michigan MI	Puerto Rico PR
Colorado CO	Minnesota MN	Rhode Island RI
Connecticut CT	Mississippi MS	South Carolina SC
Delaware DE	Missouri MO	South Dakota SD
District of Columbia DC	Montana MT	Tennessee TN
Florida FL	Nebraska NE	Texas TX
Georgia GA	Nevada NV	Utah UT
Hawaii HI	New Hampshire NH	Vermont VT
Idaho ID	New Jersey NJ	Virginia VA
Illinois IL	New Mexico NM	Washington WA
Indiana IN	New York NY	West Virginia WV
Iowa IA	North Carolina NC	Wisconsin WI
Kansas KS	North Dakota ND	Wyoming WY
Kentucky KY		

HBJ material copyrighted under notice appearing earlier in this work.

Letter Writing: Social Notes

The Thank-You Note. The thank-you note is a friendly letter written to thank someone for a gift or a favor. The best thing to do about a thank-you note is to write it! Putting it off is bad manners.

Many thank-you notes become long friendly letters. These are probably the best kind. However, a brief, sincere acknowledgment of a gift will do very well. Be sure to write a thank-you note promptly, and always mention specifically the gift or favor.

The form of a thank-you note is the same as the form of a friendly letter.

> 625 Redwood Street
> Aurora, Illinois 60506
> January 26, 1986
>
> Dear Aunt Ida,
>
> Thank you for the sweater you sent for my birthday. Mother says you knitted it yourself. I'm sure she's right, for it's beautifully made. The unusual pattern fascinated my friends when I wore the sweater to school yesterday.
>
> The whole family celebrated with me on the twenty-fourth. I selected the menu, and my selections were apparently popular. Uncle Arthur ate three helpings of everything. Grandmother and Aunt Edith were here too. There wasn't a cake crumb left!
>
> Are you coming down for Father's birthday? I hope so.
>
> Love,
> Ellen

A Model Thank-You Note

HBJ material copyrighted under notice appearing earlier in this work.

WRITING ASSIGNMENT. Write a thank-you note. Make the receiver of your letter know that you genuinely appreciate the gift or the favor. Be as specific as possible. Below are suggestions for this assignment.

1. Write a thank-you note for a gift you received during the holidays or on your birthday. Be sure to mention the gift by name. Give reasons why you like the gift.
2. Write to someone (the newspaper deliverer, a postal clerk, a neighbor, the driver of the school bus) who habitually goes out of the way to be kind or courteous to you.
3. Write a senator or a representative to thank him or her for voting for or against an important bill.

The Bread-and-Butter Note. A bread-and-butter note is a brief, friendly letter written to your hosts to thank them for their hospitality and for the good time you had during a visit. Write a bread-and-butter note very soon after your return from a stay at someone else's home. If you have been visiting a friend of your own age, you should write your note to his or her parents (or whoever were your hosts). This does not mean, of course, that you need not write a letter to your friend, too. You should write two letters—one to your friend and one to his or her parents—under these circumstances.

Your hosts will appreciate your mentioning particular things that you especially enjoyed about your visit. They will also want to know that you arrived home safely.

The form of a bread-and-butter note is the same as the form of a friendly letter.

> 14 Riverview Avenue
> Memphis, Tennessee 38107
> July 15, 1986

Dear Mr. and Mrs. Perez,
    Today I spent most of my time telling my family what a good time I had at Greenacres. I think they're tired of hearing about the things Louise and I did, but I'm enjoying reliving everything as I tell them about it. The trip to Berg Mountain on Wednesday and the party Saturday were wonderful.
    My train was on time and Dad met me at the station. He hardly knew me, I was so tanned.

> Love,
> Eleanor

WRITING ASSIGNMENT. You have spent a weekend at the home of one of your friends. Following the suggestions above, write a bread-and-butter note to your hosts.

HBJ material copyrighted under notice appearing earlier in this work.

Letter Writing: The Form of the Business Letter

Since a letter represents you, its appearance is very important. A business letter should be written on business stationery, a white sheet 8½ × 11 inches in size. The letter should be centered on the page. It should be neat and, if possible, typewritten.

The parts of a business letter are shown below.

1. The letter is centered on the page with equal margins at top and bottom and on both sides.

2. The *heading* is the same as the heading of a friendly letter. On business stationery with a printed heading, write only the date.

3. The *inside address* begins at the left margin a small distance below the heading. In three lines it gives the name of the person or firm to whom the letter is written, the street address, and the city, state, and ZIP code. City and

Heading	188 Penbroke Street Anchorage, Alaska 99504 October 3, 1986
Inside Address	NASA Maryland Avenue, S.W. Washington, D.C. 20546
Salutation	Gentlemen:
Body	I understand that you are distributing free of charge a booklet entitled "There's a Future for You in Space Research." Please send a copy of the booklet to me at the address above. It will be helpful in a report I am making to my high-school science class.
Closing	Very truly yours,
Signature	*Arnold Zimmerman* Arnold Zimmerman

A Model Business Letter

HBJ material copyrighted under notice appearing earlier in this work.

state are separated by a comma. A letter written to a person in a firm will have a four-line inside address. The person's name will then be the first line.

4. The *salutation* begins at the left margin. In a business letter it is *Dear . . .* followed by a colon (:). If you know the person's name, you will use it: *Dear Mr. White:, Dear Ms. Kennedy:.* If you do not know the specific name but have addressed the letter to Manager, Principal, etc., the salutation will be *Dear Sir:*, although it is understood that the person could be a man or a woman.

If you are writing to a firm, the salutation will be *Gentlemen: (Dear Sirs:* is also acceptable).

5. The first line of the letter is indented.

6. The proper complimentary close for a business letter is *Yours truly, Very truly yours, or Sincerely*, followed by a comma. Only the first word is capitalized.

7. The signature is your full name. Do not put *Mr.* or *Miss* before your name. An unmarried woman may put *(Miss)* in parentheses before her name if she is writing to a stranger.

EXERCISE A. On a sheet of paper, write the following inside addresses in correct form, adding omitted punctuation. Below each example, write the salutation that should be used with it.

1. 50 West 44th Street
   New York New York 10036
   Scholastic Magazines
   Mrs. Caroline Chesterton

2. 26 Broadway
   American Export Lines Inc.
   New York New York 10004

3. Sales Manager
   6465 Turtle Creek Drive
   Waco Texas 76710
   Republic Plastics Corporation

4. 501 Madison Avenue
   New York New York 10022
   Space Digest

EXERCISE B. Write neatly in ink or type the business letter outlined below, arranging the parts correctly to make an attractive letter. Plan your arrangement on a piece of scrap paper before actually writing the letter.

Home address: your own
Date: today's
Write to: Western States Electric Company
          16 Bantam Road
          Tucson, Arizona 85706

Supply the correct salutation.

Body of letter: Our high-school science club has been studying the applications of electronics in everyday life. Will you please send us any literature on this subject which you have for free distribution?

Add the proper closing and your own signature.

HBJ material copyrighted under notice appearing earlier in this work.

Letter Writing: The Contents of the Business Letter

While business firms are always pleased to receive mail orders for their mechandise, they often are forced to waste time and money because the orders are not clear. Sometimes the articles ordered are not clearly described; sometimes important details like the quantity or size are omitted. When you write an order letter, be sure the company receiving the letter will know exactly what you want.

Study the following order letter:

483 Lincoln Street
Topeka, Kansas 66606
May 21, 1986

Ace Sporting Goods Company
245 Jefferson Road
St. Louis, Missouri 63119

Gentlemen:

    Please send me the following articles as listed
in your spring catalogue:

1 dozen Ace tennis balls	$18.00
2 prs. Walker tennis shorts, size 30 @ $13.00	26.00
Total	$44.00
Taxes and Postage	5.56

I am enclosing a money order for $49.56.

                    Very truly yours,

                    Robert Mitchell

                    Robert Mitchell

A Model Order Letter

WRITING ASSIGNMENT. Write to the Murphy Cycle Company, 825 Cook Avenue, Mobile, Alabama 36605. Order 2 Roadking tires No. 25B, @ $9.50; 1 Roadking lamp No. 2, price $8.89.

HBJ material copyrighted under notice appearing earlier in this work.

INDEX

HBJ material copyrighted under notice appearing earlier in this work.

HBJ material copyrighted under notice appearing earlier in this work.

282

INDEX OF VOCABULARY WORDS

(Page numbers refer to definition in text.)

HBJ material copyrighted under notice appearing earlier in this work.

Key to *English Grammar and Composition**

The following chart correlates lessons in *English Workshop, Third Course* to the appropriate rules in the Liberty Edition of *English Grammar and Composition, Third Course* and the Benchmark Edition of *English Composition and Grammar, Third Course.*

Workshop Lesson	Text Rule	Workshop Lesson	Text Rule
1	1a/12a	65	24k–l/22k–l
2	1b/12b	66	24h/22h
3	1c/12c	67	24j/22j
5–6	1d/12d	68	26c–g/24c–g
7–8	1e/12e	69	27a–d, 27h/25a–d, 25h
9	1f/12f	70	27g/25g
10	1g–h/12g–h	74	32c/27c
14	31b/30b	75	5b/16b
15	2a–b/13a–b	77	5c–f/16c–f
16	2d/13d	78	5g–i/16g–i
17	2c/13c	79	5k, 5m/16k, 16m
18–19	2e–g/13e–g	81	5r/16r
20–21	2a–b, 10a–e/10a–b, 13a–e	84	31f/30e
24	29c/30c	86–91	6a–c/17a–c
26	2h–i/13h–i	92	6d/17d
27	2j/13j	96	31b/30b
28	2k/13k	97	7a/18a
31	32d–h/27d–h	98	7b/18b
32	31d/30c	99	7c–d/18c–d
33	3a–c/14a–c	100	7e/18e
34–35	3c/14c	102	7g/18g
36	4a–c/15a–c	108	11a/11a
37	4d/15d	109	11d–e/11d–e
38	4e/15e	110	11b–c/11b–c
39	4f/15f	111–113	11f/11f
44	10a, 10c–e/10a, 10c–e	116	13a/2a
45	10b, 10e/10a, 10e	117–118	13b, 14f/2b
46–47	10a–e/10a–e	119	13f, 14g/2e
48	24a–d/24a–d	120	13c, 14h/2c
49	10f/10f	121–122	13g, 14i/2f
52	32e, 32g–h/27e, 27g–h	123–124	15a–e/3a–e
53	31f–g/30e–f	125	15f–j/3f
54	23c/21c	126	15l, 31d/3g, 30c
55	23c–d/21c–d	127	15e/3e
56	23e/21e	128	15n–p/3h
60	32e, 32g–h/27e, 27g–h	129	15k–m/3g
62	24f–g/22f–g	130	16e/4e
63	24k/22k	134	20a–c/8a–c
64	24j–k/22j–k	135	20e/8e

*References printed in red refer to the appropriate rules in the Benchmark Edition of *English Composition and Grammar, Third Course.*

284

HBJ material copyrighted under notice appearing earlier in this work.